Psychosomatic Specificity

Collaborating Authors

Franz Alexander, M.D.
Donald W. Fiske, Ph.D.
Thomas M. French, M.D.
Charles Kligerman, M.D.
George J. Mohr, M.D.
George H. Pollock, M.D.
Richard E. Renneker, M.D.
Louis B. Shapiro, M.D.
Lucia E. Tower, M.D.
Edoardo Weiss, M.D.

Psychosomatic Specificity

Volume 1
Experimental Study and Results

Edited by
Franz Alexander, M.D.
Thomas M. French, M.D.
George H. Pollock, M.D.

The University of Chicago Press
Chicago & London

Library of Congress Catalog Card Number: 68–16711

The University of Chicago Press, Chicago 60637
The University of Chicago Press, Ltd., London W.C.1

Published 1968
Printed in the United States of America

Acknowledgments

The authors of this volume are acutely aware of their indebtedness to a great many individuals and institutions through the pilot and project years of this research. We wish to express our deep appreciation:

To the Chicago Institute for Psychoanalysis, its Director and its staff, for their unfailing scientific, moral, and financial support over the project's span of more than fourteen years.

To all those persons and groups who have contributed funds to the project, most notably the United States Public Health Service, the State of Illinois, the Foundations' Fund for Research in Psychiatry, and Miss Charlotte Rosenbaum of Chicago.*

To the many internists and hospitals who referred the patients utilized in the study, including the Illinois Research and Educational Hospital, the Department of Psychiatry of the University of Illinois, Michael Reese Hospital, the University of Chicago Hospitals and Clinics, and the Veterans Administration hospitals in the Chicago area.

To a number of psychiatrist colleagues who participated in the research at different periods: Drs. Helen B. Carlson, Robert Cutler, George C. Ham, Irene M. Josselyn, Morris A. Lipton, and Paul Nielson.

To our Medical Control Group: Dr. Mark Lepper as Moderator, and Drs. Arthur Billings, Nicholas J. Cotsonas, Bernard Eisenstein, Aaron M. Josephson, Armand Littman, Cyril Mendelson, Ernest Mond, R. Barratt Terry (deceased), and Hyman Zimmerman.

To our Medical Editors: Drs. S. Howard Armstrong, Jr. (deceased), Morris A. Lipton, and Milton Robin.

* United States Public Health Service Grant, M-541, October, 1952–September, 1960. The State of Illinois, Research Project 1720, July, 1956–June, 1958. Foundations' Fund for Research in Psychiatry, Grant T60-156, December, 1960–November, 1965. Charlotte Rosenbaum Fund, January, 1958, continuing.

To Dr. William Offenkrantz, Department of Psychiatry, University of Chicago, for his help in arranging a number of interviews as well as selecting a number of cases for the research.

To Barbara Page Fiske, B.A., Alice J. Holloway, Ph.D., John Van Pelt, B.A., and Donald Ross, Ph.D., for assistance to our statistician, Donald W. Fiske, Ph.D.

To Drs. Louis A. Gottschalk, John E. Gedo, and David A. Hamburg for their participation in the Interviewer Cue Detection Study.

To our earlier project secretaries, Miss Lorraine Sherman and Mrs. Evelyn Heidkamp.

To Miss C. Malvina Owens and Miss Mary C. Neff, our research assistants, without whose dedicated and competent help this project might still be incomplete.

To Mr. Glenn Miller, Librarian of the Institute, for his assistance in preparing the index.

And to Mrs. Kate Ollendorff and Dr. Gerhart Piers for their generous editorial assistance.

The original team of investigators consisted of Dr. George C. Ham as coordinator, and Drs. Franz Alexander, Helen B. Carlson, Thomas M. French, Paul Nielson, George H. Pollock, Richard E. Renneker, and Edoardo Weiss as the other investigators. For a while Dr. Irene Josselyn also collaborated. When Dr. Ham left Chicago, Dr. Renneker took over the function of coordinator. In the meantime, some team members dropped out and new members were added. In its final form the team consisted of Drs. Franz Alexander, Thomas M. French, Charles Kligerman, George J. Mohr, George H. Pollock, Richard E. Renneker, Louis B. Shapiro, Lucia E. Tower, and Edoardo Weiss. After Drs. Alexander, Mohr, and Renneker moved to California, Dr. Pollock became the coordinator. Drs. S. H. Armstrong, Jr. and Morris Lipton served as medical editors. Dr. Donald W. Fiske began as statistical consultant, but joined the research team and contributed greatly in the preparation of our research findings for publication.

Contents

Psychosomatic Specificity

CHAPTER ONE

History

This volume deals with the findings of fourteen years (1951–65) of research in psychosomatic medicine carried on by Franz Alexander and a team of co-workers at the Chicago Institute for Psychoanalysis. The project was designed as an attempt to test and possibly to substantiate a point of view which had developed over many years of previous psychosomatic and psychoanalytic experience, and which had been characterized as the "specificity hypothesis."

The notion of an interrelation between the psyche and bodily states is as old as medicine itself. The Hippocratic formulation of a connection between certain humors and specific personality types—and the role of the flow of these humors in health and disease—not only dominated the medical thinking of antiquity and the Middle Ages but persists to some degree in modern medicine. Yet, with all due respect to the ancients and to such eminent later contributors as Descartes, Claude Bernard, William Beaumont, and William James, it can be said that the first really fundamental understanding of this area derived from Freud's work. The striking demonstration in *Studies in Hysteria* (Breuer and Freud 1955), that specific unconscious contents could be symbolically expressed in the "body language" of somatic symptoms, opened a new era in the scientific approach to psychogenesis in somatic illness. After the initial work on hysteria psychosomatic phenomena did not continue to be of central interest in the development of psychoanalysis. Nevertheless, they appeared as peripheral observations in many psychoanalytic studies and at times caught the attention of some of Freud's most gifted pupils. Ferenczi published several of his short vignettes in this field (Ferenczi 1916, 1950), and Abraham dealt with certain aspects of the subject in more systematic fashion. Abraham's classic "A Short Study of the Development of the Libido" (1927) postulated a maturational sequence of zonal fixation points that were associated with specific developmental conflicts. Thus oral drives were associated with conflicts over wishes to receive, anal drives with giving and withholding, and so on. These ideas set the stage for further elaborations such as Alexander's vector theory (1935).

Freud himself did not limit his conceptualizations in the psychosomatic field to the conversion mechanism. In his paper "The Pschoanalytic View of Psychogenic Visual Disturbance" (1957) he noted that there were operative other mechanisms than conversion—that unconscious attitudes might alter physiologic functions without symbolizing any definite psychic meaning. In spite of this clear early differentiation, subsequent writers often tended to regard all sorts of vegetative symptoms as symbolic representations of unconscious content. Perhaps this trend reached its greatest degree of exaggeration in the formulations of the colorful Groddeck; but even today there are workers who use this approach almost exclusively.

Other investigators went to an opposite extreme and postulated that the exact nature of the conflict was not important—that acute or chronic emotional tension, from whatever cause, could lead to dysfunction or lesion in a vulnerable organ. Pre-existing vulnerability of the organ was assumed to depend either on congenital factors or on vicissitudes of some early physical disease.

The view developed by Alexander and his associates at the Chicago Institute lies midway between these extremes. The assumptions underlying their work might be summarized as follows:

1. There is at present no unitary theory to account for all psychosomatic disorders: some seem purely hysterical while others seem to be vegetative concomitants of chronic emotional tension.

2. Nevertheless, most syndromes in the group that we loosely call "psychosomatic illness" or "vegetative neurosis" seem to be fairly regularly associated with certain characterological patterns or emotional constellations.

3. In all cases a constitutional factor "*X*" is assumed. This factor may bear a reciprocal relationship to the degree of intensity of the psychological factor in accord with Freud's well-known concept of the "complementary series."

4. The emotional constellations mentioned above play an etiological role in association with other complex factors in the genesis of the disease.

The convictions of the Chicago group gradually emerged as a result of impressions culled from individual experiences in the psychoanalytic treatment of patients with psychosomatic illness. Anamnestic or biographical studies such as the profiles of Dunbar (1943) helped bring into focus certain observational fields in the complex and overdetermined data of individual psychoanalyses. When these observations and experiences were compared, it appeared that similar characterological patterns tended to recur in certain diseases and that certain types of trauma often seemed to initiate a chain of events culminating in a somatic breakdown.

To study and evaluate these impressions more systematically, Alexander and his associates in 1932 began a series of psychoanalytic studies of patients suffering from chronic organic ailments in the causation of which emotional conflicts had been suspected as a primary or contributing factor. These investigations dealt mainly with seven diseases: bronchial asthma, rheumatoid arthritis, ulcerative colitis, essential hypertension, neurodermatitis, thyrotoxicosis, and peptic ulcer. Most of these studies have been thoroughly reported in the literature and are listed in the Bibliography.

As a result of these investigations, the original impressions were greatly strengthened and expanded. Yet despite the considerable effort that had been expended in these researches and the increased conviction that developed in the minds of the investigators concerning the presence of significant psychosomatic correlation ("specificity") in these diseases, the concept still remained at the level of hypothesis. Therefore it appeared important to devise new research that would approach the problem by a different method and possibly add further corroborative evidence to our hypothesis.

In an unfinished essay prepared for this volume shortly before his death Alexander wrote:

> The initial impetus for undertaking a validation of these findings was my conviction that conclusions drawn from the psychodynamic material of case histories are subject to the same uncertainties which are common to all historical and biographical studies. The number of variables is so great and their mutual correlation is so complex that one can arbitrarily select psychodynamic patterns which are clearly demonstrable in one group of patients, but which are also present and demonstrable in many other case histories. We find anxiety, dependent needs, oedipal constellations, castration fear, phallic ambitions, competition, envy and jealousy, hostile impulses, hope and disillusionment, progressive and regressive trends in every

patient, whether he suffers from organic or purely psychological symptoms. We also find these patterns in normal individuals.

In our field what an author selects as particularly characteristic for a group of cases may be determined not only by actual similarities but also by the focus of his interest. That certain correlations, such as with compulsion neurosis and depressive reactions, have nevertheless been established with a fair amount of certainty in a few conditions is the strongest corroboration of the general validity of psychodynamic observation and reasoning. It should be emphasized, however, that one never succeeds in designating as characteristic single entities such as anal tendencies or oral fixations, because these are present in all nosological entities and even in so-called normal persons. It turns out that what is characteristic is always the total gestalt in which the omnipresent individual psychological trends appear in a unique combination. Oral deprivation often intensifies anal retention (holding on to possessions) but may also intensify oral aggressive and acquisitive tendencies. The resulting personality picture will depend (in addition to many other factors) upon the predominance of one of these two reaction patterns: seeking security by retentiveness or seeking it by aggressive acquisitiveness. Occasionally both patterns may be present in an equal distribution or the one or the other may predominate. Also in the psychoanalytic study of patients with organic illness it was found that only the total dynamic patterns and not single psychological entities are characteristic for a disease.

As the clinical investigations progressed, the Chicago workers became more and more impressed by the regularity with which certain psychodynamic patterns appeared as central features in different diseases. For example, they regularly found a characteristic and pronounced conflict about dependency needs in duodenal ulcer patients. A conflict about crying and confiding in a mother image whom the patient is afraid of losing was a constant finding in asthma, confirming an early discovery of Weiss (1922). A characteristic difficulty in handling hostile impulses appeared again and again in hypertension. Many of these findings were also corroborated or described independently by other psychoanalytic and psychiatric authors. Masculine protest reactions in female arthritics were too obvious to be overlooked. Associated with this was an early restriction by tyrannical parents (mostly mothers) of muscular expression and a conspicuously intense muscle eroticism, all this leading to continuous self-control of aggressive impulses that were flowing toward the extremities.

In neurodermatitis cases the presence of an intense craving for physical closeness combined with a conflict about exhibitionistic tendencies was described by Miller (1942, 1948) and by others in earlier papers. And finally, the Chicago investigators recognized the central role which basic fear of biological death plays in thyrotoxicosis, together with a highly characteristic way of handling such fear by counterphobic mechanisms and denial. A tendency toward early maturation and self-sufficiency was another regular finding in these cases.

It was equally impressive to find that the psychological situation in which the patient found himself at the onset of his physical symptoms—which we call the onset situation—consisted precisely in the activation of the characteristic psychodynamic conflict pattern that had been present from childhood on.

The regularity with which these patterns appeared was very gratifying. It was gratifying because the psychodynamic findings made sense from the physiological point of view. Thus in ulcer patients, it makes physiological sense that frustrated dependent, help-seeking desires should have a specific correlation to stomach activity, the connecting link being the association between the wish to be loved and helped and the wish to be fed.

Similarly we found in asthma patients marked inhibition of the urge to communicate with others or to cry, which is the first communication of the child with the mother. The asthma attack consists physiologically in the inhibition of the expiratory phase of the respiratory function, which is involved in crying and verbal communication.

Again, the patient who develops thyrotoxicosis shows an early tendency toward maturation. Thyroxine is an accelerator of metabolism and of the whole maturational process. Thyroxine increases alertness and is called upon when the organism faces long-term effort. Moreover, the close psychophysiological correlation between thyroxine and anxiety has been firmly established.

In the light of Cannon's studies (1929, 1932), it seems logical that sustained and insufficiently expressed hostile impulses should affect the circulatory system, and hence correlate with hypertension.

The arthritic process is unfavorably influenced by the increased muscle tonus that results from the simultaneous mobilization of aggressive impulses and their inhibition—a kind of straitjacket situation.

In neurodermatitis the emotional factors are connected both with exhibitionistic tendencies and with the frustrated desire for physical contact as an expression of intimacy and love, a kind of contact hunger. (Blushing clearly demonstrates the involvement of the skin in exhibitionism: the blushing person betrays his hidden feelings in spite of himself.)

It is only in colitis that the psychophysiological correlation found in our studies has no readily apparent physiological meaning. Yet the notion that frustrated urges for accomplishment should, through yet unknown intermediary physiological channels, lead to increased mobility or hyperemia of the bowels, may be explained if we remember that one of the earliest accomplishments and prides of the infant is derived from the excremental act.

These psychodynamic formulations, however, were not influenced by such physiological considerations. Their physiological meaningfulness dawned upon the investigators much later, but it increased their confidence that they were on the right track.

The fact that the same psychodynamic patterns can be found, and not only in traces but full-blown, in patients who have no psychosomatic symptoms whatsoever provided a major stimulus for the present investigation. The typical "ulcer conflict," for example, is frequently seen in persons who do not suffer from ulcers. It was often noted by Alexander in a type of delinquent youth who overtly appears to be an aggressive, independent go-getter but is actually, upon closer scrutiny, seen to be an extremely dependent, insecure individual. The surface picture of independence is a defense against his unconscious help-seeking tendencies. Similarly, the continued struggle against expression of hostile impulses motivated by the need to be loved is a constant finding in hypertensives, but at the same time it is a very widespread pattern found in a great many persons without any circulatory disturbance. It was obvious from the beginning that these psychological findings in themselves did not offer an etiological explanation of these diseases. Even though the specific psychological factors seem to be characteristic for certain disease entities, they do not in themselves cause the disease except in the presence of a specific organ vulnerability, which we have called the *X* factor. This factor was also postulated by other authors such as Deutsch (1939), Binger (1945), and particularly Grinker (1953).

This preliminary hypothesis which postulates the coexistence of at least two categories of factors—a psychological and a pre-existing organic factor—resolved the first theoretical dilemma. For cases of duodenal ulcer, the hypothesis has since been validated by Mirsky and his co-workers (Weiner, Thaler, Reiser, and Mirsky 1957 Mirsky 1953).

Alexander's view that psychological factors play an important role in the etiology of the disease makes no claim for *specificity of causation*. He wrote:

> I assumed that in some cases the psychological factors may be etiologically significant, in others less so. My contention was only that they are conspicuously present in a specific distribution in the seven disease entities that the Chicago team has investigated. Moreover, the reliability of the clinical approach is limited. Clinical observations can give good hunches, which, however, have to be checked by other methods. It is easy to select psychological configurations from the immense variety of psychological events and discover in every patient just the pattern one wants to discover. In spite of this skepticism, the investigators were increasingly confident in the validity of their psychodynamic formulations.
>
> As the original clinical studies continued over more than seventeen years, the investigators became increasingly impressed with the consistent correlations between psychological and somatic findings. These studies indicated that some organic diseases have not only a specific pathophysiology, but possibly also a specific psychopathology. Independent of etiological speculations about which pathology is responsible for the other, the mere fact of their regular coexistence opens up a new chapter for medical research and theory.
>
> The fact that the psychological phenomena antedate the appearance of the organic symptoms allows only two conclusions. Either these phenomena contribute to the etiology of the organic symptoms, or they are the psychological expression of certain basic qualities of the organism which manifest themselves on the somatic side as an organic predisposition. This does not preclude the possibility that the psychological features and the organic predisposition, even though they are parallel manifestations of the same underlying organismic quality, may have a mutual secondary influence upon each other. For example, in the case of duodenal ulcer Mirsky showed that the organic factor consists in hypersecretion but also confirmed the previously discovered psychological factor—the conflict about dependency needs (Weiner, Thaler, Reiser, and Mirsky 1957). These two variables may both be contingent on a basic constitutional quality. This does not contradict the possibility that the oral conflict may influence stomach secretion, or that changes in stomach secretion may influence oral impulses.
>
> While both of these theoretical possibilities were being considered, the need grew steadily to test the reliability of the underlying clinical

observations. It made no sense to go on speculating about etiological problems before the basic facts were more solidly established.

To put the question quite bluntly, the members of the research group wondered whether they were not deluding themselves. Knowing that the patient has an ulcer or asthma may influence one to discover in him the pattern that was described in previous similar cases. Since aspects of all these patterns exist in practically everybody in varying degree, self-deception cannot be excluded. To cope with this problem, a new research was designed. A plan was evolved to undertake a "blind diagnosis" type of team investigation. If specific psychological features are characteristic for certain diseases, it should be possible to diagnose a given disease purely from psychological data. The problem was to find a method by which the reliability of psychodynamic formulations could be tested. Such a test requires two independent methods that can be checked against each other. An ulcer can be established by X-rays, with a high degree of certainty. The reliability of the claim that the presence of an ulcer can be concluded from psychodynamic formulations alone can be quickly checked by X-ray and by other non-psychological medical procedures.

In constructing this method the researchers were guided by three basic operational concepts that had been developed during the previous years of study.

The first is the *psychodynamic constellation*, the central conflict pattern together with the primary defenses employed against it.

The second variable is the *onset situation*, the psychodynamic situation in which the patient found himself during the time his first symptoms developed. The onset situation includes the external life situation as it affects the patient. The same external life event may have different meaning for different persons. For example, being left by his wife may mean a great loss for one patient and a relief for another. The term "onset situation" therefore refers to life conditions immediately preceding the illness as they affect the patient emotionally at that time. These conditions must be understood in terms of the genetic background of each patient, usually by the reactivation of old conflicts.

As previously stated, it was necessary to postulate the existence of a third set of variables, the *X factor*, primarily because the same psychological pattern history and even the corresponding onset situation may be present in patients who do not develop organic disease. Some of these patients may never develop the disease, some may conceivably do so at some future date, and some may have it in a "silent" form. There are many persons who have the type of defense against their hostile impulses that is found in hypertensives but never develop hypertension—even though their life situations stimulate aggressive impulses and at the same time prohibit their free expression. Those persons who may have, in addition to these psychological factors, a constitutional vulnerability of the vascular system (the *X* factor) may respond with hypertension.

In general terms the operational hypothesis of this work can be reduced to the following statement: A patient with vulnerability of a specific organ or somatic system and a characteristic psychodynamic constellation develops the corresponding disease when the turn of events in his life is suited to mobilize his earlier established central conflict and break down his primary defenses against it. In other words, if the precipitating external situation never occurs, a patient may, in spite of the presence of the predisposing emotional patterns and of organ vulnerability, never develop the disease.

These three variables—inherited or early acquired organ or system vulnerability, psychological patterns of conflict and defense formed in early life, and the precipitating life situation—are not necessarily independent factors. It is possible that constitution at least partially determines both the organ vulnerability and the characteristic psychological patterns. At present little is known about the interdependence of these two variables. There is strong indication, however, that the correlation between constitution and characteristic psychiatric patterns is not a simple one. Constitution alone without certain emotional experiences of early life, particularly the early mother-child relation, may not produce a consistent pattern.

Neither is the onset situation considered an entirely independent variable. It is not purely a chance factor. Patients with certain psychological predispositions may unconsciously seek out life situations which complement their predispositions. For example, hypertensives who are characterized by the tendency to carry on their work dutifully even under difficult and harassing conditions are more apt to get into life situations in which they are exploited by their environment. Such a "beast of burden" type of patient may subtly invite heavier and heavier loads just because he so patiently submits to indignities.

The Seven Diseases

It seems appropriate now to present the tentative formulations for the seven diseases with which we began this investigation.

Bronchial Asthma

The central conflict in cases of bronchial asthma stems from internal impulses that threaten a person's attachment to mother or a mother substitute. Some mothers react to the first signs of the little child's sexual strivings directed toward them with withdrawal or rejection. Sexual strivings thus become an internal danger that threatens to alienate mother's affection. Later in life a very common precipitating situation for asthma attacks is a pending marriage. These patients are apt to procrastinate about marriage, and long periods of engagement have been observed in a number of patients. The son senses the mother's disapproval of his planned marriage and is caught between his love for his fiancée and his fear of losing mother's love. A girl, too, may sense her mother's unconscious jealousy and be torn between sexual desires and fear of maternal disapproval.

The most specific feature of these patients, however, is their conflict about crying. Crying, the child's first device for calling mother, is inhibited because of fear of maternal repudiation. Asthmatic patients' mothers show an ambivalent attitude, simultaneously seductive and rejecting. Later in life, difficulty in calling mother by crying gives place to difficulty in confiding in an unpredictable mother or mother substitute. These patients have a conflict between their wish to confide and the fear of it. Thus, the fear of alienating mother becomes centered on verbal communication, which explains the involvement of the respiratory function. Asthmatic attacks can be understood as an inhibition of the use of the expiratory act for communication, either by crying or confession.

Rheumatoid Arthritis

Like hypertensive patients persons suffering from rheumatoid arthritis have great difficulty in handling their aggressive hostile impulses. Unlike hypertensive patients, however, their solution is a combination of self-control and benevolent tyranny over others.

Most of our knowledge is derived from arthritic women patients since arthritis is much more common in women than in men. When they become mothers, they show compulsive trends and are inclined to control all the moves of their children and to demand their participation in the daily chores of the household. Interestingly, in their own childhood they were exposed to similar maternal influences, and the typical mother of the arthritic patient is a restrictive one. We hear consistently the story that as children they were mostly punished by deprivation of physical freedom. "Stay put" is the characteristic command of the mother of the arthritic patient. As young girls in the prepuberty period, they react to this physical restriction by becoming tomboys—competing with boys, climbing trees and fences, and so on. This muscular activity is highly eroticized. In this way they drain the pent-up rebellion against maternal restrictions. Later in life the tomboyish physical expression of rebellion becomes transformed into a tendency to tyrannize others. This they can do without guilt because they exert a helpful type of tyranny. They are strict but take care of the interests of their underlings. In men, the central finding is a feminine identification against which they defend themselves in the same way as women.

The arthritic condition often develops when this drainage of hostile impulses, by helping and ruling at the same time, is blocked by some change in the external life situation. Loss of a person whom the patient previously dominated is one common precipitating condition. Very often the disease is precipitated when the husband or a child makes a successful attempt to stand up against domination.

Ulcerative Colitis

The central dynamic constellation in ulcerative colitis consists in losing hope that a task involving responsibility, effort, and concentration can be accomplished. These patients are inclined to give up hope easily in the face of obstacles. Even though they may continue their external efforts toward achievement, they have already lost confidence and work under internal compulsion. In early childhood they were exposed to challenges beyond their capacity. Very often their ambitious parents—usually mothers—had high expectations for the child's performance, transplanting their own ambitions into the child, who felt required to perform in order to secure the mother's love. The relative weakness of an ego that is pushed to achieve a goal beyond its capacity often manifests itself in a disintegrative process of paranoid coloring which may explain the frequent combination of psychotic symptoms with ulcerative colitis. The typical onset situation is a hopeless struggle for achievement. This formulation, particularly in the latter phase of the research, underwent important modifications, which will be presented in the second volume.

Essential Hypertension

In cases of essential hypertension the central findings are the patient's continuous struggle against expressing hostile aggressive feelings and his difficulty in asserting himself. These patients fear losing the affection of others and so control the expression of their hostility. Yet such patients were prone to childhood attacks of rage and aggression. Sometimes rather suddenly, sometimes gradually, a change in personality occurred. The formerly aggressive child changes into a person who cannot assert himself and is overtly compliant. The experience of losing the parents' and other people's affection by aggressive behavior induced them to control their hostile impulses.

Another related trend is the dogged perseverance of such persons in pursuing even insuperable obstacles. Their life history is often that of the "beast of burden." They frequently have long-standing job records and stay with the same company even when underpaid for many years. If they are promoted to executive positions they encounter difficulties because they cannot assert themselves and make others follow orders. Their inclination is to do the job of others instead of insisting on discipline.

Such an overconscientious, overresponsible attitude results in increased feelings of resentment, demanding in turn greater and greater control of these hostile feelings. A vicious circle develops, leading to a chronic state of tension.

The characteristic onset situation consists in life circumstances that mobilize hostility and the urge for self-assertion and at the same time prohibit their free expression. The characteristic job situation exists when a person is required to achieve more without added recompense and at the same time is threatened with losing his job should he show the least sign of discontent or rebellion.

Neurodermatitis

In cases of neurodermatitis we find a complex configuration between exhibitionism, guilt, and masochism, combined with a deep-seated desire to receive physical expression of love from others. In the history we usually find undemonstrative mothers who create in the child a great hunger for the type of skin stimulation—stroking and cuddling—that accompanies mother's physical expression of love toward the child. In general, such patients lacked close physical contact in early life and now try to get attention by the means of infantile exhibitionism (the attempt to induce adults to cuddle the child).

The early exhibitionistic techniques for getting attention and love are aimed at winning one parent's attention away from the other parent or a sibling. If the child is successful, he may suffer from feelings of guilt which later manifest themselves in a tendency to put the wrong foot forward, to appear in a bad light, to make embarrassing faux pas. The sexual impulse in these patients, in which skin eroticism is accentuated, is deeply linked with guilt feelings.

The disease, as a rule, is precipitated after the patient achieves some form of exhibitionistic victory. The victory arouses guilt and creates a need for suffering in the precise part of the body that is involved in the exhibitionistic success. By scratching, which is a substitute for autoerotic masturbation, the patient both relieves sexual tension and at the same time inflicts pain upon himself. Some patients vividly describe the pleasure that they derive from scratching, referring to it as a *vicious* kind of pleasure. In these scratching orgies, they attack their bodies mercilessly, experiencing pleasureful pain or painful pleasure of a high order.

Thyrotoxicosis

The central dynamic issue in thyrotoxicosis is a constant struggle against fear concerning the physical integrity of the body and, more specifically, fear of biological death. Even more characteristic is the attempt to master fear by denying it and counterphobically seeking dangerous situations and coping with them alone. In the history we often find frequent exposures to deaths of near relatives and other traumatic events that constituted childhood threats to survival. Equally characteristic is the rapid maturation of these patients. A typical example is a six-year-old motherless girl who cooked for the whole family and took care of her younger siblings. Dreams about dead persons in coffins are common. The precipitating situation is often some kind of threat to survival, in which the counterphobic defense breaks down. Thyrotoxicosis immediately following a traumatic event such as an accident is common and has come to be called "Shock-Basedow." In other cases, only careful, methodical scrutiny can reveal the threatening event immediately preceding the outbreak of the disease. Such trauma, however, will produce thyrotoxicosis only in predisposed individuals—predisposed not only by heredity and constitution but also by the type of a life history in which threat for mere survival repeatedly occurred.

Duodenal Peptic Ulcer

The central dynamic feature in duodenal peptic ulcer is the frustration of dependent desires originally oral in character. The craving to be fed appears later as a wish to be loved, to be given support, money, and advice. This fixation on early dependent situations of infancy comes in conflict with the adult ego and results in hurt pride, since the infantile craving for help is contrary to the standards of the adult, to his wish for independence and self-assertion. Because of this conflict, the oral craving must be repressed. Oral receptiveness when frustrated often changes into oral aggressiveness, and this also becomes repressed because of guilt feelings it provokes. Both oral dependent and oral aggressive impulses may then be frustrated by internal factors—shame and guilt.

The most common defense against both oral dependent and oral acquisitive impulses is overcompensation. The latently dependent or acquisitive person overtly appears as an independent, hard-working individual who likes responsibility and taking care of others. He responds to challenges with increased activity and ambition, works hard and assumes greater and greater responsibilities. This in turn increases his secret longing to lean on others. To be loved, to be helped is associated from the beginning of life with the wish to be fed. When this help-seeking attitude is denied its normal expression in a give-and-take relationship with others, a psychological regression takes place to the original form of a wish to ingest food. This regressive desire seems to be specifically correlated with increased gastric secretion.

Not all patients suffering from duodenal ulcer overcompensate for their dependent desires with an outward show of "gogetting" activity. Many of them are overtly dependent, demanding, or disgruntled persons. In such individuals, the dependent tendencies are frustrated not by internal repudiation, but by external circumstances. But even in these overtly demanding patients, a definite conflict about dependent cravings can be discovered. The crucial psychological finding in all ulcer patients is the frustration (external or internal) of passive, dependent, and love-demanding desires that cannot be gratified in normal relationships.

Onset of illness occurs when the intensity of the patient's unsatisfied dependent cravings increases either because of external deprivation or because the patient defends against his cravings by assuming increased responsibilities. The external deprivation often consists in the loss of a person upon whom the patient has been dependent, in leaving home, or in losing money or a position that had given the patient a sense of security. The increased responsibility may take the form of marriage or the birth of a child or the assumption of a more responsible job.

These original formulations utilized at the beginning of the project are now considered only approximately correct. Our study was aimed at testing the researchers' ability to diagnose the seven diseases by a method that will be described in the following chapter. It was both inevitable and fortunate that these studies furnished an opportunity to improve the original formulations. We hope to be able further to revise them with greater precision and thus to increase their value in prediction and explanation. The improved and revised formulations will be presented in the second volume.

CHAPTER TWO

Research Design and Procedure

Early clinical studies provided strong evidence for the association of distinct personality constellations with seven medically identified psychosomatic disease entities. Now a new research was undertaken to investigate further the area of psychosomatic specificity. The overall hypothesis to be tested was this: It is possible to make the correct diagnosis of any one of seven specific organic disorders, without the help of any organic-medical clues, merely on the basis of the formulation of psychodynamic and psychogenetic patterns derived from the study of psychiatric-anamnestic interview protocols. The assumption underlying this research was that each of the seven disorders is associated with a typical psychological configuration that is characteristic for (though not unique to) the specific disease.

Essentially the research design consisted of getting primary data from patients having one of the seven diseases, abstracting from this clinical information a pattern or configuration which could be matched with the previously stated disease formulations, and arriving at a somatic diagnosis from the psychological material. As a validity check, we used the objective diagnosis made by a discipline outside of psychoanalytic psychiatry, namely that of internal medicine.

Data Collection: Criteria and Procedures

The nuclear operating principle of our research involved testing our ability to arrive at a somatic diagnosis from a formulation based on the psychogenetic and psychodynamic construction of the personality structure of the patient and of the relationship of the onset and exacerbating periods of the disease to this personality structure.

One of our first tasks was the selection of patients to be interviewed by a member of the research team. This involved the establishment of uniform medical criteria for the diseases studied, and these were obtained from recognized specialists in internal medicine. Additional specific requirements established for case selection were the following.

1. The patient had to have only one of the seven organic conditions.

2. The present disease must have been active at the time of the interview, and no drastic medical or surgical therapeutic device could have been employed. Thus patients receiving drugs affecting psychological patterns, such as ACTH, or individuals who had had surgical extirpative procedures for their disease were excluded.

3. The disease had to have its onset after the completion of puberty, and the patient could not be over age 70.

4. The patient had to be capable of verbalization, not be overtly or manifestly psychotic, be available for additional interviewing if this was deemed necessary, and be generally cooperative with the referring physician or hospital.

If a patient met all of the predetermined criteria, he still had to be approved by our medical consultant before being interviewed so that an additional medical diagnostic evaluation could be obtained on each case. Seriously ill patients were usually excluded.

Our patients came to us from the private practice of recognized internists or from the clinical facilities of teaching hospitals in Chicago. Rarely did we use more than two or three cases from any one referring practitioner. We utilized both hospitalized and ambulatory cases, feeling that the ambulatory patient would provide a check on the possibility that hospitalization might affect our data. We included patients who had been ill for some time as well as individuals who had only recently developed their somatic condition. Our patients came from various socioeconomic and cultural settings. After statistical consultation, we decided that we would require a minimum of ten cases in each of the seven disease categories that we were investigating. Further, subjects were so chosen that there were at least five male and five female patients in each disease category.

The second step of our procedure was the interview. The interviewer role was rotated among the members of the analytic group, all of whom were familiar with the categories of information needed in our study.

The entire interview was recorded on a Gray Audograph. The recording was explained to the patient before the actual interview, and the recording apparatus was visible to him throughout the interview.

We used the associative interviewing method described by Felix

Deutsch, augmented by standardized questions asked of each patient. One set of standardized questions was designed to fill out the historical background, to secure dreams, associations, fantasies, answers to projective questions, and memories; another set of questions, routinely asked at the end of each case interview, touched upon essential criteria for onset dynamics and specific characterological traits associated with the seven diseases.

After transcription of the interview, the interviewer edited the verbatim record, deleting medical clues and other extraneous information and substituting the words "disease discovered" or "omission." Usually one exacerbation and remission episode was permitted to remain in the record; all medical data around this episode, of course, were eliminated. The exacerbation report kept in the record was usually that episode about which the greatest amount of psychological material was elicited. The record was edited in such a fashion that onset times were rarely given in exact months or seasons. The word "omission" appearing in the final record could mean that anything from a few words to several pages of material had been removed; there was no way of knowing how much. The name of the interviewer or other physician did not appear in the record. The censored record was then sent to a medical editor, who went over it once more, applying various standardized criteria, to screen out any remaining medical clues overlooked by the analyst interviewer. The resulting final, doubly expurgated record was retyped on a stencil, and multigraphed copies of the interview were prepared.

We were aware of the limited amount of information we could get about an individual case with the single or double interview method. At the outset, however, we felt that for purposes of this specific experimental approach, we would limit ourselves to the data that could be obtained from one, two, or three interviews prior to any psychotherapy. We found that if a patient with one of these diseases was interviewed after a prolonged and intensive therapeutic relationship had been established, it was no longer possible to elicit the kind of information that was helpful to us in preparing a psychodynamic and psychogenetic formulation from which a somatic diagnosis could be made. Instead, one found insights and transference reactions which contaminated and colored the available information so that, unless one had an opportunity to read the complete record of the treatment, the entire dynamic trend was likely to be lost. Shifting defensive positions also assumed different significance after therapy had commenced. Thus another criterion for case selection was that the patient must have had no previous psychotherapy or intensive psychoanalytic experience.

We interviewed only patients having one of the seven diseases that we were studying. Our theoretical position does not assume an exclusive and unique correlation between the psychological constellations and the existing organic disease. Thus patients not having the organic disease could conceivably have a psychological pattern similar to that found in patients with the somatic condition. Without an indicator of somatic or constitutional predisposition, our discrimination of psychological constellations could not yield meaningful data; hence we excluded from our patient population anyone not having one of the seven disorders.

The final processed interview was distributed to two groups of predictive judges. The experimental team was the analytic group, and the "control" team was the medical internist group headed by Mark Lepper. All members of the analytic group were trained and experienced psychoanalysts. The internist group, closely matched in terms of training and experience, consisted of physicians whose practice was primarily that of internal medicine, who came in contact with the particular types of patients studied by us, and who were neither identified with nor biased against a psychosomatic approach. We selected the members of this group after consultation with recognized medical authorities in Chicago. The main function of the group was to serve as a check against the possible use of subtle medical clues that might have remained in the record despite double censorship. Since all of the analytic team members were medically trained, this "control" measure seemed to be indicated.

During the pilot study certain information did often remain in the record, and this allowed the internist group to make diagnoses with considerably more accuracy than chance would predict. These performances of the internists were checked by the medical censors, who became increasingly skilled at deleting particular kinds of information of somatic diagnostic significance. In this way, the internist group contributed to the efficiency of the medical censorship. It was hoped that ideally the medical censorship could get to the point where there would be no clues for the medical team. This goal was, of course, an impossibility, since physicians who have had contact with particular types of patients over long periods of time, or with many patients of a particular diagnostic category, intuitively perceive sociological and psychological reaction patterns that can be used in making a diagnosis. Certain factual information such as age and sex could not be eliminated. Although this might be of diagnostic importance, we did not view it as necessarily interfering with the type of hypothesis testing that we were engaged in. The internists could use whatever data and logic they wished, provided they listed the reasoning and evidence employed in arriving at a particular diagnosis.

We utilized a retrospective predictive methodology in our research. The internist group attempted to arrive at a medical diagnosis by studying the identical interview material that the analytic group used for their dynamic reconstructions. We required that both groups list the data, inferences, deductions, documented rationale, reasoning, and various other components that led them to the particular diagnosis that they made. Thus both the internists and the analysts were required to spell out their specific reasons for a diagnosis. These might include pure hunches, undetected medical clues, or psychological and sociological data.

The reports of the internist group were not available to the analytic group, and the analytic formulations were not distributed to the internists. In order to keep the predictive teams apart, no research communication was maintained between the two groups. Only after all the cases had been interviewed and processed was there a study by the data analysis team of the internists' reports and the evidence or inferences they used in arriving at diagnoses. This procedure is more fully reported in chapter 4.

The individual members of the analytic predictive team received the multigraphed doubly censored case protocol several weeks prior to the session in which it was to be discussed. A two-hour seminar, at which an individual case was discussed, was held each week. Before a case meeting each analytic judge prepared a carefully documented and written personality construction of the patient to be discussed, an analysis of the onset situation and the exacerbating or remission period, an assessment of the interpersonal relationship that was manifested during the interview, as well as a discussion of the reported dreams, fantasies, and other characterological aspects of this particular patient. On the basis of this multifaceted formulation, the analytic judge attempted to reconstruct the genetic, dynamic, and psychoeconomic status of the patient. From this formulation the somatic diagnosis was made. A discussion of alternative diagnoses was also presented. Evidence for and against particular diagnoses was put forth. We were interested in the somatic diagnosis and in the differential diagnoses considered with the documented positive and negative evidence for and against particular diseases.

To indicate the degree of certainty with which the diagnosis was made, each analytic judge subjectively rated his diagnosis "A," "B," "C"—"A" indicating the highest degree of diagnostic certainty and "C" the lowest. As there were seven diagnostic possibilities, each pre-group diagnosis could be quantatively weighted from one to seven. Thus one might have a high degree of certainty about the adequacy of case information for formulation, coupled with only one diagnosis, and this would be reported as, for example, "peptic ulcer 7A." A divided judgment with less certainty about diagnosis might be designated "peptic ulcer 4, ulcerative colitis 3," but "A" about adequacy of information.

If a diagnosis was given less than four points, it was not counted as a positive diagnosis even though it happened to be correct. For example, if in a particular case the diagnosis was given as "peptic ulcer 3, ulcerative colitis 3, asthma 1," this would be recorded as incorrect whether the diagnosis actually was peptic ulcer, ulcerative colitis, or asthma. We strove to have only one diagnosis. Such splitting, however, has enabled us to identify certain cluster foci that help us to understand points of confluence in some of the syndromes studied. These clusters will be useful in our later studies.

In his written formulation, prepared before the meeting, each analytic judge tried to discuss all the points mentioned above. At the start of the seminar, before any discussion, the secretary recorded the initial qualitative diagnostic impression of each participant, as well as the specific weighting he gave to it. The analytic interviewer of the particular case, though present at the meeting, sat at the back of the room, hidden from the judges by a screen. He was thus able to avoid possible contamination of the group communication process by his presence while listening to the group deliberations for the purpose of later discussion. After each member had given his initial diagnostic impression, the previously prepared formulations were read aloud. Individuals making the same diagnosis read their presentations consecutively. Members with the strongest conviction about the validity of their formulations usually presented their material last, since we found that this procedure minimized excessive defensiveness on the part of the other participants and influenced the uncommitted judges less. At the time of the reading we were primarily concerned with understanding the clinical material and so did not focus upon the diagnostic considerations. As the discussion proceeded, individuals attempted to spell out areas of agreement and divergence. The quantity and quality of psychodynamic evidence in these areas was carefully reviewed and evaluated. A single case might be discussed for several meetings to allow complete exploration of all points. All meetings were recorded on a Gray Audograph to give us a record of the spontaneous discussion as well as to allow a later study of the group dynamic interactions.

Occasionally we discovered that the initial 40- to 100-page interview had serious information gaps. It might be decided, for example, that a particular point of interpretive divergence was due to a different emphasis upon a given fact, incident, or affect expression in the history, which might be clarified by additional data. Again, in some instances, members of the group were unable to arrive at a diagnosis even though they had prepared a written psychological formulation. They gave as their diagnostic impression "no diagnosis." This response was most often used when the interview had yielded inadequate information or when the available information could not be understood in terms of the patterns characteristically associated with the disease. The possibility was not eliminated from consideration that other previously unidentified psychological patterns might be correlated with the disease, but these findings were explicitly stated at the time of formulation discussion.

If it was felt that disagreements based on a lack of information could be resolved by another interview containing specific facts, this was requested and the case remained open. At the end of each discussion period, however, whether or not a further interview was requested, a tentative diagnostic commitment was made by all the analytic judges. The purpose of this diagnostic commitment was to provide data that might later indicate how much a particular individual had been convinced either by other members of the group or by particular information that he may have overlooked or misunderstood in the first interview and which came to light during the group discussion.

Requested additional interviews were subjected to the rigid censoring procedures described above, but they differed in several aspects from first interviews. The group directed the interviewer to ask specific questions in a direct fashion to elicit particular information. If such questions had been asked in the first interview, they might have been interpreted as "cuing."

Having the patient talk about how he felt after the first interview sometimes was of diagnostic significance. For example, it had been our experience that patients with bronchial asthma usually felt better or had a remission after their first talk with the analytic interviewer. The meaning of this remission ties in very directly with our psychodynamic hypotheses about a major conflict area in asthma. Thus in such an instance the group might be very much interested in knowing what happened after the first interview. In the second interview there was also an opportunity to get reports of dreams that might have occurred in the intervening period. For example, one patient told a dream that threw light on the transference implications of his first interview, and these permitted greater understanding of certain components of this patient's personality.

The requested interview was processed in the same way as the initial interview, and each member prepared an amended formulation, which might be much different from the one he had prepared previously. A meeting was held to discuss the additional information, and once more the new initial diagnostic impression was recorded before any specific comments were made. Again the group discussed the entire question of alternative diagnosis, based upon the additional information.

When the analytic group finally agreed that an end point had been reached for discussion of the available interview data and that more information would not aid in gaining formulation or diagnosis consensus, the closing procedure took place. Each member of the group went on record with his final diagnosis, and after this point the interviewer, who had been sitting behind the screen during the hours of discussion, emerged and revealed the actual medical diagnosis. He also discussed the case as he understood it, and he evaluated the group's performance individually and collectively. The next session might be devoted to a "post mortem" a critical examination of the diagnostic agreements or disagreements. The formulations were checked for factual consistency, for sufficiency and also for any undue emotional influencing by a single member who might have "stampeded" the group into premature diagnosis, or persuaded them with the slanted weighting of his particular interpretive version. Through this type of meeting, the group learned of its technical and emotional errors and functioned at increasingly higher levels of reconstructive efficiency (though not necessarily concomitant diagnostic accuracy). We also gained additional information for revising the specific formulations for the disease and were able to understand, identify, and enumerate features that had not previously been considered in the initial formulations for some of the diseases.

Before the analytic group heard the actual somatic diagnosis from the interviewer, it was decided whether or not the case protocol was an accepted one and could be sent to the internist group. In this way, we spared our internist group the processing of inadequate protocols that would have had to be eliminated. The number of these rejected cases was 25. At times a case was disqualified for various technical reasons even where we later learned we had 100% diagnostic accuracy. We eliminated 14 cases where there was inadequate information for formulations and further interviews were impossible, even though one might make an enlightened speculation about the diagnosis. Six cases were found not to meet the criteria of having just one of the specified seven diseases. Five cases were rejected because of obvious though previously missed cuing.

Forty-one cases were processed in the initial pilot period. In September, 1953, the formal research project commenced. Primary clinical data were obtained from 108 different patients. After the 25 cases mentioned above had been rejected, 83 cases remained. This group consisted of 46 male patients and 37 female patients.

Our formal experimental data consisted of approximately 1,500 different analytic formulations with accompanying qualitative and quantitative diagnostic judgments, and of 1,500 different diagnostic judgments made by our medical internist predictive group.

Reliability and Validity

This research employed multiple judges making multiple judgments over time. Thus at any one time there was an average of eight analytic predictive judges, ten medical predictive judges, and three to four interviewer cue detection judges, most of whom participated in the entire project. This has permitted us, for each case, to check each judge's performance against that of every other judge carrying out the same role. Studies of this form of consistency of performance, or reliability were made.

The validity of the diagnoses by the analysts and by the internists could be checked quickly and objectively, since the medical diagnosis was available immediately upon completion of a case study. The criterion was provided by a discipline (internal medicine) other than the one involved in the collection of the data for predictive diagnosis and for the interpretive theoretical framework of understanding the primary data. This research dealt only with psychosomatic correlations, not causative factors. Thus the research did not attempt to establish the etiological contributors to the disease process, and did not attempt to demonstrate the absolute correctness of the underlying formulations of the seven diseases studied. In evaluating the diagnostic formulations of each analytic judge, one must recognize the possibility that for a particular case or disease category, implicit and intuitive factors may have played a part in identifying psychodynamic patterns different from the explicitly stated formulations of the research. For purposes of testing the specificity hypothesis, however, the objective medical diagnosis proved entirely adequate as a criterion for assessing diagnostic accuracy.

A further methodological consideration related to this objective diagnostic criterion, however, requires discussion. Because the actual medical diagnosis was established and so could be used to validate a diagnostic prediction, it also became a source of potential methodological error, namely, interviewer cuing. This problem is discussed more fully in chapter 5. Methodologically, whenever a result is already known and a "blind" retrospective predictive study is undertaken, the danger of potential illegitimate communication must be kept in mind and cannot with absolute certainty be eliminated. On the other hand, if one makes anterospective predictions where outcome or end product is not yet available, a check on the validity of the predictions is not immediately, and in some instances may never be, possible, thus interfering with this crucial phase of the research. We attempted to consider these issues as carefully as possible and report our results with these contingencies in mind.

Data Processing and Analysis

After our collection of primary data had been completed, the initial task of processing and analyzing these data belonged to our statistician and our research secretary.

The research secretary recorded the quantitative and qualitative diagnostic commitments of the analytic group and served as the main communication link with the internist group. She sent the case material to the internists and received their diagnostic formulations. These were available to no one but the statistician. The research secretary also acted as coordinator with the case-selection medical consultant and regulated interview traffic from interviewer to case editor to analytic and internist groups; in addition she was the sole custodian of all of the qualitative and quantitative judgments that were collected. She recorded these on forms provided by our statistician and periodically sent the recorded data to him. In accordance with previous methodological discussions he processed the results and prepared them for subsequent analysis.

As indicated earlier, our patient distribution was a minimum of five male and five female cases for each disease category. This does not mean that every disease group had only ten cases; in some categories there were larger numbers. The flow and regulation of types of cases needed was arranged by the medical consultant and the statistician.

The statistical results of our study were prepared and presented to the core research group, which has written the explanatory sections to augment the statistical tables and charts in this volume.

Data Presentation

Scientific method does not make discoveries but is a way of testing a discovery and so increasing the probability of its validity. When we can identify a pattern, understand its components, recognize its genetic roots, appreciate its purpose in the past and in the present (even if it is inappropriate to the present), we are in a better position to understand what can be done about altering it if this is indicated as possible. After we have obtained refined data, we can present results and conclusions which may add to or modify existing theory.

No conclusions are final or complete; they are intermediate until newer questions and findings require additional investigations. We do not view this research as a final definitive study of psychophysiological correlations. Various additional projects relating to further analysis of some of the data already collected have been started, and clinical and theoretical research needed to present further elaborations of the specificity theory have begun.

CHAPTER THREE

Quantitative Findings for the Analytic Judges

This chapter presents the results of quantitative analyses of the diagnoses made by the analyst judges. Its main focus is on the success of these diagnoses and on some of the factors that may have contributed to their correctness. Although these findings are of major importance, they cannot be definitely evaluated by themselves; final interpretation must be withheld until the findings of the medical control and interviewer cue data, presented in later chapters, have been considered.

An Overview of the Findings

A large proportion of the diagnoses made by the analytic judges were correct. Of the initial diagnoses, those made before the final group discussion of the cases, 41% were correct. Fifty-one per cent of the final diagnoses, made after the last discussion, were correct.

These average levels of success hide a considerable degree of variation. The analysts did better on some diseases (such as arthritis) and less well on others (such as hypertension and ulcer). The variation was even greater for the 14 disease-sex categories, the cases grouped by disease and sex. The success range among the initial diagnoses was from 58% for males with arthritis to 16% for female ulcer cases.

Even within each of the disease-sex categories, there was marked variation. On the one hand, each category contained at least one case for which no analyst made the correct initial diagnosis; on the other hand, in all but two categories, there was a case for which 75% or more of the analysts made correct initial diagnoses. Looking at the data another way, the majority of the analysts were correct on 40% of the cases, few or none of the analysts were correct on 46%, and about half the group were correct on the remaining 14%.

What might account for such wide variation? One possibility was that some wrong diagnoses might stem from confusion between the actual disease and another disease for which a similar psychological pattern had been postulated. Detailed examination indicated that such a tendency was true only to a limited extent. More generally, the data suggest that some kinds of confusions between diseases were more likely than others: for a given actual disease, the wrong diagnoses often specified one disease more frequently than any other.

Each analytic judge had a general level of diagnostic success exceeding that expected on the basis of chance (one out of seven, or about 14%), although the judges varied considerably in their overall level of correctness. Those who were more successful on male cases tended also to be more successful on female cases. Unsuccessful efforts were made to relate these individual differences to certain personal data on the analysts, such as their degree of interest in particular diseases and their judgment about which of these diseases they themselves would be most likely to have. There was some evidence that the analysts were more likely to be correct when they specified one disease and mentioned no alternative or second choice.

The changes from initial to final diagnoses were also studied. Although the same diagnosis was made in most instances, there were more changes from incorrect to correct diagnosis than changes of any other kind.

Finally, we attempted to account for the different degrees of success on the various cases. The analytic group did not do better or worse on cases where the duration of the disease had been especially long, nor on the cases where the protocol included more than one interview.

A Detailed Picture of the Findings

For most of the findings reported here, all available data were used. In studying the performance of the individual analytic judges, however, the data are limited to the nine who participated in 50 to 74 cases each. Three judges who worked on only 10 to 17 cases, early in the series, were not studied separately.

The data presented below are based on 83 cases of the basic series begun in the fall of 1953. There were 46 males and 37 females. For each disease, at least five male and five female cases were used, and in some instances there were six or seven cases of the same sex. The only unusual frequency was 12 for the male ulcer category.

Although at least five cases of each category were seen by the group, an individual judge usually saw fewer than that number, for various reasons: he could not participate because he was the interviewer or was ill or because the case was seen before he joined the group. Thus the average (mean) number of cases in each disease-sex group seen by each judge was four. On the other hand, the typical (modal) case was judged by eight analysts, with a variation from five to nine for different cases.

Whenever a judge made a diagnosis, he could name one disease, name more than one disease, or refrain from making a diagnosis. In the data reported below, unless otherwise indicated, every opportunity to make a diagnosis is counted, even the instances of refraining, or "no diagnosis."

The only question about what comprises a correct diagnosis arose when an analyst mentioned more than one disease. Such instances were counted as correct if the analyst indicated that one disease (the actual one) seemed to him more likely than not. Thus a judge might indicate as his diagnosis, "ulcer or colitis, but more probably ulcer." Another might say "ulcer, but possibly colitis, asthma, or neurodermatitis." If the case were actually ulcer, both judges would be credited with a correct diagnosis.

On the other hand, one judge might say "ulcer or colitis—I can't decide." Another might say "ulcer, colitis, or asthma." Still another might say "no diagnosis, but a preference for ulcer." All three of these would be counted as wrong, whatever the actual disease. Thus the criterion of correctness was a strict one: no credit was given for diagnoses that were partially correct. Hence the findings present a conservative picture of the success of the diagnostic judges.

In the statistical analyses, the initial diagnoses will be emphasized. These were the last diagnoses made independently by each judge. When the judges received all the interview material (consisting of one or more interviews) at the same time, only one set of initial diagnoses was made and reported before the group discussion. When additional interview material was requested by the group after a discussion, another set of initial diagnoses was made after seeing this additional material, and this set was used in the statistical analyses. Such diagnoses were presumably influenced by the preceding discussion and therefore were not as independent as the initial diagnoses. It is also possible that the second set might be more correct, a possibility studied in the research and reported later in this chapter. Yet, in those cases where two blocks of interview information were given the judges at different times, it would clearly be inappropriate to use only the diagnoses based on the first block.

Thus in whole or in large part the initial diagnoses were based on the psychodynamic pictures constructed by each analyst individually and independently. These diagnoses provided better evidence of the capacity of each analyst to make a correct formulation of each case than the final diagnoses, which might in any one case be greatly influenced by the persuasiveness of one judge in convincing others that he was right in the group discussion. Since the statistical treatment of the data assumed that diagnoses were made independently, the initial diagnoses were given primary emphasis in the studies reported below.

Moreover, for most cases, the final diagnoses of the analysts equaled or exceeded the initial diagnoses in accuracy (see "Shifts in Diagnoses from Initial to Final" below). So once the statistical significance of the initial diagnoses had been determined, it was unnecessary to make the same statistical analyses of the final diagnoses.

The Overall Results for Analysts' Diagnoses

Percentage of Correct Initial Diagnoses

Table 1 shows the percentage of correct initial diagnoses made by the analysts. Each entry is the average (mean) of the values for the nine analysts who judged a majority of the total series of cases. For example,

Table 1

Analysts' Correct Initial Diagnoses

(Per Cent)

Bronchial Asthma	Neurodermatitis	Rheumatoid Arthritis	Hypertension	Ulcerative Colitis	Peptic Ulcer	Thyrotoxicosis	Mean
42	42	51	32	44	32	46	41

the proportion of asthma cases on which each analyst made a correct initial diagnosis was determined; these nine values had a mean of 42%. This procedure was followed so that the overall value would not be biased by one particularly successful or unsuccessful judge who happened to judge more cases than the others.

For the seven diseases, the mean proportion correct is 41%, but the means for different diseases range from a high of 51% for arthritis to a low of 32% for both hypertension and ulcer.

Table 2

Analysts' Correct Initial Diagnoses: by Sex

(Per Cent)

	Bronchial Asthma	Neurodermatitis	Rheumatoid Arthritis	Hypertension	Ulcerative Colitis	Peptic Ulcer	Thyrotoxicosis	Mean
Male cases	45	27	58	42	42	49	38	43
Female cases	39	57	44	22	46	16	53	40

The same data broken down by the sex of the case are shown in Table 2. The accuracy of the analytic group is slightly higher for the male cases generally. The striking fact, however, is the greater diagnostic accuracy for one sex or the other within a single group. For neurodermatitis cases the group got 57% right for females but only 27% for males. On the other hand, 49% of the group's diagnoses of ulcer were correct for males but only 16% for females. The 42% and 22% figures for hypertension are also divergent. Some fluctuation in percentage is to be expected between different samples, especially when the samples are small. But statistical tests indicate clearly that diagnostic success varied not just with disease but (and more especially) with disease-sex grouping also.

Statistical Significance

These figures are impressive, but the question arises how much confidence can be placed in them. To obtain an answer, we evaluated the data statistically to determine how often such results might occur on the basis of chance.

The procedure can be illustrated by the results for one group: male cases of thyrotoxicosis (see Table 3). Looking at Case T1, we ask how

Table 3

Statistical Significance of Results
Male Cases of Thyrotoxicosis, Analysts' Initial Diagnoses

Case Number	Number of Correct Diagnoses	Total Number of Diagnoses	Probability of this or better result
T1	5	6	.00002
T2	3	8	.021
T3	1	7	.442
T4	0	7	1.000
T5	4	7	.001

often one would expect to find five correct diagnoses out of six, on the basis of chance alone. The answer depends upon the likelihood of each diagnosis being correct: if there were two diseases, each judge could be expected to be right half the time; with seven diseases, the probability of success is theoretically one out of seven.

But there is a complication stemming from the fact that the analysts did not use each of the seven diagnoses equally often. On male cases, the distribution of stated diagnoses was as follows: arthritis 13%, asthma 17%, colitis 19%, hypertension 11%, neurodermatitis 11%, thyrotoxicosis 8%, and ulcer 21%. For female cases, the distribution was somewhat different: arthritis 16%, asthma 15%, colitis 11%, hypertension 11%, neurodermatitis 18%, thyrotoxicosis 18%, and ulcer 10%. Since the analysts used the diagnosis of colitis for more than one-seventh of the male cases, and the diagnosis of thyrotoxicosis for less than one-seventh, they were more likely on the basis of chance to be right when they called a case colitis than when they called it thyrotoxicosis. (This relationship can be seen clearly at the extreme: if they had called all cases colitis, they would have been right on every case that was actually colitis and wrong on all other cases. The principle as stated ignores the frequency of actual cases of each disease because we are considering the probability of being correct on a single case which was actually colitis, as the first step toward assessing the success of the analysts on all colitis cases.) In testing the statistical significance of the data in Tables 1 and 2, the probabilities used were the proportions of all cases that were diagnosed as each disease (given above): for example, for all the male cases the diagnosis of thyrotoxicosis was made 8% of the time, and this was the probability used in the statistical analysis.

It may occur to the reader that some analysts might use a given diagnosis more than other analysts did; if so, perhaps a different proportion should be used for each analyst. A study of this point indicated that although some analysts did show clear deviations of this sort, the total number of marked deviations was little more than would be expected from fluctuations in small samples (each analyst typically saw only four cases of each sex for each disease).

Returning to Case T1, how often would one find a result as good as or better than five out of six correct? The answer can be obtained from tables of the binomial distribution, which show, for example, how often one would expect, when tossing six coins, to obtain six heads, five heads, and so on. They also give the expected frequencies when the probability for each event is some value other than .50. In the present case, where the probability is .08 for each analyst, the table shows that six out of six would occur by chance only three times in ten million trials (.0000003), and that five out of six would occur slightly less than twice in one hundred thousand trials (.0000181). So the chances of five or six correct diagnoses out of six is the sum of these values, .0000184, or roughly .00002. This is the value in Table 3 for Case T1.

Note that the value sought is not the probability of just the obtained result (five out of six), but rather the probability of that result and of any more favorable one (five *or* six out of six).

The probability for each of the other cases can be determined by the same method. The probability is 1.000 for Case T4 because zero or better includes all possible results.

The five probabilities in Table 3 show marked variation. What is the likelihood of obtaining a set of probabilities as good as or better than these? To answer this question, a more complex statistical procedure is necessary. Each empirical probability can be converted into a statistic known as chi-square and (unlike the probabilities) these converted values can legitimately be added. The likelihood of obtaining the total chi-square or a higher one can be determined from standard tables. For the male thyrotoxicosis cases, the value is less than .001 (which is as far as the standard tables go). Hence the findings for the male thyrotoxicosis cases cannot be attributed to chance.

A similar procedure was carried out for the other sets of cases. The results are given in Table 4. They are reported in terms of the levels commonly used in statistical analysis: thus .01 indicates a result which by chance would occur less than once in 100, but more than once in 1,000.

Table 4

Statistical Significance of Results for Analysts' Initial Diagnoses

	Bronchial Asthma	Neurodermatitis	Rheumatoid Arthritis	Hypertension	Ulcerative Colitis	Peptic Ulcer	Thyrotoxicosis
Male cases	.01	.01	.001	.001	.01	.001	.001
Female cases	.001	.001	.001	.05	.001	.70	.001

NOTE: Each entry is the obtained level of statistical significance, the probability of obtaining the given result by chance.

Most of the results are clearly significant. The value of .05 for female cases of hypertension is just within the conventionally acceptable level. The .70 value for female ulcer cases, however, is not statistically significant —it obviously could have occurred by chance. Although 16% of the diagnoses were correct for this group, this is little better than 14% (one out of seven) or 12%, the actual frequency of such diagnoses. The lack of success for these cases presents a problem requiring further investigation and study.

The overall conclusion is clear: the analysts were, in general, able to diagnose cases of the seven diseases with better than chance accuracy. The picture is so definite that there is no need to determine the significance for all cases of each sex, or for all cases of each disease.

Percentage of Correct Final Diagnoses

Proportional values of correct final diagnoses are presented in the upper part of Table 5. Note that the individual values for all cases (male and female) of each disease are very close to the total mean for all diseases—51%. The exceptions are arthritis (66%) and ulcer (34%). These combined values, however, hide the differences for each sex and between sexes, as shown in the second and third rows of the table. For male cases,

Table 5

Summary of Analysts' Correct Diagnoses (Per Cent)

	Bronchial Asthma	Neurodermatitis	Rheumatoid Arthritis	Hypertension	Ulcerative Colitis	Peptic Ulcer	Thyrotoxicosis	Mean
FINAL DIAGNOSES								
All cases	50	52	66	40	58	34	54	51
Male cases	49	44	80	47	56	54	49	54
Female cases	51	60	53	33	61	13	59	47
INITIAL DIAGNOSES[a]								
All cases	42	42	51	32	44	32	46	41
Male cases	45	27	58	42	42	49	38	43
Female cases	39	57	44	22	46	16	53	40
DIFFERENCE								
All cases	8	10	15	8	14	2	8	10
Male cases	4	17	22	5	14	5	11	11
Female cases	12	3	9	11	15	−3	6	7

[a] Reproduced from Tables 1 and 2 for comparison.

the final diagnoses were very successful on cases of arthritis: among the other six diseases, there was not much variation in success. For female cases, the analysts did well on colitis and neurodermatitis, fairly well on thyrotoxicosis, arthritis, and asthma, poorly on hypertension, and very poorly on ulcer.

The lower section of the table makes a comparison between initial and final diagnoses. This comparison will be considered more fully in a later section, but it may be noted here that there is an overall gain of 10% for final diagnoses. The gain in accuracy varies with disease and sex. The largest gain is 22% (from 58% to 80%) for male arthritis, and there is actually a loss (from 16% to 13%) on female ulcer, the group on which the analysts did so poorly.

Differing Degrees of Success on Individual Cases

As Table 3 suggests, some cases were diagnosed correctly by a majority of the analysts and some cases were missed by most of the group. The distribution of success rates for all cases is indicated in Figure 1.

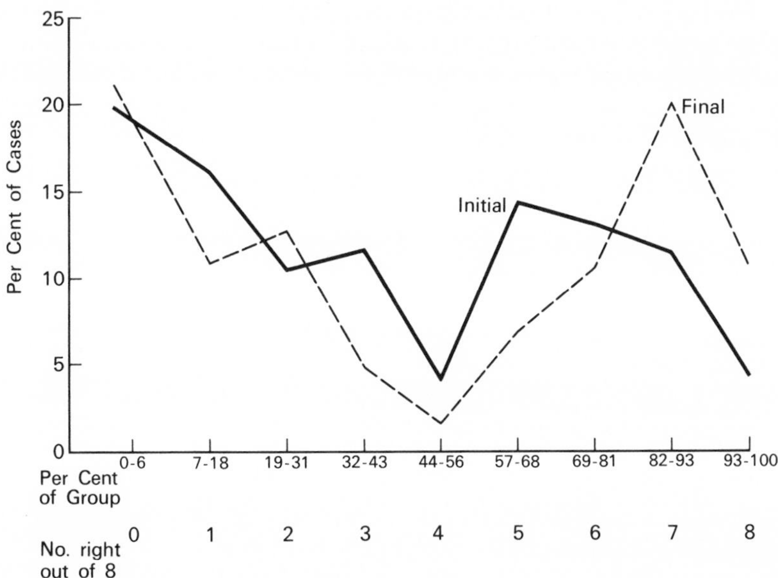

FIG. 1. Distribution of relative success (portion of analytic group correct) for initial and final diagnoses.

The height of the solid line shows how often the group obtained a given degree of success in the initial diagnoses. Degrees of success are indicated along the horizontal axis in terms of the percentage of the group who were correct and also in terms of the number correct out of eight. (Since not all cases were judged by exactly eight analysts, these are merely for ease in interpreting the percentage figures.) Thus, starting from the left end of the solid line, the graph shows that in 20% of the cases, none of the analysts was correct; one was correct in 16%, two were correct in 10%, and three were correct in 11%. Then comes a peculiar dip: four analysts were correct in only 4% of the cases. For five, six, and seven correct, there were 13%, 12%, and 11% of the cases respectively. Finally, all analysts were correct in 4%.

The striking feature of the graph is the piling up of cases toward the extremes. If all cases were equally difficult to diagnose, the graph would show the most frequent occurrence to be cases where three analysts were correct; very often, four or two would be correct; almost never would we find seven, eight, or none correct. This theoretical distribution is shown in Figure 2. A statistical test confirms the clear implication that the obtained distribution is different from such a theoretical one. We must therefore conclude that some cases were distinctly easier to diagnose than others or, conversely, that the errors tended to be concentrated on certain cases.

The broken line in Figure 1 gives the distribution for the final diagnoses of the analysts. At the left side, it resembles that for the initial diagnoses: 44% of the cases fall at the first three points. The dip in the middle,

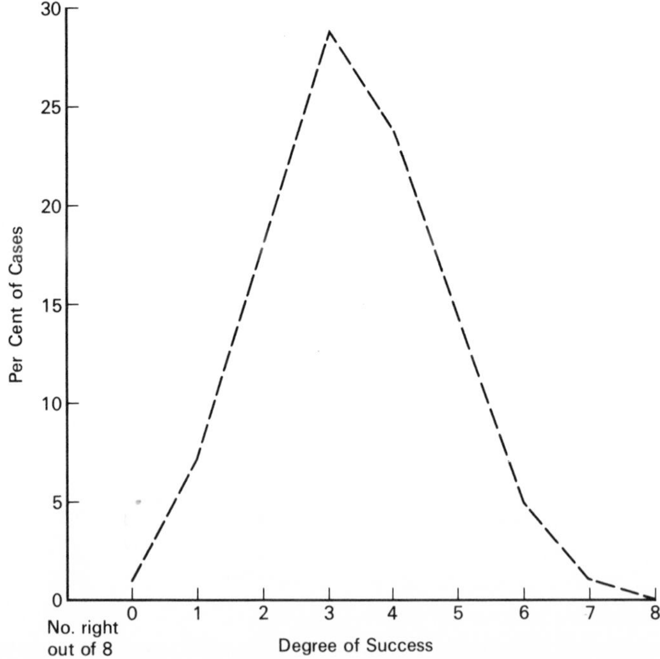

FIG. 2. Theoretical distribution expected when 41% of diagnoses are correct (41% represents the overall success of the analytic group's initial diagnoses).

however, is even more pronounced, and the piling up at the right is more marked. Thus the final diagnoses show this "mostly right or mostly wrong" trend even more than the initial ones. The differences between the distributions suggest that, in cases where three or more analysts made the same diagnosis (and the correct one) initially, other analysts tended to be convinced and to change their diagnoses to that one. (Studies of such shifts in diagnoses are reported later.) On the other hand, the presence of almost half the cases at the low or failure end of the distribution suggests that for a large block of cases, even the group's discussion did not facilitate accurate diagnoses.

The cases appear to fall into two groups with respect to the correctness of the analysts' diagnoses: for 46%, no more than two analysts out of eight made correct initial diagnoses; for 40%, at least five of the group were correct. From the data already presented, two points can be made. The failures were not confined to cases of either sex. Table 2 shows that the group was about equally successful with males and females; detailed studies show that the separate distributions for the two sexes are quite similar. Also, the failures were not restricted to certain diseases. Certain disease-sex groups, however, contributed more than their share to the incorrectly diagnosed cases: for instance, no female case of ulcer was diagnosed successfully by a majority of analysts.

Given the finding that the analysts were successful in about half the cases, why did they fail in the other half? The informational content of the interview protocol may have been insufficient. Again, the transcribed censored protocol omitted the richer material available in a face-to-face interaction, with its auditory and visual cues. The incorrect diagnoses might also be due to an analyst's limited experience with a particular psychodynamic pattern. In addition, the analyst may have been unable to see the correspondence between the patient's pattern and the theoretical formulation for the disease. Finally, there is the possibility that the theoretical formulations were limited or insufficient: for instance, for each of the seven diseases, there may be subtypes in which the basic conflict takes a form not previously recognized. A diagnosis might be incorrect for any one or more of these reasons.

Differences Between Diseases in the Analysts' Accuracy

Initial Diagnoses

The results reported above show that the analysts, as a group, did better on some diseases than on others. Another way of comparing the different diseases is to study the best performances of the several analysts: for any one disease, some of the analysts may have high accuracy even though the others do poorly and hence pull down the group average. So an examination of best performances can yield an estimate of the degree to which the psychological constellations of these patients could be matched with the pattern that had been identified with the patients' actual diseases in the conceptualizations of the analytic group.

The data presented below are based on conservative estimates of the success of each analyst on each disease. The results for Analyst C on male colitis cases can be used to illustrate the procedure. He participated in two such cases and was correct on both. But this 100% value is misleading.

Table 6

Correct Initial Diagnoses for the Nine Analysts on the Seven Diseases: Male Cases
(Per Cent)

Bronchial Asthma	Neurodermatitis	Rheumatoid Arthritis	Hypertension	Ulcerative Colitis	Peptic Ulcer	Thyrotoxicosis
57	40	75	83	50	83	75
50 } 50	33 } 34	67 } 67	67 } 69	33 } 36	60 } 66	50 } 55
43	29	60	57	25	55	40
43	25	60	50	25	50	40
40	25	50	50	25	50	40
33	25	50	25	25	38	33
29	20	40	25	15	36	25
25	0	40	20	11	33	25
20	0	40	0	0	33	0

NOTE: The values in each column are in order of size, regardless of the analyst. The single value to the right of each column is the mean of the top three values.

He used the diagnosis of colitis six times, and so he was right only 33% of the time. It can be argued that his success on colitis cases was in part due to his calling so many cases colitis. Hence a conservative estimate of his success is 33%, the lower of these two figures.

As another example, Analyst E was correct four of the five times (80%) he used the diagnosis of ulcer (for male cases). Of the 11 male cases of ulcer that he saw, however, he was correct on only four (36%). Again the conservative estimate of his success is the lower of these two figures, 36%.

Table 6 gives the results for the nine analysts on each disease, for male cases. The values are arranged in order of size, not by analyst. Each value is the lower one of the two figures discussed above: the number of correct diagnoses divided by the actual number of cases, and the number of correct diagnoses divided by the number of cases for which the analyst used the given diagnosis.

Even with this very conservative approach, the great majority of the values are above 14% (one out of seven). Only six of the values for males (10%) and 13 of the values for females (21%) are below that figure (see Table 7).

What was the level of the best performances for each disease? This question can be answered in various different ways. For example, one

Table 7

Correct Initial Diagnoses for the Nine Analysts on the Seven Diseases: Female Cases
(Per Cent)

Bronchial Asthma	Neuroder- matitis	Rheumatoid Arthritis	Hyper- tension	Ulcerative Colitis	Peptic Ulcer	Thyro- toxicosis
60	80	60	50	100	33	67
50 } 53	67 } 69	50 } 53	40 } 38	67 } 76	33 } 33	60 } 62
50	60	50	25	60	33	60
50	50	44	25	40	25	60
33	40	40	25	33	20	40
33	40	33	0	33	0	40
29	22	33	0	25	0	25
17	0	0	0	25	0	22
0	0	0	0	20	0	20

NOTE: The values in each column are in order of size, regardless of analyst. The single value to the right of each column is the mean of the top three values.

could look at the top performance by any analyst, such as the 75% for thyrotoxicosis. But this value is based on only four cases: if the analyst saw two more cases and missed on both, his value would drop to 50%.

A reasonable solution is to take the mean of the top three values. Since this method uses a larger number of observations, it avoids the problem of discriminating between relatively small and unreliable differences and provides a fairly stable estimate of the best performance. These means, typically based on about 13 cases, are given beside the three top values.

Examination of these means suggests three groups. For males, the values for arthritis, hypertension, and ulcer are near 67%, or two out of three correct. Those for asthma and thyrotoxicosis approximate half correct, and those for colitis and neurodermatitis are near 33%, or one-third correct. The psychological formulations postulated for the seven diseases presumably enable the analysts to do much better on the first three diseases than on the last two, but even on the best three, the performance is substantially less than 100%.

Comparable results for female cases are given in Table 7. The top diseases are colitis (76%), neurodermatitis (69%), and thyrotoxicosis (62%). The values for arthritis and asthma are near 50%, and those for hypertension and ulcer approximate 33%. As noted above in connection with the mean success of the whole group (Table 2), performance varies not just with disease but with disease and sex: the three diseases most successfully diagnosed for males are different from the top three for females.

These figures suggest that some diseases were easier for the analysts to identify, by means of the psychological pattern associated with the disease, than others. A number of other factors must be kept in mind, however. Data to be presented later show that accuracy of diagnosis varied with the analyst-judge and with the interviewer. Since the interviewer was always eliminated from the judging and since the assignment of interviewers could not be systematically controlled, the best performance on a disease is affected by who interviewed the several cases and was consequently eliminated as judge.

Another factor is the difference between patients. As shown in Figure 1, the group tended to be fairly successful or fairly unsuccessful on each case. Table 8 presents the proportion of the group who were successful on each case. For example, in the five cases of female neurodermatitis, the group was highly successful on four (71% or better), but no one was correct on the fifth. Why? Was this a case showing a new personality pattern not previously recognized? Was there something about the content or the course of the interview which misled the group? Or was the difficulty of another kind?

With respect to female hypertension, the group did fairly well on one case, fairly poorly on a second, about chance on a third, and completely missed the last two of the five. These data may indicate that the postulated psychological formulation fits only a small part of such cases. It is also possible that the proportion of cases in the general population that fit the formulation is much larger than these figures suggest and that the low proportion of successfully diagnosed cases is an accident of sampling: in the selection of only five cases we may by chance have obtained an unusually high proportion of cases not fitting the formulation. In Table 8, for every disease-sex group there is at least one entry of 0%: this means that there was at least one case in which no analyst was correct. In most of the groups, there was also at least one case on which all or all but one of the analysts were correct. The exceptions are female cases of colitis and hypertension, for which only a majority were correct on the most success-

Table 8

Ranking of the Cases by Percentage of Analysts Making Correct Initial Diagnoses on Each Case

Bronchial Asthma	Neuroder-matitis	Rheumatoid Arthritis	Hyper-tension	Ulcerative Colitis	Peptic Ulcer	Thyro-toxicosis
MALE CASES						
88	80	100	88	83[a]	100	83
67	62	88	75	43	86	57
57	12	67	50	28	71	38
40	0	38	50	25	62	14
17	0	0	25	0	62	0
12			20		57	
0			0		50	
					25	
					14	
					12	
					0	
					0	
FEMALE CASES						
88	83	88	62	75	33	100
75	75	75	25	62	25	71
43	71	38	12	38	14	62
14	71	17	0	28	12	29
12	0	0	0	0	12	0
0					0	

[a] Subsequent to the group's processing of this early case of spastic colitis, it was decided that this disease category should be restricted to cases with ulcerative colitis. This case was inadvertently included in all the analyses presented in this chapter and in the study of interviewer cues presented later. Without this case, the performance of the analytic group on male colitis cases would clearly be less favorable. Since it was one of the few cases not given to the internist group, it does not affect the essential comparison of the performance of the analytic group with that of the internists.

ful case, and female cases of ulcer—a group on which the analysts were consistently unsuccessful.

Various factors that may account for these findings have been noted in the preceding section. Whatever the interpretation, the striking fact remains: the analysts' success varied greatly from case to case, much more than could be expected on the basis of chance. The tendency of the group to be mostly right or mostly wrong, shown in Figure 1 for the entire set of cases, seems to hold for most of the separate disease-sex groups.

Final Diagnoses

The performance of the analytic group on final diagnoses (and, for comparison, figures given earlier for initial diagnoses) are shown in Tables 9

Table 9

Correct Final and Initial Diagnoses for the Nine Analysts on the Seven Diseases: Male Cases
(Per Cent)

Bronchial Asthma	Neuroder-matitis	Rheumatoid Arthritis	Hyper-tension	Ulcerative Colitis	Peptic Ulcer	Thyro-toxicosis
FINAL DIAGNOSES						
50	50	83	83	50	67	67
50 } 50	50 } 47	80 } 79	67 } 70	40 } 41	60 } 61	60 } 59
50	40	75	60	33	56	50
50	40	75	43	33	56	50
43	33	75	43	29	56	50
40	25	67	33	27	55	50
33	25	67	33	25	50	40
33	25	60	25	25	45	40
25	20	60	20	20	44	0
INITIAL DIAGNOSES						
57	40	75	83	50	83	75
50 } 50	33 } 34	67 } 67	67 } 69	33 } 36	60 } 66	50 } 55
43	29	60	57	25	55	40
43	25	60	50	25	50	40
40	25	50	50	25	50	40
33	25	50	25	25	38	33
29	20	40	25	15	36	25
25	0	40	20	11	33	25
20	0	40	0	0	33	0
DIFFERENCES IN MEANS OF TOP THREE ANALYSTS						
0	13	12	1	5	−5	4

NOTE: The values in each column are in order of size, regardless of analyst. The single value to the right of each column is the mean of the top three values. Data on initial diagnoses are reproduced from Table 6 for comparison.

and 10. The final values are generally higher than the comparable ones for initial diagnoses. Only one value for males and nine for females are below 14% (one out of seven).

The means of the three highest for each disease also tend to be above those for the initial diagnoses, as shown in the bottom part of each table. For males, the values for arthritis and neurodermatitis are clearly higher, but the value for ulcer drops a few points. The values for female cases of arthritis, asthma, and (especially) hypertension also are definitely above

Table 10

Correct Final and Initial Diagnoses for the Nine Analysts on the Seven Diseases: Female Cases
(Per Cent)

Bronchial Asthma	Neurodermatitis	Rheumatoid Arthritis	Hypertension	Ulcerative Colitis	Peptic Ulcer	Thyrotoxicosis
FINAL DIAGNOSES						
75	67	100	75	100	33	67
67 } 67	60 } 61	60 } 70	75 } 67	75 } 81	33 } 29	60 } 62
60	57	50	50	67	20	60
60	50	50	40	60	17	60
50	40	43	25	60	17	50
50	33	40	20	60	0	40
40	30	40	0	50	0	33
25	0	33	0	40	0	33
17	0	33	0	33	0	25
INITIAL DIAGNOSES						
60	80	60	50	100	33	67
50 } 53	67 } 69	50 } 53	40 } 38	67 } 76	33 } 33	60 } 62
50	60	50	25	60	33	60
50	50	44	25	40	25	60
33	40	40	25	33	20	40
33	40	33	0	33	0	40
29	22	33	0	25	0	25
17	0	0	0	25	0	22
0	0	0	0	20	0	20
DIFFERENCES IN MEANS OF TOP THREE ANALYSTS						
14	−8	17	29	5	−4	0

NOTE: The values in each column are in order of size, regardless of analyst. The single value to the right of each column is the mean of the top three values. Data on initial diagnoses are reproduced from Table 7 for comparison.

the initial values, but the values for neurodermatitis and ulcer are lower.

The relative order of the diseases with respect to accuracy is about the same as for initial diagnoses. In addition, the contrast between male and female cases appears again. Colitis is highest for females but lowest for males. Asthma and neurodermatitis are higher for female than for male, but the reverse is true for ulcer. On final diagnoses, the group clearly made its poorest performance on female ulcer cases.

Table 11

Percentage of Analysts Making Correct Final Diagnoses on Each Case

Bronchial Asthma	Neuroder-matitis	Rheumatoid Arthritis	Hyper-tension	Ulcerative Colitis	Peptic Ulcer	Thyro-toxicosis
			MALE CASES			
100	100	100	88	83[a]	100	83
86	80	100	75	75	100	75
86	50	88	62	57	100	71
17	0	88	60	28	86	0
12	0	25	40	0	75	0
0			25		75	
0			0		50	
					25	
					14	
					12	
					0	
					0	
			FEMALE CASES			
88	86	100	88	100	25	100
88	83	100	62	88	25	100
62	75	25	25	71	12	57
43	71	20	0	38	11	29
14	0	12	0	0	0	0
0					0	

[a] See note to Table 8.

The proportion of analysts whose final diagnoses were correct on each case is given in Table 11. Once again, we find a marked range for each disease, typically from 88% to 0%. For every disease-sex group except female ulcer there were one or more cases where all analysts, or all but one, were correct. But for every disease-sex group except arthritis, there were one or two cases on which no analyst was correct. As with the initial diagnoses, the group tended to be generally correct or generally incorrect.

Studies of Errors in Analysts' Diagnoses

Diagnostic Associations between Diseases: Incorrect Diagnoses

Whereas the number of errors provides one kind of information, the type of errors provides a different and potentially more fruitful type of information. For example, the fact that one disease was frequently diagnosed as another suggests either that the psychological pictures for the two diseases were similar or that the members of the analytic group perceived them as similar. This suggestion could be explored by reviewing the interview protocols for cases with the two diseases.

When the analytic judges began work on the series of cases reported here, they felt, with varying degrees of conviction, that there were certain disease "families"—pairs of diseases—with similar pictures. The consensus of the group was that there were three families: ulcerative colitis and peptic ulcer; arthritis and hypertension; bronchial asthma and neurodermatitis. Thyrotoxicosis was left by itself. The research reported in this volume was oriented, of course, toward the differentiation of the seven diseases, not the differentiation of disease clusters.

Table 12

Mean Percentage of Diagnoses in Correct Disease Family

	Bronchial Asthma and Neurodermatitis	Rheumatoid Arthritis and Hypertension	Ulcerative Colitis and Peptic Ulcer
INITIAL DIAGNOSES			
Male Cases	51	58	57
Female Cases	66	58	42
FINAL DIAGNOSES			
Male Cases	62	65	64
Female Cases	64	60	44

One way of studying the question of disease families is to see how successful the analytic group was in identifying the family in which each case fell. Table 12 gives this information for both initial and final diagnoses. Each entry is the mean of the values for the two diseases involved (so that a greater number of cases of a particular disease does not give that disease more influence on the mean than the other disease). It can be seen that the group was highly successful: in general, the majority of the group placed each case in the correct disease family. The overall level of success for each family can be roughly estimated by comparing these figures with the result expected on the basis of chance: two out of seven, or 29%.

Of even more interest is the picture for each disease. Table 13 presents the data for initial diagnoses. For male ulcer cases, the most frequent incorrect diagnosis was colitis, the other disease in that family. But the line above shows that the most frequent error for colitis cases was not

Table 13

Distribution of Analysts' Initial Diagnoses for Each Actual Disease

(Per Cent)

Actual Disease	Bronchial Asthma	Neurodermatitis	Rheumatoid Arthritis	Hypertension	Ulcerative Colitis	Peptic Ulcer	Thyrotoxicosis	Other[a]
MALE CASES								
Bronchial asthma	*45*	17	0	4	19[b]	12	0	4
Neurodermatitis	13	*27*	21[b]	0	10	11	11	8
Rheumatoid arthritis	0	4	*58*	9[b]	8	7	3	10
Hypertension	13	3	6	*42*	20[b]	6	8	2
Ulcerative colitis	18[b]	6	0	6	*42*	6	0	23
Peptic ulcer	11	5	4	1	17[b]	*49*	0	13
Thyrotoxicosis	10	8	0	7	18[b]	3	*38*	16
Means of errors	11	7	5	4	15	8	4	11
FEMALE CASES								
Bronchial asthma	*39*	17[b]	4	6	3	8	11	12
Neurodermatitis	19[b]	*57*	11	6	6	0	0	2
Rheumatoid arthritis	10	6	*44*	21[b]	0	11	0	10
Hypertension	0	4	29[b]	*22*	6	2	20	17
Ulcerative colitis	6	18[b]	0	2	*46*	12	2	13
Peptic ulcer	11	17	4	6	10	*16*	22[b]	14
Thyrotoxicosis	15[b]	3	5	4	3	10	*53*	6
Means of errors	10	11	9	8	5	7	9	11

NOTE: Each entry is the mean of the values for the nine analysts. The entries in italics are those for correct diagnoses.

[a] Includes all diagnoses which did not clearly emphasize a specific disease, and all instances where an analyst refrained from making a diagnosis.

[b] Modal (most common) error.

ulcer but asthma. Thus, in males, although ulcer tends to be called colitis, colitis tends more frequently to be diagnosed as asthma. Arthritis also has its most frequent error in its own disease family. But asthma is most frequently called colitis, neurodermatitis is called arthritis, and hypertension is called colitis.

The data for female cases show a somewhat different picture. For the asthma-neurodermatitis and for the arthritis-hypertension families, the most frequent error is the other disease in its family. But colitis is most frequently diagnosed as neurodermatitis and ulcer is most often called thyrotoxicosis.

The row of means indicates the extent to which a disease was used in incorrect diagnoses. Thus colitis was given 15% of the time as the diagnosis for male cases of other diseases. In female cases, neurodermatitis was the erroneous diagnosis that was most frequently used. In both male and female cases, asthma was the next most prevalent error. In the incorrect diagnoses for female cases, however, the errors were much more evenly distributed among the seven diseases.

Table 14 presents data for final diagnoses. For male cases, the picture for five diseases is similar to that for initial diagnoses. The most frequent error for asthma, however, is now within its family (neurodermatitis), but arthritis is now most often called ulcer. The lower part of the table, for female cases, shows more differences. Neurodermatitis is called arthritis more often than it is called asthma. Hypertension is most frequently called thyrotoxicosis and, almost as frequently, arthritis, and ulcer is now called neurodermatitis oftener than thyrotoxicosis.

The rows for mean errors show that in male cases colitis and asthma are again the commonest errors, whereas in female cases neurodermatitis and thyrotoxicosis are the most frequent.

The data in Tables 13 and 14 provide limited support for the disease groupings postulated by the group. For both sexes asthma is typically misdiagnosed as neurodermatitis and arthritis as hypertension. On the other hand, neurodermatitis is called arthritis oftener than it is called asthma. Colitis is mistaken not for ulcer but for asthma in male cases and for neurodermatitis in female cases. In males, ulcer is misdiagnosed as colitis, but so is hypertension.

We can also see that the confusions are typically not reciprocal: neurodermatitis is frequently diagnosed as arthritis, but arthritis is only infrequently called neurodermatitis.

Quantitative Distribution of Errors

Statistical analysis of the quantitative distribution of errors may be of value as a guide to improving our formulations.

Table 14

Distribution of Analysts' Final Diagnoses for Each Actual Disease

Actual Disease	Bronchial Asthma	Neurodermatitis	Rheumatoid Arthritis	Hypertension	Ulcerative Colitis	Peptic Ulcer	Thyrotoxicosis	Other[a]
MALE CASES								
Bronchial asthma	*49*	24[b]	0	4	15	4	0	4
Neurodermatitis	8	*44*	22[b]	0	10	6	6	5
Rheumatoid arthritis	0	2	*80*	3	0	15[b]	0	0
Hypertension	13	0	0	*47*	25[b]	6	6	4
Ulcerative colitis	23[b]	0	0	10	*56*	3	0	8
Peptic ulcer	8	7	4	1	16[b]	*54*	0	9
Thyrotoxicosis	10	8	0	7	18[b]	3	*49*	4
Means of errors	10	7	4	4	14	6	2	5
FEMALE CASES								
Bronchial asthma	*51*	11[b]	2	0	0	6	10	21
Neurodermatitis	6	*60*	12[b]	0	9	0	11	2
Rheumatoid arthritis	6	6	*53*	14[b]	0	8	0	14
Hypertension	0	4	19	*33*	6	2	21[b]	15
Ulcerative colitis	0	24[b]	0	2	*61*	9	0	4
Peptic ulcer	6	33[b]	11	2	6	*13*	16	14
Thyrotoxicosis	13[b]	3	3	4	0	4	*59*	13
Means of errors	5	14	8	4	4	5	10	12

NOTE: Each entry is the mean of the values for the nine analysts. The entries in italics are those for correct diagnoses.

[a] Includes all diagnoses which did not clearly emphasize a specific disease, and all instances where an analyst refrained from making a diagnosis.

[b] Modal (most common) error.

In Tables 13 and 14 there are a few suggestive trends. Let us consider only the errors whereby a particular disease was specified; that is, we shall ignore the last column in these tables. In male colitis cases asthma was initially the mistaken diagnosis in half of all errors. In the final diagnoses this trend was even more pronounced; almost two-thirds of the male colitis cases incorrectly diagnosed were called asthma. In the initial diagnoses of female cases of colitis, neurodermatitis was the most prevalent error, accounting for slightly less than half the incorrect diagnoses. Again in the final diagnoses the trend became more pronounced, with two-thirds of the errors going to neurodermatitis.

In the initial diagnoses of male cases of ulcer, slightly less than one-half of the errors were colitis; in the final diagnoses, colitis was still the most frequent error, but the proportion was somewhat less.

In both male and female cases of neurodermatitis, arthritis and asthma were the two most frequent initial diagnostic errors—with arthritis first and asthma second in the male cases, asthma first and arthritis second in the female cases. In the female cases these two mistaken diagnoses constituted almost three-quarters of all errors.

In the final diagnoses for male asthma cases, the majority of errors were neurodermatitis; for arthritis the majority of errors were ulcer.

On the other hand, in many diseases, the errors were more evenly distributed. Moreover, every disease was called every other disease by at least one analyst on at least one case, with but one exception: colitis was never called arthritis.

The statistical significance of these trends was also evaluated (see Table 15). The technique was the same as that used to assess the extent of correct diagnoses (see pp. 30–33). In this instance, of course, we examined the frequency not of the correct disease but of the modal, or most common, error. For example, the modal error for male cases of neurodermatitis was arthritis. For each such instance, the proportion of analysts diagnosing it as arthritis was determined and the probability of this observation was obtained. The probabilities for the several male cases of neurodermatitis were combined by the procedure outlined earlier in this chapter. As shown in Table 15, the probability of the combined result is .20, a value that is not usually accepted as statistically significant. On the other hand, for all neurodermatitis cases (male and female together), the probability for arthritis is .05, which is just within the usually accepted limits for statistical significance.

The table shows further that, for males, there were significant tendencies for colitis to be called asthma, for ulcer to be called colitis, and for hypertension to be called colitis. For females, the significant trends are for hypertension to be called arthritis, for thyrotoxicosis to be called asthma and for colitis to be called neurodermatitis.

When male and female cases are combined, there are significant tendencies for thyrotoxicosis to be called asthma, for ulcer to be called colitis, and for neurodermatitis to be called arthritis.

In Table 15, the diseases are arranged by families. There is no clear support for the family groupings, but only weak trends. For no family pair is there a significant tendency for the modal error of each disease to be the other in its pair.

Table 15

Statistical Significance of Modal Errors in Analysts' Initial Diagnoses

Actual Disease	Male Cases		Female Cases		All Cases	
	Modal Error	p	Modal Error	p	Modal Error	p
Bronchial asthma	Ulcerative colitis	.70	Neurodermatitis	.70	Neurodermatitis	.20
Neurodermatitis	Rheumatoid arthritis	.20	Bronchial asthma	.50	Rheumatoid arthritis[a] Bronchial asthma	.05 .70
Rheumatoid arthritis	Hypertension	.20	Hypertension	.10	Hypertension	.10
Hypertension	Ulcerative colitis	.05	Rheumatoid arthritis	.01	Rheumatoid arthritis	.20
Ulcerative colitis	Bronchial asthma	.01	Neurodermatitis	.05	Neurodermatitis[b] Bronchial asthma	.10 .10
Peptic ulcer	Ulcerative colitis	.01	Thyrotoxicosis	.70	Ulcerative colitis	.02
Thyrotoxicosis	Ulcerative colitis	.20	Bronchial asthma	.02	Bronchial asthma	.01

NOTE: Each numerical entry is the obtained level of statistical significance, the probability of obtaining the given result by chance.

[a] For all cases, arthritis and asthma were tied for the largest error. (The difference between the p values for arthritis and asthma is a consequence of the difference in the way that the identical number of errors was distributed over cases. For example, one case of neurodermatitis was diagnosed as arthritis by five analysts. There was no such unusual concentration among the asthma errors.)

[b] For all cases, neurodermatitis and asthma were tied for the largest error.

Strictly speaking, some of the values in Table 15 slightly overstate the statistical significance of the concentration of errors, since the observed frequency of the modal error in each instance contributed to the selection of that error as the most common. This small bias is not serious because the purpose of the analysis was only to identify tendencies which can be used to sharpen the psychological formulations for the several diseases.

The modal errors as given in Tables 13, 14, and 15 should be interpreted cautiously. For a majority of diseases the value of the modal error is not much higher than the value for the next most common error. Furthermore, a single case can have a large effect on this value: the mode is often a result of most of the group making the same error on a single case. It is striking, however, that in female ulcer cases, the initial diagnosis of ulcer was less frequent than that of thyrotoxicosis and also less frequent than that of neurodermatitis, and in cases of female hypertension, there were more initial diagnoses of arthritis than of hypertension.

Overuse or Underuse of Particular Diagnoses by the Analyst Judges

As mentioned earlier, a judge who used one diagnosis much more frequently than any other would be more likely to be correct on cases of that disease. Conversely, a judge who rarely used a diagnosis would be more likely to be incorrect. So there is a possibility that the relative success of a given judge (or of all judges) on a particular disease is raised or lowered by the number of times the disease was used as a diagnosis.

Table 16 shows the mean proportion of cases called each disease by the analysts, the mean proportion of cases that actually were that disease, and the difference. There was no marked tendency for the group as a whole to use any diagnosis too much or too little. The diagnosis of ulcer was used slightly less than the actual frequency of ulcer cases in the sample, and colitis was used slightly more than its actual frequency. (The overuse or underuse of the several diseases contributes to the mean proportion of errors in Table 13.)

The picture is different, however, for the two sexes. Whereas ulcer was used too seldom for both male and female cases, colitis was used much too frequently for male cases and not often enough for female cases. We can also see that neurodermatitis was used too often for female cases and hypertension was not used often enough for male cases. None of the differences are great, and reference back to Table 2 shows no strong relationship between these figures and accuracy.

The values for individual analysts, from which these were derived, tend to be larger. Differences as large as 27% and 20% occur, and these may show that an analyst occasionally overused a particular diagnosis to a significant extent. But the typical difference is 5%, which is clearly trivial in view of the very small number of observations on which each figure is based. When the data for both sexes are combined, the discrepancies tend to become even smaller. No judge overused or underused a diagnosis to a marked extent on both sexes.

The differences can be interpreted in any of several ways. Perhaps the formulations for colitis were so broad and comprehensive that they frequently seemed to fit cases of other diseases, at least with males. Perhaps the formulations for ulcer contained elements which were thought to be always present in such cases but do not actually occur in all cases. Perhaps individual analysts, or the analysts as a group, were somewhat preoccupied with, or especially interested in, certain diseases (a hypothesis presently to be examined). The choice among the possible explanations is not an easy one because the effects are small. Although more elaborate examination showed that the relative success of each analyst on a disease was somewhat related to the extent that he used the disease diagnosis,

Table 16

Distributions of Initial Diagnoses and Actual Diseases (Per Cent)

Actual Disease	Called This Disease	Actually This Disease	Difference
Male Cases			
Bronchial asthma	17	15	2
Neurodermatitis	11	12	−1
Rheumatoid arthritis	13	14	−1
Hypertension	11	16	−5
Ulcerative colitis	19	9	10
Peptic ulcer	21	26	−5
Thyrotoxicosis	8	10	−2
Female Cases			
Bronchial asthma	15	16	−1
Neurodermatitis	18	12	6
Rheumatoid arthritis	16	14	2
Hypertension	11	13	−2
Ulcerative colitis	11	14	−3
Peptic ulcer	10	16	−6
Thyrotoxicosis	18	15	3
All Cases			
Bronchial asthma	16	15	1
Neurodermatitis	15	12	3
Rheumatoid arthritis	14	14	0
Hypertension	11	14	−3
Ulcerative colitis	15	11	4
Peptic ulcer	16	21	−5
Thyrotoxicosis	13	12	1

Note: Each entry is the mean value for the nine analysts.

there was no tendency for the most successful analysts to be those whose accuracy was most closely related to their use of particular diagnoses. The latter finding might be expected, since differential usage could reduce the likelihood of being correct for some diseases and raise it for others. One major point is clear. The general success of the analytic group as a whole is not a function of the way they distributed their diagnoses over the diseases.

Personal Characteristics of the Judges

The analysts filled out a Personal Data Questionnaire after the 83 cases had been completed. This instrument was designed to elicit information about the particular meaning of the several diseases for each analyst.

The most interesting results involved answers to the following item:

> Listed in the order of probability, (a) Which of these diseases could you possibly have in the future? (b) Which of these diseases would you most likely never have?

The majority of the group listed hypertension and ulcer as diseases they could have and thyrotoxicosis as one they would be unlikely to have. The diseases were arranged in order by the number of analysts mentioning them for each part of the question. As might be expected, the first of these orders was almost the complete reverse of the second. When the two orders were compared to the rank order of the diseases in terms of the overall group accuracy, striking relationships were found. For female cases, the analysts' diagnoses were more accurate on diseases they felt they were unlikely to have and less accurate on diseases they felt they might have. The relationships for male cases were the reverse, but were not as marked: they did less well on diseases they thought they would never have. Separate studies for the eight male analysts as a group yielded the same total picture as that for the group of nine (including one female analyst) who provided the major data in this study.

It might be conjectured that the analysts could be more objective and impersonal in diagnosing female cases with disease syndromes they felt they could never have. But on the other hand, they could empathize better with males having diseases they might sometime have. The data are too limited to provide a definitive answer.

Although these findings are curious and provide opportunities for speculation, it must be recalled that they may have occurred by chance and that they are group results. No clear picture emerged from the study of the responses and accuracy of each analyst separately.

In connection with these statistical analyses, the question of the relative accuracy of each analyst on male cases as against female cases is of interest. There was no relationship between the diseases on which an analyst did better on male cases and those on which he did better on female cases; he was not consistently better or worse on some diseases for both sexes.

The analysts were also asked which diseases interested them particularly. Some had analyzed cases of one or more of the diseases and some had done research on particular diseases. There was no general tendency for individuals to be more accurate on the diseases in which they had such interests.

The analysts also reported the approximate time they spent on each case before the group meeting. The median (middle value) was four hours, the range being from two to twelve hours. There was no relationship between this estimate and the analyst's overall accuracy of diagnosis.

None of the analysts reported that they had a history of any of these seven diseases.

The Success of the Individual Analyst

Some judges were more successful than others. Table 17 presents the mean accuracy per disease for each analyst. We can see immediately that every judge had an average success that was well above chance (14%, one out of seven) on both male and female cases. There is, however, considerable range in the success rates, from 26% to 58% for initial diagnoses and from 33% to 64% for final. We have found no factor that is related to these differences. The differences between analysts, however, are dependable. The relative success of the several analysts on male cases had

Table 17

Total Correct Diagnoses for Each Analyst
(Per Cent)

Analyst	Initial Diagnoses		Final Diagnoses	
	Male Cases	Female Cases	Male Cases	Female Cases
A	37	42	59	41
B	56	58	66	64
C	48	26	55	48
D	29	36	49	42
E	48	48	50	48
F	41	41	54	46
G	41	28	52	33
H	33	33	39	38
I	53	43	61	59
All	43	40	54	47

Note: The values in this table represent the mean for all seven diseases.

a positive correlation with their success on female cases (the rank order coefficients are .51 for initial diagnoses and .65 for final).

Whatever the source of the analysts' differential accuracy, this table, together with the detailed information on how well each analyst did on each disease, can be used to locate analysts who were especially successful. Their psychological formulations for each case should provide suggestions for refining the general formulation for each disease or a guide for putting the elements together.

Similar data on differences between analysts are presented in Table 18, but here the value for each analyst is based on the conservative method used for Tables 6 and 7. Two indices were computed. One was the number of correct diagnoses for each disease divided by the number of actual cases with the disease. This is the conventional "per cent correct" index,

Table 18

Indices of Diagnostic Accuracy of Individual Analysts (Per Cent)

Analyst	Initial Diagnoses		Final Diagnoses	
	Male Cases	Female Cases	Male Cases	Female Cases
A	33	32	51	33
B	49	50	57	61
C	37	24	45	43
D	26	26	42	34
E	42	44	45	48
F	38	39	49	42
G	36	23	45	27
H	29	32	33	35
I	50	31	48	50

NOTE: See text for explanation of indices. The values in this table represent the mean for all seven diseases.

the one used in Table 17. The other was the number correct divided by the number of times that the analyst used the diagnosis. Each value in Table 18 is the smaller of these two indices. The rationale for this procedure has been presented earlier (pp. 37–40). The patterns in Tables 17 and 18 are very similar.

Studies of the success of each judge on each disease revealed that judges were not consistently successful or unsuccessful on the several diseases. A single judge might do poorly on one disease but quite well on another, or poorly on male cases of the disease but well on female cases. This lack of consistency may be due in part to the small number of cases of each disease-sex group that were diagnosed by any one judge. The data provide leads, however, for possible refinement of the psychological pictures for the diseases.

It was also possible that the performance of a judge might improve with experience in diagnosing from the protocols and in discussing cases with the group. In checking whether each judge did better on the second half of the cases he saw in each disease-sex group than on the first half, we found no evidence of definite improvement: judges might improve on some diseases but do worse on others. No judge clearly improved on both male and female cases. There was no relationship between a judge's overall accuracy in diagnosis and the number of diseases on which he improved.

This apparent lack of improvement with experience admits two explanations. It may be that the several cases within each disease-sex group were so separated in time that experience with previous cases was of little help on later cases: the average analyst saw only four or five cases per disease-sex group over five or six years. It is also possible that the group improved its understanding of the disease but that this gain was offset by more vigorous censoring of later cases by the interviewers and medical censors.

A similar temporal analysis was made by disease. A majority of the analysts improved on hypertension cases and on female cases of asthma and colitis. But, a majority did more poorly on the second half of the female cases of neurodermatitis and thyrotoxicosis. In view of the marked differences between cases in the proportion of analysts making correct diagnoses and of the small numbers of cases of each disease, it is probably wisest to view these results as accidents of sampling.

Other Factors that May Have Affected Diagnostic Success

Duration of Illness

One factor which might have affected the diagnostic success of the analytic group was the duration of the illness: Was the analytic group more—or less—successful on cases with recent onset of the disease? Correlations were computed between the duration of disease and the proportion of the analytic group making correct initial diagnoses for each of the 14 disease-sex combinations. For no disease was there a strong relationship for both sexes. For each sex there was no general tendency toward a relationship in the correlations for the several diseases. Thus the data showed no systematic relationship between duration of illness and accuracy of initial diagnoses by analysts. (The duration of the disease was more than a year for 71% of the cases and between six months and a year for another 20%.)

Number of Interviews

Another factor possibly affecting accuracy was the number of interviews with the patient: cases for which there was more material might be more successfully diagnosed. The data indicate that this was not true. If anything, there was a slight trend toward less successful diagnosis of cases with more than one interview before the group meeting. Such cases were those in which the interviewer was unable in one interview to obtain the usual information: an adequate account of the patient's history and of the onset of the disease and answers to the standard questions.

A similar kind of factor is the reinterviewing of a case after an initial meeting. In 31 of the 83 cases, the group requested an additional interview and gave the interviewer specific questions to ask the patient. Although it might be expected that the group would be more successful when it had such specific information, no such trend was found: the group did as well when they received all of the interview material at one time as they did with cases for which they requested a further interview. Such additional information apparently provided the group with no more adequate a total picture, although it is possible that the advantage from such specific inquiries was offset by the fact that the case was basically more difficult to interview or to diagnose.

In this connection, it must be recalled that the diagnoses used in these analyses were the ones made after receiving the requested interview but before the subsequent group meeting. (These were used because they were based on all available interview material.) These diagnoses could have been influenced by the discussion at the first meeting. If this prior discussion contributed to the group's success on such a case, its effect must have been offset by the inherent difficulty of the case.

Specificity of Diagnosis

As indicated at the beginning of the chapter, the analysts were permitted to make diagnoses involving more than one disease. They could assign a total of seven points to one, two, or more diseases. Two-thirds of the initial diagnoses were univocal and specific. A fifth gave major weight to one disease but mentioned one or more others. (About a tenth were mixed, with no one disease favored, or were instances where the judge refrained from making any diagnosis.)

The degree of weight the analyst placed on a disease can be viewed as an index of the clarity of the psychological picture presented; it may also be interpreted as a reflection of the judge's confidence in his diagnosis.

There was a marked tendency for the judges to be more accurate on cases where they made a single diagnosis than on cases where they gave a major weight to only one disease. This finding suggests that when the judges felt they could make a specific diagnosis, mentioning only one disease, they were more likely to be right than they were when they felt that the case might be one of two or more diseases.

Shifts in Diagnoses from Initial to Final

As one would expect, specific initial diagnoses limited to a single disease were less likely to be changed after the group discussion than were other diagnoses. Thus specific diagnoses were more likely to be unchanged and to be correct.

Most diagnoses were not changed from initial to final. The same disease was given major weight both times in 72% of the instances.

Viewing the diagnoses in terms of correctness or incorrectness, only 3% were changed from correct to incorrect. (No analyst changed from correct to incorrect on more than one case in any disease-sex group.) About 12% of the diagnoses were changed from an incorrect disease to the correct one.

Thus most of the diagnoses were not changed as a result of the group discussion, but most of the changes were in the correct direction: there was greater agreement between the judges on their final diagnoses. Frequently an analyst changed when he was not certain of his diagnosis and the consensus of the group was for another diagnosis. In such cases he was likely to move in the right direction. Examination of the cases in terms of the number of judges who had the same diagnosis indicated that the larger this mode, the more likely it was that the selected diagnosis was correct. Hence there was some changing of diagnosis to that of the majority.

There were exceptions, however. In one outstanding case, only one judge made a correct initial diagnosis. None of the other seven even mentioned the actual diagnosis as a possibility. But after they had heard the one analyst's interpretation of the case, they were so convinced by him that each of the seven changed to his diagnosis, the correct one. There were, of course, other less dramatic cases of analysts changing their diagnoses because they were convinced by the formulation presented by another analyst. In addition, the group was aware that some of their members were generally more successful. Although no analyses were made on this question, it seems probable that shifts in diagnoses toward agreement with such judges were more frequent than toward agreement with other judges.

We have seen that the final diagnoses tended to be more accurate than initial diagnoses. This was true not only for each analyst and for every disease-group except female ulcer, but also for most analysts on most diseases. In only 14 of the 126 possibilities did an analyst do less well on his final diagnoses for a disease-sex group.

The same picture is found for the cases. On 34 of the 83 cases, the group's final diagnoses were better and on only 11 were they worse. (Three of these cases were female ulcer.)

CHAPTER FOUR

The Medical Control Study

The Problem of Medical Control

A brief review of the basic rationale for the whole research project seems appropriate at this point. A psychological formulation was postulated for each of the diseases studied. Each of these seven patterns was viewed as discrete, as different in many essential features from that for each of the other six diseases. Therefore (the fundamental argument stated), a person knowing these seven individual formulations and having a protocol containing appropriate material should be able to reconstruct the psychogenetic and dynamic pattern of the patient, see its correspondence with the pertinent theoretical formulation, and thus identify the actual somatic disease.

Since the members of the analytic group were moderately successful in making correct diagnoses, the major findings presented in chapter 3 can be held to provide evidence in support of the guiding rationale. Such evidence, of course, is not conclusive, since the analytic group may have made successful diagnoses on the basis of material other than that pertinent to the formulation postulated for the actual disease. The results may also reflect the presence in the protocols of medical information providing a basis for correct diagnoses. To minimize the amount of such information, each protocol was subjected to rigorous editing by the interviewer who sought to eliminate all direct references and obvious clues to the disease before the protocol was distributed to the analytic judges. But there remained a further problem. Since all the analytic judges were physicians with prior general or specialized training in organic medicine, was it possible that they might be consciously or unconsciously influenced by remaining medical non-psychological data that might lend weight to a given diagnosis? Would careful re-editing by a medical editor solve this problem? The medical editing in turn raised difficult problems of what should or should not be eliminated or altered. Any and all information about a patient may be contributory to the etiological understanding of his illness or relevant to its natural history and thus be of diagnostic value to the sagacious clinician. Not all such information constitutes an illegitimate medical clue. Therefore, areas of information requiring selective deletion had to be defined. The name of the disease, pathognomonic or significant symptomatology, references to medical procedures or medications which would reveal the disease (such as the use of antacids for duodenal ulcer) would be totally eliminated. Some significant historical information, however, posed a more serious problem for the medical editor: for example, a long asymptomatic period followed by accidental diagnosis during physical examination, as in hypertension; or a chronic, serious illness with a course of many exacerbations—characteristic of colitis but very unlikely in hypertension, which pursues a relatively uninterrupted course, or in thyrotoxicosis, where definitive medical or surgical intervention would usually be rapidly instituted.

The medical editor had to give careful consideration to the diagnostic implications of such factual data as: sex; race; age at the time of discovery of the disease; number and rhythmicity of exacerbations, seasonal and otherwise; geographical and other spatial relationships; liking for and participation in or prohibition of particular foods or activities; patient's own appraisal of the bothersomeness and seriousness of his condition. These factors, often important etiologically, could not easily be removed from the record without seriously distorting the psychological picture. Sometimes a compromise was necessary, requiring fine judgment on the part of the medical editor and consultation with the analytic interviewer—often with a post hoc evaluation of the censorship by the analytic group. In this way, during the pilot phase of the study, a number of basic principles were established.

Although it was proved impractical to edit out all reference to sex, race, nationality, and age, phraseology related to specific somatic symptoms and conventional medical or surgical therapy was deleted from the record. In the application of this rule a very considerable borderland was encountered wherein verbal expression could be construed either as emotionally significant or as potential medical cuing. There are many phrases of psychodynamic importance that in common knowledge and usage are also associated with certain somatic diseases. Thus: "My pressure got too high but I didn't blow up" can be readily interpreted as either a hypertensive describing a headache, or an ordinarily normal person controlling his temper. Application of this rule involved many individual judgments.

Similar difficulties presented themselves in regard to editing of references to medical and surgical procedures that were of psychological significance and to patients' descriptions of relationships with various physicians. Naturally both the names of doctors and all potential references to an area of specialization were censored. As a rule, it was possible to keep in the record a fairly undistorted, uncensored description of the patient's emotional relation to the doctor. With reference to the timing of the discovery of the disease, it became important to insist on the uniform use of the phrase "disease discovery," in such a fashion that it carried no information whether this discovery was made by a physician or by the patient. Quite frequently hypertension is the adventitious discovery of an examining physician, whereas several of the other syndromes manifest themselves directly to the patient by prodromal symptons, e.g., duodenal ulcer, neurodermatitis. Again, certain of the diseases, asthma and atopic dermatitis, for example, are not treated surgically. So references to operative procedures were omitted.

Some of our patients had surgery that, though unrelated to the specific psychosomatic disease, was temporarily associated with the disease onset and was of psychodynamic importance either in demonstrating a characterologic response or in actually playing a role in the genesis of the disease. An example of the former is a hypertensive patient who became somewhat paranoid about a hemorrhoidectomy he felt had been clumsily performed. One could also cite the patient who, after incidental benign surgery, developed thyrotoxicosis seemingly in relation to anxiety about dying. Another patient developed arthritis after an appendectomy, presumably because the immobilization blocked his usual muscular discharges. These instances taxed the ingenuity of the medical editors, but the general rule followed was that if the operative procedure was directed toward the psychosomatic illness or a sequela, it was omitted entirely. When a surgical episode was mentioned, it was rewritten by the medical editor so that the nature of the operation was concealed, but the fact remained that there was some operative procedure that bore only a temporal relation to the onset or exacerbation of the psychosomatic disease. It was often important to specify whether the operation antedated or followed the psychosomatic illness, since some conditions might arise in anticipation of an operation.

In general, statements about the timing of disease discovery and exacerbations presented an important problem because some diseases, such as asthma, are often characterized by a sudden, dramatic onset, whereas others like hypertension or arthritis typically may undergo a slow, insidious development. Rather than adopt an arbitrary period of time during which the onset is designated, the medical editor tried to present the exact timing of the onset or exacerbation in such a way as to retain the events which seemed of psychodynamic importance. As the project progressed, the medical editors became increasingly skillful in solving this problem.

As far as possible, specific reference to seasons was altered in such a way as to preserve the sequence of events leading to onset without designating the season. In regard to religious holidays, the strict application of this rule sometimes fell in the no-man's-land between potential significance for psychodynamic formulation and for educated medical guessing. Application or waiving of this rule was decided in conference between the interviewing analyst and the medical editor.

Similarly, descriptions of the household and of urban or rural geography were edited in such a fashion as to remove reference to place names, to certain classes of objects (such as food and pets), and to climate. This rule, requiring individual judgment when used, could not strictly be applied without some distortion of the psychodynamic material. On the other hand, names of places in which an allergic patient might seek relief by reason of pollen-free atmosphere were usually successfully edited with preservation of the psychodynamic significance of the trip.

Among specific object classes, sections dealing with pets again lay in the borderland of combined psychodynamic significance and potential cues. Such a section was retained if the interviewing analyst felt it was crucial to the formation of a psychodynamic appraisal, and if left in, the medical editors rewrote the section to minimize its medical cue value.

Finally, to test the efficiency of our medical editing procedures we decided early in the pilot study to set up a "medical control group" of internists. They would receive the same censored protocol given to the analytic group and would likewise hold meetings for discussion, review, and revision of the diagnoses. The results of this group were separately recorded.

The original purpose of this medical control group was not to function as a "control" in the sense of experimental design in the physical sciences, for the success of our predictions would be measured against chance by purely statistical methods. Thus such a "control" would bear only a superficial resemblance to the methods of exact science. Nor was it meant to provide a competition between the internist and psychoanalyst to see who could score better in such a blind study, using their respective methods and reasoning. (Some such aspect of a competitive atmosphere did creep in and was actually fruitful, as will be discussed later.) The purpose of this "control" group was twofold: (1) to provide data for increasing the stringency of medical editing so that nonpsychological information could be reduced to a minimum; and (2) when such an irreducible minimum had been reached, to use the score of the internist group as an indication of the results obtainable by medical judges without special psychological training. The significance of this score will be considered later.

The internists selected for this study had to meet certain criteria. They had to be clinicians of some standing, with recognized diagnostic acumen, without either an antipathetic bias toward the psychological approach to medicine or an unusual interest in and knowledge of psychological concepts (especially a knowledge of the formulations of our specificity hypothesis). Internists who had undergone personal analysis were also disqualified. Many checks and crosschecks were devised for screening the internists considered, but these need not be discussed here.

When the internists first began to scan the censored protocols for medical cues, they spotted many cues quite easily. By the time the formal study started, however, most of the problems had been worked out, and only such information as sex, race, age at onset, and general pattern of life with and without the disease remained. This meant that in the final study the medical control group members all operated with meager medical information. Rather than supercensors, they became essentially a comparison group, a group that could show the typical success and the variation in such success attained by ten different persons in the interpretation of the information that remained—information that the analytic group might also use. It is important to emphasize that since the remaining cues were gross and nonspecific, what was needed was a sample of the performance of a nonanalytic group for purposes of comparison. Hence the size of the matched medical control group was determined by the approximate size of the analytic group. Although the medical control group was selected partly on the basis of lack of familiarity with the "specificity" formulations, some of these concepts have become part of general medical knowledge. This factor, which could not be totally eliminated, was checked by requesting the internist to list the evidence on which he based his diagnosis, so that later review would show whether the internists used psychological data in their formulations and diagnoses.

It was important that the nonpsychiatric group be interested in, or at least not openly hostile to, psychodynamic thinking, so that sufficient motivation would be present to carry the group through the entire study. The choice of the internists was made principally by the medical editors who were familiar with the clinical habits and training of the selected individuals. In addition, the internists were asked to fill out a questionnaire which confirmed their status in regard to interest and training in psychiatric aspects of medicine and their own personal disease experiences.

Some individuals, as would be expected, had more knowledge in the psychological area than others since they practiced in a specialty, such as gastrointestinal disease, requiring attention to some of the theories concerning etiology. From observation of the medical group at work, it was obvious that attitudes toward the analytic formulations varied. Several of the most strongly motivated individuals had as their principal stimulus a desire to show that the hypotheses were wrong by having the internists "do better" than the analysts. The apparent lack of interest of some other members was evidenced by the long delay in getting in their reports, failure to attend meetings, and cursory reports.

An element of necessary frustration, which may have contributed to a slackening of interest in some of the internists, was the fact that they were never advised of the relative success of their efforts in this diagnostic "guessing game" in relation to the analysts. In fact, neither group was aware of the results of the other until the entire study was completed.

To make the activity of the medical control group comparable with that of the analytic group, it was decided that they would have two reviews of the protocols. First each individual would privately read the material and submit his impression in writing, noting his reason for the choice of diagnosis. Each report was then circulated to the entire group. At the group meeting each participant was expected to reconsider his opinion in light of the others' and to then decide on his final diagnosis. For the first ten cases of the definitive study this review was done on an individual basis. It was then decided that since the analysts met to support their views and discuss each other's formulations before arriving at the final diagnoses, the medical control group should have similar meetings. These discussion meetings were carried on from Cases 10 through 45 but were abandoned after that because of scanty attendance and delay. Thereafter, individual and final diagnoses without group meetings were again used. The modification of the procedure after Case 45 is probably not a significant alteration in the method: the individual impressions of the medical control group probably provided a better index than the group meetings of ability to use the material of the protocols to arrive at a diagnosis. In the group sessions there was a tendency at times to engage in various forms of detective work involving non-protocol considerations, such as attempting to guess probability of diagnosis according to the number of cases already seen in each category.

Some of the internists did not complete all of the cases. One member had a fatal illness and several others had major changes in professional situations that required them to leave the project when the statistical consultant indicated that this could be done without disrupting the study.

Quantitative Results of the Medical Control Study

The internists in the medical control group saw 70 of the 83 cases diagnosed by the analyst group. Although it was originally planned that the internists should see all cases, practical circumstances led to the decision to reduce the number to this 84% subgroup. The 70 cases included four or more cases in each of the 14 disease-sex categories, that is, from 71% to 100% of those seen by the analyst group. The 13 eliminated cases came from the earliest ones.

Proportion of Correct Initial Diagnoses by Internists and Analysts

For each disease, the proportion of correct diagnoses by internists and by analysts is shown in Table 19. Each entry is the mean of the value for the set of judges. (It should be noted that the values given here for analysts differ slightly from those presented in Table 1, since some cases included in Table 1 were excluded here.)

Table 19

Correct Initial Diagnoses by Internists and Analysts
(Per Cent)

	Bronchial Asthma	Neurodermatitis	Rheumatoid Arthritis	Hypertension	Ulcerative Colitis	Peptic Ulcer	Thyrotoxicosis	Mean
Internists	18	30	16	22	30	25	15	22
Analysts	42	44	54	32	38	33	39	40

NOTE: Values are for the 70 cases seen by both groups.

The success of the internists ranges from 15% to 30% for the seven diseases, with a mean of 22%—slightly better than one out of five. On the whole, the analysts were much more successful than the internists: for the several diseases, the margin was from 8% to 38%. Over the seven diseases, the mean success of the internist group was 8% above chance (14%) whereas the mean success of the analysts was 26% above chance.

Table 20 presents the results of disease-sex distribution. The internists did about equally well on male and female cases. Because the frequencies in each group of cases are only half of the total, the percentage of successful diagnoses fluctuates more widely, for example, from 10% to 40% for female and male ulcer cases respectively. The difference between the analysts and the internists is slightly larger for female cases than for male cases. Although the differences for the 14 categories show considerable range, the internists were more successful in only one diagnostic category, male neurodermatitis.

Statistical Significance of the Internists' Results

The statistical significance of the findings for the internists was determined in the same manner as that for the analysts (see chapter 3, "Statistical Significance," especially Table 4). These results can be found in

Table 20

Correct Initial Diagnoses: By Sex

	Bronchial Asthma	Neurodermatitis	Rheumatoid Arthritis	Hypertension	Ulcerative Colitis	Peptic Ulcer	Thyrotoxicosis	Mean
MALE CASES								
Internists (% correct)	10	35	12	30	31	40	12	24
Analysts (% correct)	43	20	58	41	31	50	25	38
Number of cases	5	4	5	5	4	10	4	37
FEMALE CASES								
Internists (% correct)	25	26	20	13	28	10	18	20
Analysts (% correct)	41	68	50	24	46	16	53	43
Number of cases	5	4	4	4	5	6	5	33

Table 21. For 11 of the 14 disease-sex categories, the success of the internist group does not reach the minimal level conventionally accepted as significant (.05). Although their average performance exceeds one out of seven (14%), it typically does not depart sufficiently to yield a reliable gain over chance. (The attentive reader who compares Table 21 with Table 20 may be puzzled by some apparent discrepancies. For example, the significant value for female thyrotoxicosis in Table 21 is surprising because the corresponding degree of success in Table 20 is not very high. The explanation lies in the basis for determining statistical significance: namely, the proportion of all called diagnoses specifying the given disease. The internists used the diagnosis of thyrotoxicosis for only 7% of the female cases, each of the other six diseases being used more frequently.)

Table 21

Statistical Significance of Results for Internists' Initial Diagnoses

	Bronchial Asthma	Neurodermatitis	Rheumatoid Arthritis	Hypertension	Ulcerative Colitis	Peptic Ulcer	Thyrotoxicosis
Male Cases	.70	.01[a]	.20	.20	.05[a]	.10	.30
Female Cases	.10	.20	.10	.10	.50	.90	.02[a]

NOTE: Each entry is the obtained level of statistical significance, the probability of obtaining the given results by chance.

[a] These are the only values that reach .05, the minimal level conventionally accepted as significant.

Proportion of Correct Final Diagnoses by Internists and Analysts

Table 22 presents the success of the final diagnoses of the two groups. On the whole, the analysts were twice as successful as the internists. The differences, however, vary greatly: from 3% for ulcer up to 56% for arthritis.

The sex-distribution comparisons are given in Table 23. There are three diseases in males for which the internists exceed the analysts by small margins (1 to 5%): neurodermatitis, hypertension, and ulcer. On the other hand, the maximum differential success of the analytic group is now 72% (for male arthritis) and its margin is substantial for most other categories.

Differences between Final and Initial Diagnoses

For the entire group of 70 cases, the internists were only slightly more successful (3%) in their final diagnoses than in their initial judgments (see Table 24). The mean performance of the analysts rose 10% from initial to final. For the separate disease-sex groups, the internists actually

Table 22

Correct Final Diagnoses by Internists and Analysts (Per Cent)

	Bronchial Asthma	Neurodermatitis	Rheumatoid Arthritis	Hypertension	Ulcerative Colitis	Peptic Ulcer	Thyrotoxicosis	Mean
Internists	20	40	13	29	29	31	16	25
Analysts	51	54	69	41	55	34	46	50

NOTE: Values are for the 70 cases seen by both groups.

Table 23

Correct Final Diagnoses by Sex (Per Cent)

	Bronchial Asthma	Neurodermatitis	Rheumatoid Arthritis	Hypertension	Ulcerative Colitis	Peptic Ulcer	Thyrotoxicosis	Mean
MALE CASES								
Internists	11	43	8	47	23	57	8	28
Analysts	47	38	80	46	49	56	37	50
FEMALE CASES								
Internists	28	38	18	11	35	5	24	23
Analysts	55	71	58	36	61	13	56	50

Table 24

Correct Final Minus Correct Initial Diagnoses: Percentage Difference

	Bronchial Asthma	Neurodermatitis	Rheumatoid Arthritis	Hypertension	Ulcerative Colitis	Peptic Ulcer	Thyrotoxicosis	Mean
ALL 70 CASES								
Internists	2	10	−3	7	−1	6	1	3
Analysts	9	10	15	9	17	1	7	10
MALE CASES								
Internists	1	8	−4	17	−8	17	−4	4
Analysts	4	18	22	5	18	6	12	12
FEMALE CASES								
Internists	3	12	−2	−2	7	−5	6	3
Analysts	14	3	8	12	15	−3	3	7

had lower values for final diagnoses on almost half the categories whereas the analysts dropped on only one. It may be that the group discussions of the cases were more valuable to the analysts than to the internists.

Differential Success for Individual Cases

The internists were more successful on some cases than on others. The solid line in Figure 3 represents the frequencies for different degrees of success. Among the 70 cases, there were 10 cases for which no internist gave a correct initial diagnosis and 23 cases where only one was correct. At the other end of the distribution, there was no case correctly diagnosed by all internists, one case correctly diagnosed by all but one internist, and one case missed by only two of that group. In spite of the small frequencies, the total curve is systematic, with only one deviation from regularity.

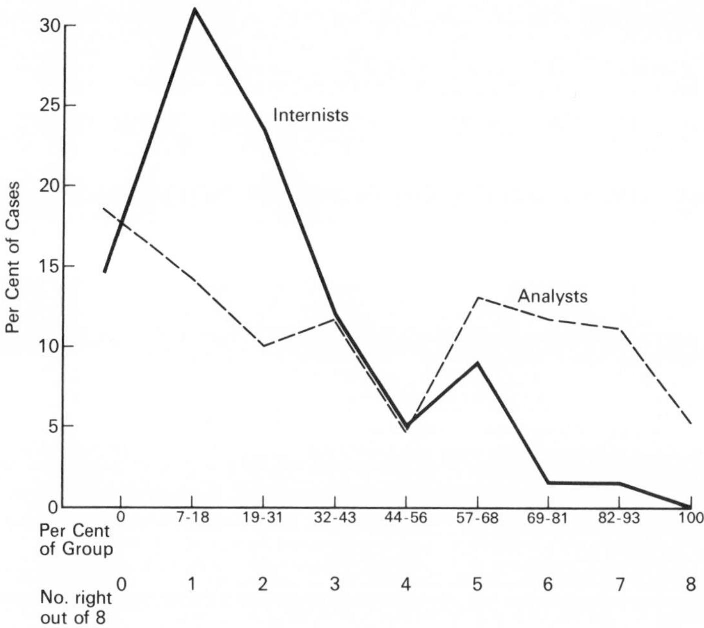

FIG. 3. Distribution of cases in terms of per cent of group making correct initial diagnoses for the 70 cases seen by both groups.

Figure 4 shows the expected theoretical distribution if all cases were equally difficult for the internists to diagnose. (This was obtained in the same way as Figure 2.) The most common expected finding would be one judge correct; the next most common would be two judges correct. Cases with 75% of the judges correct would almost never occur. It will be seen that this theoretical curve is very similar to the one actually obtained for the internists (the solid line in Figure 3). The slight discrepancy is not statistically significant. The result supports the interpretation that these cases as a whole were of about equal difficulty for the internist group to diagnose, the degree of difficulty being estimated as about 22% success. This situation is consistent with what would be expected if the internists could usually eliminate two of the seven possible diagnoses but had no basis for selecting one among the remaining five. This is further discussed in the "Appraisal of the Medical Control Study," below.

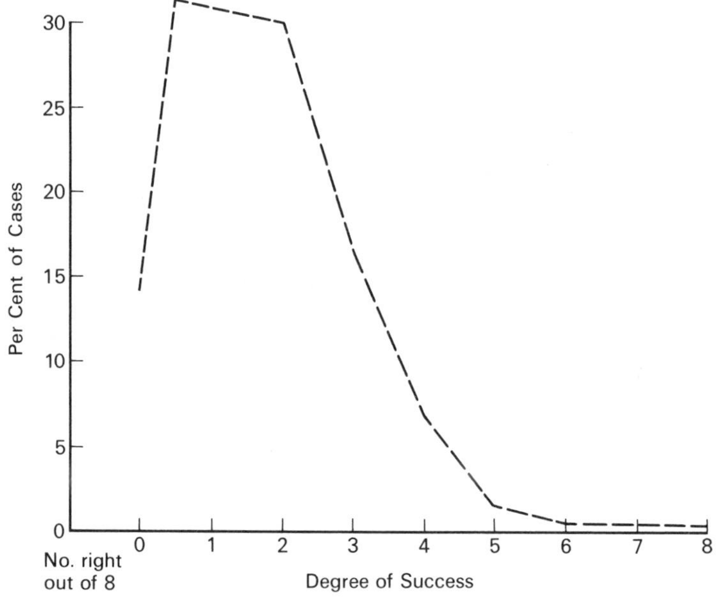

FIG. 4. Theoretical distribution expected when 22% of diagnoses are correct (22% represents the overall success of the internist group's initial diagnoses).

The distribution for the internists in Figure 3 (the solid line) differs considerably from that for the analysts on these 70 cases (the broken line). The dissimilarity between the two distributions is statistically significant. In this figure (as in Figure 1) the curve for the analysts is rather flat. More than half of the analytic group gave correct initial diagnoses for 27 of these cases.

As one final check on the general observation that the performance of the analytic group was generally better than that of the internists in terms of correct initial diagnoses, a count was made of the number of cases on which the analysts did better (43 cases) and the number where the internists excelled (22 cases). The two groups did equally poorly (0 to 12%) on the remaining five cases. This difference (43 vs. 22) is statistically significant.

The different shapes of the two curves in Figure 3 is congruent with the prior expectation that the analysts and the internists would arrive at successful diagnoses by different routes. One additional statistical analysis supports this interpretation. For the 70 cases, the correlation between the proportion of the analysts making correct initial diagnoses and the corresponding proportion of the internists is .27. Although this value is statistically significant, its absolute magnitude is far from that for a perfect correlation (1.00) and leaves a great deal of variation which is specific to one measure or the other.

This small degree of association could be a consequence of common factors determining the success of the two groups: the fact that both groups consisted of physicians with the same basic medical training; alternatively, or in addition, the possibility that the internists used some psychological material in the protocols and that the analysts were influenced by occasional tangential medical facts that had not been censored.

The correlation strongly suggests that the great majority of the factors affecting success in diagnosis were different for the two groups. This interpretation is supported by inspection of the differences between the groups in the proportion of successful diagnoses for each case. For 22 cases, one group exceeded the other by more than 30% (in 20 of these 22, the analytic group was more successful). Conversely, the two groups differed by 15 percentage points or less in 26 cases: in 17 of these, no more than one judge in each group was correct.

Looking at the data another way, there were no cases in which 75% or more of both groups were correct. The internists had two cases above this point, cases which were less successfully diagnosed by the analytic group. On the other side, the analysts had 14 cases in which 75% or more of them were correct while the internists did less well. This examination gives further evidence that the groups were successful for different reasons.

Differences between Internists in Correctness of Diagnoses

There were individual differences among the internists in the proportion of correct initial diagnoses. For male cases, the range was from 7% to 38%; for female cases, it was from 7% to 34%. For each sex, the distributions were fairly even, each distribution having one or two judges who were clearly much better or much worse than their colleagues. Indices of diagnostic accuracy were computed for the internists in the same manner as those for the analysts (see chapter 3). These values gave essentially the same picture. Both the distribution of mean proportion correct per internist and that of the indices of diagnostic accuracy were similar to the comparable distributions for analysts, although the latter had central tendencies about 20% farther up the scale. Thus in the internist group as in the analytic group, some judges were more successful than others in determining the actual disease from the interview protocols. There was no relation between success on male cases and on female cases, however, as there was for the analysts. Hence the differences among internists in degree of success are probably less reliable than those among analysts.

Differences as a Function of Personal Characteristics

The internists completed the same Personal Data Questionnaire that was given to the analysts. Like the analysts, the internists tended to pick hypertension and ulcer as diseases they could have in the future and thyrotoxicosis as one they would be unlikely to have. Another unlikely disease was asthma. The relations between these group selections and group accuracy of initial diagnoses were the same as those for the analysts: for male cases, the group did better on the diseases they thought they might have, but for female cases they did better on the diseases they thought they would never have.

The internists also reported the diseases in which they were particularly interested or which they saw often in their practice. In the limited data on such differential experience, no systematic relationship to diagnostic accuracy could be discerned.

Their estimates of the time they spent on each case varied from 45 minutes to four hours, with a median of two and a half hours. (These values are well below those reported by the analysts.) These estimates had a positive relationship with their success on female cases and a negative relationship with success on male cases; the relationship to average performance over all cases was only slightly positive.

Summary of the Quantitative Findings

These statistical analyses have shown that the internists had a small average degree of success in making diagnoses from the censored protocols used by both groups of judges, with greater success for some disease-sex groups and lesser success for others. In comparison, the analysts did better with each disease group although they were not consistently better with each of the very small samples for the separate disease-sex groupings. The differences between the two sets of judges were more than quantitative differences in degree of success. First, the analytic group achieved a statistically significant level of success for most of the disease-sex groupings whereas the internists' performance reached this level in relatively few instances. Second, the internists gained only slightly from group discussions of the cases whereas the analysts gained appreciably. Third, the proportion of cases for which a majority of the analysts was correct was much greater than the corresponding proportion for the internists. Fourth, and most important of all, there was only a slight tendency for the internists and the analysts to achieve their highest levels of success on the same cases.

These analyses permit the conclusion that the success of the analytic group was not a result of utilizing medical cues. They do not allow us to conclude, however, that the seven psychological formulations for the separate diseases are valid. All the quantitative analyses that have been presented have dealt with the end products, the labels or diagnoses. They have not directly considered the formulations or the inferential processes by which each judge arrived at his diagnosis. The latter factor will be examined in the next section.

An Appraisal of the Medical Control Study

The preceding section makes it clear that the medical control group was more proficient in certain areas than in others. Several factors might be considered. Some diagnoses were often used not only when the diseases were present but also when they were not present. Other diseases were infrequently mentioned, present or not. The other possibilities—a disease being mentioned infrequently but appropriately and a disease being mentioned rarely and generally incorrectly—were also encountered. In retrospect, some of the errors were based on mistaken concepts of the general natural history of the disease and the fact that in the selection of the patients usual age and sex distributions were distorted. In general, however, the principal mode of making a diagnosis by the internists was by the exclusion of the unlikely disease, followed by a choice among the remaining possibilities.

During the pilot phase, an analysis of the results of the medical control group was made by the late S. Howard Armstrong, Jr. After initial elimination of some rather gross leaks by tightening the censorship, the internists were still able by astute medical reasoning to narrow the diagnostic possibilities from one in seven to one in three. They then would make the diagnosis from three possibilities. Further work on the stringency of editing reduced this narrowing from one in three to one in four, and this ratio persisted more or less without further change, and is roughly the statistical score achieved by the medical control group in the research (22%). Thus, both from meeting reports of the medical control group and by inspection of the protocols, there is general agreement that the medical control group worked deductively mainly by narrowing the field of choice by exclusion and then making intuitive or calculated selections among the remaining possibilities.

The following is an example of a typical protocol submitted by a medical control judge.

Case: Mrs. S. U. [Actual diagnosis: rheumatoid arthritis]
(Medical Control Group No. 47)
Age: 32
Sex: Female

Caucasian. Plump.

Disease has lasted about eight and one-half years. Started while her child was an infant. Implications that disease started abruptly. "What happened day before that?"

Probably would be allowed pets if she wanted them.

She would wish for health. Implies concern and bother by symptoms.

Onset not related to mother's death.

Has put on too much weight. Eats too much. No limitation on eating.

Worried that condition will get worse. Implies a rather progressive disease for which she has been given a *guarded* prognosis.

Had second child after onset. First child delivered prematurely by cesarean section. Husband is afraid wife would be unable to care for more children.

Question on page 7, second interview, by analyst: "About the onset—the first symptoms that you had—I have to ask you some more questions. Did you feel that you were away from somebody, your family, your husband, lost somebody—or what?" Sounds like fishing for hyperthyroidism.

Apparently gave up bowling.

Question on page 7 concerning anger also most leading.

Question on page 9 concerning crying suggests probing for asthma.

Has done well in the interval between interviews. Husband said: "You've been doing real good."

At first symptoms came and went and then she had second pregnancy. Got worse one year after birth of second child. Chronic progressive disease for nine years with more intermittency at first and two periods of worsening from which recovery has been incomplete. Patient sounds resigned to ill health and her husband feels she could not care for more children and he notices her condition.

Hypertension, hyperthyroidism, and neurodermatitis seem most unlikely. Asthma is less likely than other three. Because of the plumpness and the lack of diet change I prefer arthritis.

Diagnosis: Arthritis 5 Colitis 2

This brief record demonstrates that the internist is sensitive to psychological clues in his concern with the interviewer's technique on certain pages. But whereas pointed probing about crying may indeed suggest asthma, the notion that questioning about object separation "sounds like fishing for hyperthyroidism" was based on an erroneous conception of the psychosomatic specificity formulation. Nevertheless, this internist, though alert to the presence of what he felt were psychological cues (both correct and incorrect), was not led astray but actually rejected them and chose the correct diagnosis on the basis of medical reasoning and careful deduction. The report also shows some of the limitations of editing—in connection with the presence of pets and the hint of abrupt onset. Such inferences were used to great advantage by a skillful internist, especially when other diagnostic evidence was lacking.

This method of diagnosis is in marked contrast to that of the analytic group, where almost every diagnosis was made on the basis of a lengthy, elaborate, inductive, closely reasoned psychological formulation and where diagnosis by exclusion was seldom used. (See the specimen case of Mr. A. O., Appendix.) In addition, the protocol above, though terse in comparison with the analytic records, was a fuller than average report for the medical control group. In fact their records were often quite sparse, sometimes consisting only of the diagnosis, such as "general impression—peptic ulcer."

This raises the question of motivation in the medical control group. Except for a competitive desire to beat the analysts in a diagnostic contest, the personal investment and consequent zeal of this group was not comparable with that of the analysts. On the other hand, two factors operating to the advantage of the medical control group tended somewhat to mitigate this discrepancy. (1) The patients had all presented themselves for medical treatment and were referred to the analysts only for purposes of the study. This produced a research population whose productions in regard to their illnesses were not primarily "psychological." (2) The deductive diagnosis-by-exclusion method was a fairly uncomplicated one which could be applied by a skillful internist with a high degree of rapidity and efficiency (without becoming involved in the sustained attention required for psychological formulation).

Some of the internists, in spite of initial screening, may have used psychological thinking influenced by the "specificity formulations" to reach their diagnoses. Some forms of psychological thinking have become time-honored concepts and are considered quite legitimate components of the internists' armamentarium: for example, the role of fright in hyperthyroidism (shock Basedow) or of pressure in "businessman's ulcer." To check on the possible use of the specific psychological formulations, every one of the internist protocols was carefully studied from this point of view. This might be termed a "psychological control of the medical control group." In many protocols where the data were meager or limited to a diagnostic impression, it was impossible to reach any conclusions. Conversely, the positive evidence for use of such formulation was negligible.

The primary task of limiting medical cues to an irreducible minimum was conscientiously carried out and could hardly have been extended further within the limitations of a project of this type. We believe that there was only minimal leaking of obvious medical information that led to an accurate diagnosis. One of the cue detection judges (see chapter 5) who was exceptionally zealous in searching for "medical cues" failed to show any important incidence.

But with respect to the possible use of the medical control group as an experimental control, the matter is not so clear. The problem of "control" in the biological and behavioral sciences is a complex one, and it is impossible to manipulate the variables as adequately as can be done in the physical sciences. Although the available data were identical and the number and level of experience of each team comparable, the two groups were quite different in their general approach and mode of reasoning. In examining the statistical results, we conclude that the 25% (one in four) achieved by the medical control group as a mean score for the final diagnoses of the entire series (see Table 22) probably represents the limitation of our method in censoring medical cues—the "irreducible minimum." One might now argue that any performance possible by the medical control group was also possible by the analysts because of their previous medical training, provided the analysts were sufficiently keen on the diagnostic significance of small items of the protocol. Hence one might subtract the score of the medical control group from the score of the analysts and represent this as the true performance of the analysts using the "specificity hypothesis." This extreme position would be pictorially represented as in Figure 5.

On the other hand, it might also be argued that the analysts and internists arrived at their results by different modes of reasoning or by the use of entirely different concepts to which the data were related in order to arrive at a diagnosis. Thus the analysts, intent on making coherent and convincing psychological formulations, would tend to ignore potential medical items, whereas the internists would not be interested in building

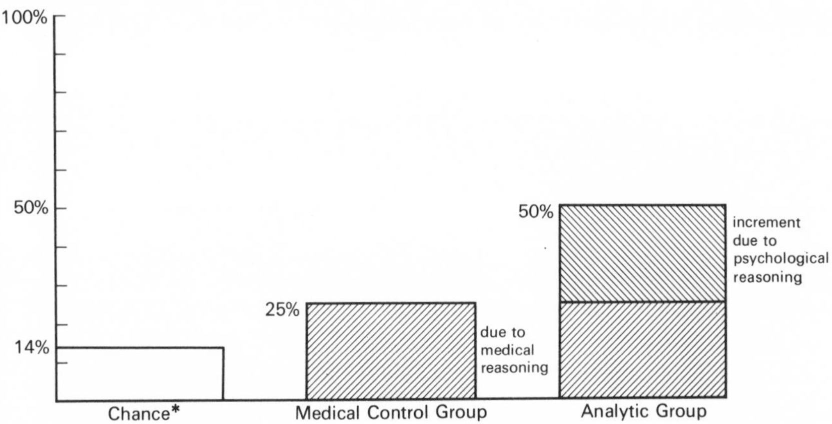

FIG. 5. Incremental success in diagnosis due to psychological reasoning.

* The 14% "chance" result is included here for purposes of comparison. The reader might wonder why the "chance" factor is not subtracted from all the scores represented above. Since the performance of each group was based upon a systematic method of interpreting the protocols, it would be incorrect to attribute a part of their performance to factors ordinarily implied by the term "chance." In other words, the total performance of each group should, strictly speaking, be attributed to the type of reasoning it used.

a psychological picture, but would focus on information of possible medical diagnostic significance. In this case, the scores attained by the two groups would stand separately, and would represent the performance reached by two independent methods of data analysis and reconstruction. This second extreme would be represented as in Figure 6.

Although it is not possible from our data and with our method to prove the point definitely, certain lines of evidence suggest that the actual state of affairs lies in the latter direction and that each group, operating from its particular "set," tended to focus on the data needed theoretically to complete its task and to ignore other data.

Careful perusal of the protocols shows that the manifest approach of the two groups is completely different: the internists are preoccupied with medical data; the analysts are overwhelmingly absorbed with making consistent psychological formulations and seem to be resentful, sometimes to the point of negativism, when some potential medical cue obtrudes itself. Nevertheless, the possibility that the analysts responded unconsciously to medical cues cannot absolutely be excluded.

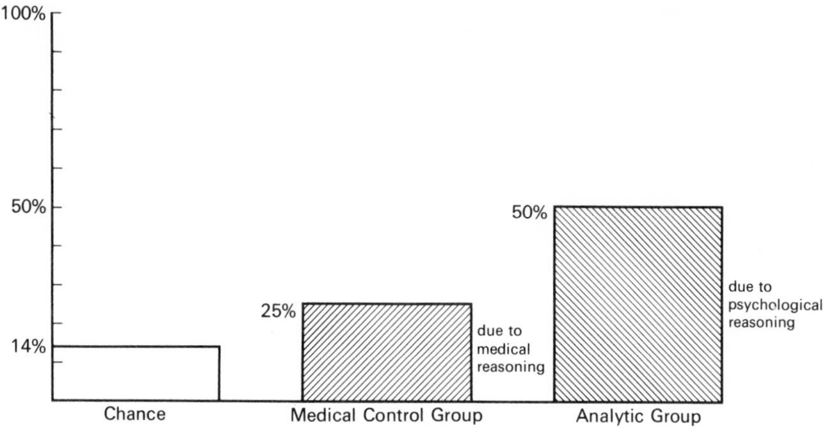

FIG. 6. Overall success in diagnosis.

If we look at the quantitative findings (Table 23) we note that the internists actually exceeded the analysts in three disease-sex categories—male hypertension, male ulcer, and male neurodermatitis. In the first two the difference is so slight as to be almost negligible, but in male neurodermatitis it is sizeable. The question arises: Why should the medical control group have exceeded the analysts in this disease category or, for that matter, in any disease category? One might think that in certain cases where the medical cues are particularly subtle, the internists would be able to employ to their own advantage very sophisticated medical thinking unavailable to the analysts. But neurodermatitis is one of the most easily diagnosed diseases in terms of its natural medical history. It pursues a chronic, relatively benign course, seldom incapacitating, necessitating few major changes in the life of the patient and not subject to any dramatic type of therapy. On such medical grounds the internists often made the diagnosis while the analysts were simply not thinking in those terms.

As an illustration let us compare the style of the analytic group with that of the medical control group on a specific case: Mr. K. A., male, neurodermatitis (Medical Control Group No. 63).

When this case of neurodermatitis was first discussed by the analytic group, five out of eight made an initial diagnosis of arthritis, and neurodermatitis was scarcely mentioned, even as a secondary diagnosis. After a second meeting with an intensive discussion, the final diagnoses were unanimous for arthritis in spite of a great deal of uneasy feeling in the group. The following written formulation of one of the analysts represents quite typically the thinking of the analytic group on this case.

> The outstanding impression this patient gives us is latent homosexuality, against which he uses different defense mechanisms. This repressed unconscious passive homosexual trend manifests itself:
>
> 1. In his deep attachment to his father. They enjoyed each other's company, and the patient has an intensive sense of gratification in being with his father and discussing matters with him. Father's loss affected him deeply and his depression lasted for four or five months.
> 2. He enjoys male company and prefers it to being with women.
> 3. Patient developed a strong father-son relationship toward one of his superiors, Peter, with whom he became very chummy.
> 4. He has an intensive reaction when accosted by homosexuals and is extremely sensitive to feminine traits (over-politeness) in men.
> 5. In his dream he is attacked by monsters, and at the beginning of the dream he cannot defend himself.
>
> The interviewer even mentions that it seems that he wants to be attacked. The defenses that the patient uses against this passive homosexual trend are: great emphasis on aggressive physical activities; an outwardly fearless masculine attitude; helpful and considerate for others, particularly toward his father. He helps father financially to realize his dream to go to Europe. Patient attacks in others his own passive trend by making "pinches" as a policeman, arresting homosexuals and also taking a great satisfaction in making other arrests, i.e., of gangsters.
>
> Patient is an ambitious man, but when he had an opportunity to fill the position of an inadequate superior he refrained from reporting the shortcomings of this man to the administration.
>
> Patient, apart from his passive homosexual tendencies, also shows a great amount of aggression. This hostile aggression finds outlet primarily by physical activities, particularly football. He loves to tackle and obviously enjoys the physical bodily contacts, scrambles and pile-ups. The genetic speculation seems to be probably that patient's passive homosexuality is a secondary defense mechanism against a deeper-seated aggressive, competitive attitude toward father. This would explain why he felt so unreasonably guilty after father's death, because he helped him to go on a trip to Europe where he died.

Patient does not repress his hostilities, but controls them to a certain extent. When it comes, however, to important situations he expresses his indignation directly, even to his superiors. He quit his job when he felt that the demands on him were excessive and the compensation not sufficient. This would directly eliminate the suspicion of hypertension. According to our theoretical concepts this patient should be diagnosed as arthritic. He has the passive homosexual component and its overcompensation. He shows a great deal of aggressiveness, but at the same time he controls himself to a very high degree. For example, when he was offered a promotion he did not accept it in spite of his ambitions, because he felt he was too young for the job. He obviously enjoys working under the direction of someone whom he likes, for example, Peter. His dependent needs and his rebelliousness are pretty evenly distributed.

His dreams are typical for arthritis, feeling paralyzed in expressing his aggression, the unconscious wish to be attacked, but finally succeeding in killing the enemy. Dreams of being paralyzed, not being able to run, are common in arthritics. They may appear also in hypertensives.

The most difficult problem in this case is to account for the onset situation. My only possible answer to this is that he was striving hard and had to control himself to a considerable degree. He wanted to make a good impression, turn out good work under some pressure, and there was a let-down in his physical activities. It is not quite certain whether this let-down was true, both for the exacerbation and for the onset situation. It seems to be unquestionably the case so far as the exacerbation is concerned. The exacerbation also coincided with the time of his marriage. Even more difficult is to precisely account for the fact that his symptoms subsided after his father's death. The possible explanation would be that all the latent hostility which he so successfully overcompensated by passive, sublimated homosexual love suddenly subsided when father died. His passive longing for the lost father came to the fore. The idea is that when hostile aggressive impulses decrease, their control becomes unnecessary and the psychodynamic constellation for the arthritic condition disappears. Further indications of arthritis are that mother's disciplinary methods were restriction of freedom, and mother was very strict. Patient loved the outdoors and felt this type of punishment very seriously. The exacerbation after he joined the police force might be explained by the fact that soon after he started his work they were given orders not to take out their aggression against the public and to be considerate. In other words, the patient had a wonderful opportunity to be aggressive, but at the same time to control it. Outside of arthritis, I could only think of ulcer. Conflict between his dependent tendencies and their overcompensation is marked. He was striving hard for success, and his responsibilities, because of the illnesses at home (father's and brother's), increased when the disease started. The exacerbation was connected with marriage, which for him was quite a step toward responsibility. On his nuptial night he did not know what to do and ordered a dinner (oral regression from a genital task). He likes to help, does not like to receive, and accepted with a feeling of guilt the fee offered him after the second interview.

Diagnosis: Arthritis 5
Ulcer 2

On the other hand, the medical control group voted correctly three out of eight for neurodermatitis on their initial formulations, and others had this as a secondary diagnosis. Several of these formulations were:

This 28-year-old man has an illness which began at 19 and has obviously been neither disfiguring nor disabling. While symptomatic he was able to pass the police physical examination, ruling out all but neurodermatitis and ulcer among the illnesses that last so long. Taking medication for two years without relief spells:

Diagnosis: Neurodermatitis 7

Twenty-eight year old male, whose illness started at the age of 19, nine years earlier. He states that he had prolonged symptoms before seeing a doctor, suggesting mild symptomatology, certainly speaking against symptoms one would associate with hypertension, thyrotoxicosis, probably also with asthma. Medical care could be expected to be sought quite promptly if these illnesses gave symptoms.

He moved on to another department two to three months after his illness started, i.e., he was not severely ill or hospitalized. Later on we learn that he was promoted even though he had the illness for over one month, again speaking for mildness of symptoms and/or symptoms not outwardly apparent (against arthritis, asthma).

The illness has prolonged remissions, one such lasting two years (then periods of symptomatology). In spite of his illness he has changed jobs repeatedly and actually is accepted as a police officer. Assuming he took a physical examination then, and knowing that he is performing a good job and still is on the force, this virtually eliminates all but neurodermatitis. The fact that he got married and his wife has been pregnant five times again speaks for mild illness.

Diagnosis: Neurodermatitis 6
Ulcer 1

Age 28. Onset seven years previously. Then prolonged remission. Not a physically restricting illness. Was in police training while ill.

Diagnosis: Neurodermatitis 5
Ulcer 2

Long period remissions and symptomatic exacerbations and yet no disability nor definitive therapy excludes hyperthyroidism, arthritis, asthma, hypertension. Symptomatic response to withdrawing therapy makes peptic ulcer seem less likely.

Diagnosis: Ulcerative Colitis 4
Neurodermatitis 3

A comparison of these protocols illustrates the enormous difference in approach between the two groups. The reader will also note that in this instance medical editing was somewhat loose and more than "minimal leaks" appeared. In particular, the impression got across that this patient had several exacerbations and remissions over a long period (censorship was supposed to restrict this to one exacerbation), and the knowledge that he passed a police examination while acutely ill "virtually eliminates all but neurodermatitis." The internists were able to spot this cue quite easily. The analysts missed it, not because they lacked the medical knowledge to reason in this way, but because of their lack of interest in this elementary diagnostic approach and in these data. The case also provides evidence against the argument that the analysts used such medical cues unconsciously.

Further support to this thesis came adventitiously from an unexpected quarter, the exhaustive "cue study" (see chapter 5). This study, which was designed to check unconscious contaminating communication between the interviewing analyst and the analytic judges, often revealed significant differences between the mode of operation of the medical and analytic groups. One of the "cue detection judges" was particularly zealous in searching for "medical cues," and this furnished an added check on medical data in the interviews. For example, if we look at Case No. 1958/130, Mrs. W. S., aged 25, actual diagnosis asthma, we note that the analysts were very uncertain after the first interview and only two of eight suggested asthma as an initial diagnosis, whereas five of the eight internists were correct on the initial diagnosis. After a second interview, in which the psychological picture emerged more clearly, the analytic team voted seven out of eight for asthma.

In summary, then, it is our considered opinion that the medical control group and the analytic team utilized different diagnostic methods, using different data, and that the statistical results attained by the analysts derive from psychological diagnostic methods and evidence rather than from a combination of psychological and "medical" information.

CHAPTER FIVE

The Interviewer Cue Detection Study

The Interviewer Cue Study

The meaningfulness and the character of patient interview material may be considerably influenced by the sensitivity, the orientation, and the expertness of an interviewer. Accordingly, the decision to make use of expert and psychosomatically oriented interviewers in this research was at first scarcely questioned. It was felt that only through the use of well-qualified interviewers would it be possible to obtain material clearly and sufficiently revealing those characteristic psychodynamic patterns which would enable the analytic research group to predict a patient's illness.

During the period of this research, knowledge of the psychology of communication had increased rapidly. Such knowledge included patterns of nonverbal communication between patient and interviewer in clinical interview situations. We began to speculate whether our interviewers could be assumed to have unconscious but effective motivations to communicate special interests or emphases to the research group through the medium of the interview, especially since most interviewers were also members of the research team. Unavoidably, they knew both the diagnosis of the case and the dynamic patterns that the analytic group associated with the disease. It seemed reasonable to assume that the interviewing team member would wish to provide a "good" interview, that is, one that would lend itself readily to the development of a dynamic formulation and point clearly toward the correct medical diagnosis. Hence we undertook a formal study of invalid, illegitimate, and unconscious interviewer communication.

We began to scrutinize interviewer activity in minute detail for its possible meaning in terms of interviewer communication. The experienced interviewer operates spontaneously, largely from preconscious levels. He follows a patient's leads, selecting or ignoring almost without conscious attention the areas he feels it important to pursue or not to pursue. In a project such as this he may come to operate, perhaps not consciously, within the framework of his knowledge of the design and objectives of the particular scientific experiment, and this, we thought, might result in some undesired effect on the research findings.

After some preliminary studies we arranged for a formal review of all our interview protocols and discussions to ascertain, if possible, whether unconscious interviewer activity had actually influenced our predictive results. We compiled a list of potential interviewer communications. For example, a sudden out-of-context question would be suspect, as it might have been determined by the interviewer's preconscious need to establish suitable material for making a particular medical diagnosis. So too would the interviewer's lack of interest, his haste to get on to new material, "hammering away" at a certain point, or interrupting a flow of patient material to change the subject. Undue emphasis upon any point or unnecessary repetition of a particular statement made by the patient would be similar forms of intrusive interviewer behavior. We suspected further that just as in certain interviews there might be a "cuing the group in," there might also be a "cuing the group out." The latter would be just as effective in pointing to an incorrect diagnosis as the former to a correct diagnosis.

During the original processing of a case, each analytic research judge was expected to search for illegitimate medical or analytic cue material which might have escaped the censoring editors. Several cases were judged "unsuitable" by the analytic group and eliminated from the study, even after processing, because of cuing that had slipped through. Neither this procedure nor our experimental design, however, could eliminate all possibility of interviewer cuing.

We faced a threefold problem in our cue study. First we had to determine whether interviewer cues really were present in the protocols; second, we had to find out whether cues, if present, had influenced the results; last, it was of crucial importance to examine the dynamic formulations of the individual analytic judges and the recorded analytic group discussions to determine how cues had been used. Had the intuitively derived dynamic formulations of the cases led to correct diagnosis, or did residual medical or interviewer cues, configurational patterns of the illness, or some group process determine the final diagnosis?

Two members of the analytic group who joined the project somewhat late were asked, as a preliminary study, to review all the protocols processed by the group before they had joined, that is, cases they had not studied and for which they did not know the diagnosis. They were asked to note any interviewer activity that suggested possible cuing, state why it seemed suspect, and name the disease most suggested by the amount and the nature of the cuing rather than that suggested by the dynamics of the case itself.

Each of the possible cues picked up by these first cue judges was gone over carefully by the research group as a whole. With some there was immediate agreement that a particular interviewer activity had derived from pressure toward a given diagnosis. About others there was very little agreement. It was then decided that it would be advisable to study every case protocol for evidences of cuing and to ascertain as clearly as possible the effect, if any, on the analytic group results. In the interest of objectivity it was also decided this study should be made primarily by persons other than the analytic research team.

Methodology of the Interviewer Cue Detection Study

From the pilot cue studies, categories of potential interviewer cues were established. The common factor in these cues was evidence that the interviewer showed an unwarranted or unexplained interest or lack of interest in a particular part of the patient's story. Cues were classified in the manner shown below and given to the four cue detection judges as part of their instructions. These judges were then given, one at a time, copies of the edited protocols used originally by the analytic judges. The cue detection judges were asked to read the interviews, look carefully for possible interviewer cues, and classify such cues according to the categories defined and illustrated on the instruction sheets. They were also to record their findings on a prescribed record form. The instructions given to the cue judges follow.

Instructions to Interviewer Cue Detection Judges

Aims

The purpose of this study is to determine the nature and extent of cues from the interviewer in each interview protocol, and the relationship between such cuing and the accuracy of the diagnosis made from the protocols.

Your task is to identify everything in the protocol which might be a cue. In general, cues will be departures from the intended procedure of obtaining an associative anamnesis followed by the asking of a set of standard questions. Each standard question was designed to obtain specific information. If this information had been elicited in full in the earlier part of the interview, the question would ordinarily be omitted.

The determination of what is a cue is a matter of judgment. Attached is a list of some types of cues. This list is suggestive, not exhaustive: it is expected that other types will be found.

Cues can be roughly classified as specific or general. An example of a specific cue is the use of an unwarranted word. A general or broader cue would be a persistent emphasis on a topic throughout the interview, or the omission of standard questions pertaining to one disease. In evaluating the interviewer's questions on a particular topic, however, the judge should take care to determine whether or not the interviewer may be merely following up the patient's own spontaneous interest in this topic. It is the duty of the interviewer to follow up implications of the patient's spontaneous remarks that have not been clearly enough spelled out. When the interviewer does no more than this, his questions should not be evaluated as positive cues.

Most cues can be seen as suggesting or as tending to rule out a disease or diseases. However, every cue or departure from the general plan of procedure should be noted, even though it cannot readily be related to any of the diseases. This is particularly important because it is not possible to include in the psychological formulations for the several diseases all material which might be related to them in the thinking of the members of the analytic group. For example, it is conceivable that one of the analysts might have entertained for a while, and discussed with the group, the speculation that a particular reaction was associated with colitis. If he were the interviewer for a case of colitis that showed this reaction, he might emphasize it in his conduct of the interview. This would be a cue even though he and the group might subsequently decide that this reaction was not characteristic of colitis.

Procedure

Go through each protocol looking for specific cues. Your method of doing this cannot be prescribed, but it is obvious that each question or remark of the interviewer should be examined, and frequently the preceding response of the patient must be read to determine whether the interviewer's statement or query follows or is out of context.

Each specific cue should be identified on the first page of the Record Form, together with some indication of its type. It will ordinarily be possible to interpret the cue as suggesting that the actual disease is or is not one or more of the seven possibilities. (It would be valuable to us if you would also record anything you may observe in the protocol which is direct or medical evidence for or against a disease and which should have been deleted by the censors. Such oversights should be rare and would ordinarily not be in the interviewer's communications.)

At the end of the interview, you should consider whether the interview as a whole, or some sections of it, show general cues. (This may require a quick reexamination of the protocol.) Any general cues or impressions should be noted on the second page of the Record Form.

Part of this general review should be a consideration of the standard questions. Were some omitted that should have been asked? Were the omissions those related to one or more particular disease? These judgments would be in addition to any cues in the phrasing of the standard questions or in the transition from the associative part of the systematic questioning.

The list of standard questions was developed and extended during the course of the study, from 1953 to 1959. It will be necessary to evaluate the adequacy of the standard questioning in terms of the practice current at the time of the interview. This can be done with the aid of the supplementary material on the chronological history of these questions.

It will be apparent that each interview should be reviewed as a unit, at one sitting, so that general cues and cues involving repetition or other cross-references can most readily be noted.

After you have recorded all observed cues, both general and specific, please record your impressions of the net balance of the cuing. Which diseases, if any, are clearly suggested? For which are there some hints? Which are probably ruled out by the cues? Which are clearly ruled out?

The statement of these impressions will vary from case to case. In some, you may feel that there are no definite cues, but one slight hint favoring one or two diseases. In others, you may be able to indicate two or three diseases that are suggested with varying degrees of strength, and similarly for diseases that are more or less ruled out. In still others, you may feel that there is evidence both for and against a particular disease.

It is desirable that you mention as many diseases as the cues permit, and that you indicate the relative strength of the evidence for or against each disease. This composite judgment should reflect your general impression. It may or may not correspond with the frequencies of mentions of diseases in the "for" and "against" columns of the first page of the Record Form.

Note that it is not your task to make a diagnosis of the case from the material given by the patient. Any attempt to make such a diagnosis is likely to interfere with your "set" to identify every cue that is present.

It is necessary for us to know every disease that is suggested (even though each case had only one disease) and not merely which disease seems most likely. Whether or not each cue is true or false, whether it could help or mislead a diagnostician is irrelevant to your task.

Cases With More Than One Interview

About half the cases have more than one interview. In some of these, a second interview was held by the interviewer because the usual procedure could not be completed at one time. Both interviews were given to the diagnostic judges together. In such cases, the two (or more) interviews should be treated as essentially one unit, like the cases with a single interview.

In other cases, the group held a meeting and discussed the case on the basis of the one or more interview protocols furnished to it, but decided that an additional interview was necessary because information on certain essential topics was lacking or was vague. The group would then request the interviewer to ask the patient certain questions, or to investigate further certain topics, in a subsequent interview. In such cases, the group's questions have been extracted from the transcript of the discussion and attached to the protocol. The additional interview should be reviewed, keeping in mind these questions and the fact that, under these circumstances, it was customary for the interviewer to ask about reactions and dreams following the earlier interview. The specified questions should not themselves be taken as cues.

With the exception of this particular orientation towards requested interviews, these cases should be handled like the others. After noting specific cues in the several interviews, note any general cues or impressions about the case as a whole (and *not* about each interview separately).

Categories of Interviewer Cues

Judges should be alert to possible cues of the following types:

1. Out of Context Request for Information

Out of context question, or request. It abruptly changes the topic away from an area in which the patient was still actively talking. (Assumption: The area switched away from was not concerned with the information relating to the dynamics of the actual disease.

Therefore, if the area was "typical" for asthma, this would be a cue against asthma. Also, the direction indicated by the interviewer change in topic would be regarded as a possible cue for another disease.)

2. *Unwarranted Emphasis*

Seemingly unwarranted emphasis by the interviewer of certain points of information:

a) The interviewer's statements may indicate the interviewer's disbelief that something is not present—is a cue for the disease reflected by the personality trait, conflict or historical occurrence which the interviewer persists in looking for—even in the face of a denial by the patient.

b) Interviewer can also indicate disbelief that something is present. This is a cue against the disease represented by the thing present.

c) The interviewer may tend to repeat certain points already made by the patient. He is not asking for clarification but only for repetition and a further declaration of certainty. For example:

A: "You said, didn't you that you can't cry?"

P: "Yes."

A: "I just wanted to be sure."

(However, it should also be recognized that sometimes the interviewer may have asked the patient to repeat a statement for another reason, e.g., if the patient is speaking too softly and the interviewer wants to make sure the remark gets on the record.)

d) The interviewer may exaggerate the quantity or quality of something which the patient has said, as

P: "I began to think maybe that plan wouldn't work out."

A: "So you began to believe that you were failing."

e) The interviewer may focus selectively upon a casual bit of information, dropped by the patient in the midst of a vigorous, cathected account of something else. This is a cue against any disease possibly reflected by the patient's main point, or for the disease associated with the selectively emphasized interviewer fragment.

3. *Weighted Words*

These were more common in the early years, and involved an interviewer's unsolicited introduction of verbal expressions linked in the group's mind with specific diseases. Furthermore, these terms or phrases were used to describe some aspect of the patient's behavior. Examples:

Peptic ulcer:	dependent; ambitious (very)
Bronchial asthma:	protective; couldn't communicate
Neurodermatitis:	guilt; exhibitionistic

Ulcerative colitis:	gave up; fear of failing
Hypertension:	underdog; rage; can't blow your top
Thyrotoxicosis:	premature independence in functioning; fear of corpses
Rheumatoid arthritis:	tomboy

This does not refer to the usage of such words in the standard questions, but rather in the course of playbacks to the patient of what he has just said—but reworded by the interviewer to include one of the "cue" words. Example:

A: "Let's see now if I understand. You felt that mother was too protective, but somehow you couldn't communicate this to her?"

These words were cues for the diagnosis usually associated with the particular "cue expression."

4. Selective Omissions

Failure to ask standard questions pertaining to a given disease was evidence against this diagnosis.

5. Unwarranted Assumptions

The interviewer's remark or question may reflect his presupposition that certain dynamic factors or time relations will be found (because he knew the diagnosis). Examples:

A: "I'll bet you were a tomboy as a kid."

P: "How did you know?"

A: "Your mother must have kept you under her thumb."

6. Emotional Reaction of Interviewer to Patient

Evidence that the interviewer was irritated with the patient or had some other kind of emotional reaction that may have influenced the patient's responses.

7. Medical Data

Summarizing comment: The common denominator of the various categories of cues above listed is evidence pointing toward an unexplained, and seemingly unwarranted, interviewer interest or disinterest in selective portions of the patient's story, or in particular interpretations of the patient's story.

The above list of possible cues is not complete but only illustrative. It is also applicable only to interviews that preceded the first group discussion of a case. In the group discussion, the interviewer may have been instructed to ask certain questions or investigate certain topics. Questions asked by the interviewer in accordance with such instructions should, of course, not be evaluated as interviewer cues.

We here present as an example the record form for the study of interview cues, as processed by a cue detection judge in the pilot cue study.

CASE IDENTIFICATION: Mr. J. B. JUDGE: X
DATE OF INTERVIEW: December 3, 1953 DATE OF CUE REVIEW: May 15, 1959

SPECIFIC CUES

CUE No.	PAGE No.	DESCRIPTION AND CATEGORIZATION	FOR	AGAINST
1	12	Analyst asks, "Are you often taken to be a pushover?" (Analyst thinks patient is a weak sister. Unsolicited word.)	Colitis	
2	13	Analyst does not question patient about his reaction to father's suicide. (Failure to follow patient material.)		Thyrotoxicosis
3	40	Analyst says regarding onset, "Still, it was something in connection with school." (Unwarranted emphasis.)	Colitis or Ulcer	
4	55–58	Analyst seems to be badgering patient about sex.	Asthma	

GENERAL COMMENTS AND SUMMARY

Some evidence for ruling out arthritis because of the lack of questioning in this area.

Mild hint of colitis because of interviewer's use of "pushover" and because of his feeling of irritation with the patient.

Taken all together, cues tend to suggest colitis and very weakly, asthma.

Some evidence against arthritis, and very slight evidence against thyrotoxicosis.

It was decided that the team of four cue detection judges should include one analyst from the analytic team and three analysts who had no special knowledge of the style, habits, or biases of the analytic team members, and no identification with the project. (These three judges operated independently of each other and of the research team. In allowing them no communication with each other about the cases and not allowing them to learn the diagnoses of the cases they processed, "learning factors" were kept to a minimum.) The one analytic judge was asked to function as a "cue detection judge" in order to pick up possible preconscious special communications that might not be quite so obvious to the other judges. Because this judge might remember the particular case under study and his scrutiny for cues be influenced by his remembering the diagnosis, he was expected to report whether and at what point he remembered the case. Any major difference in his performance as a cue detection judge from that of the other cue judges might alert us to other factors perhaps requiring exploration.

The fact that the interviewer had known the diagnosis added a burden to his conduct. He had been expected to use the technique of "associative anamnesis"; to follow up any and all leads given by the patient; and then to complete the process by asking all the standard questions properly, again following through on every lead. This was not possible with each patient. Nor was it possible for each interviewer to conform completely to a set style of interviewing. Deviation by the interviewer from the ideally prescribed procedures was to be viewed by the cue detection judges as possible interviewer cuing. But due care was to be exercised to differentiate as far as possible variations from the standard techniques resulting from the patient's particular personality and interests, and from idiosyncrasies of the interviewer's style.

Quantitative Analyses of the Cue Detection Judges' Reports

The study of the interviewer cues in the total group of cases was planned to have two major parts. One part was directed toward determining how many potential cues were in the protocols, how many of the cases were judged to be cued for the actual disease, and whether there was any relationship between judged cuing and success of the analytic group in their diagnostic judgments. The second part sought to determine the extent to which the potential or alleged cues seemed to have been utilized in the process by which the analytic judges arrived at their dynamic formulations of the cases and their diagnoses. These are discussed in the preceding and following sections of this chapter.

In the plan for the first part, major emphasis was placed on the relationship between the judged extent of cuing and the success of the analytic group. If the proportion of correct initial diagnoses by the analytic group did not vary systematically with the judged extent of cuing, the cuing could not have helped the analytic group. On the other hand, if the proportion of correct diagnoses increased regularly with increases in judged extent of cuing, then there was a definite possibility that illegitimate cuing had contributed to the success of the analytic group.

Quite frankly, the findings were puzzling. For this reason, it seems desirable to present the two major findings at this point and then give the details of the procedure and the analyses for this investigation. In this way, the reader will be able to weigh the several kinds of pertinent evidence, consider the evident disparity between the findings, and form his own judgment about the resolution of the puzzle.

On the one hand, the cue detection judges showed no agreement among themselves on the extent of cuing in a given case. Consistent with this finding is the fact that there was little agreement upon specific cues: those identified by one judge were rarely identified by a second judge. It seems reasonable then that there were very few clear-cut universally identified cues and that any cuing that occurred was quite subtle.

On the other hand, the analytic group tended to be more successful on cases which at least one cue detection judge felt were strongly cued for the actual disease. Surprisingly, they did as well on the cases which only one cue judge felt were strongly cued as they did on those which two or even three felt were strongly cued. Thus, instead of a gradual increase in success with higher degrees of consensus among the cue judges, there was only one abrupt jump from low success where no cue judge felt the case was strongly cued to considerable success where at least one judge felt so. In this quantitative part of the interviewer cue study, this is the only finding pertinent to possible utilization of cues by the analytic group.

These are the two separate and disparate findings that must be interpreted. The next section presents the procedures by which these results were obtained.

Procedure

Most of the controls used in this research project were built into the original design and procedures. The attempt to deal with the possible interviewer cuing was a retrospective check.

Four cue detection judges were used. Judge I was a member of the analytic group who joined the group after one-third of the cases had already been processed. The other three judges were not members of the analytic research group; two resided in other cities. They were psychoanalysts who had some general familiarity with the formulations concerning the personality constellations and onset situations postulated for each disease, but did not hold extreme views about these theories. Whereas Judge I and Judge II reviewed all the protocols, Judge III reviewed the last 59 and Judge IV reviewed the first 60, both seeing a large group of cases in the middle of the series.

Although the instructions to the judges were extensive and the judges clearly understood the objective established for them, little guidance could be given them on how to proceed. They had no precise, objective criteria for determining whether a particular response was or was not a cue. Since each judge went through all his cases with no information about the agreement between his impressions and those of other judges or about the agreement between the actual diseases and his impressions, it is not surprising that the judges tended to approach the task with somewhat different emphases. Thus one judge carefully watched for potential medical cues that had not been censored whereas another judge emphasized apparent departures from the established procedure for interviewing.

Two major parts of the reports by the cue judges were utilized. The lists of specific potential cues were used in some quantitative analyses and were important material for qualitative studies of individual cases. More central to the question of possible interviewer cuing were the cue judges' overall impressions, which weighed not only specific but also general cues.

The general impressions were recorded by the cue detection judges in their own words. One or more diseases might be mentioned as favored by the apparent cuing, along with some deemed as cued against. It was necessary to compare each of these statements of general impressions with the actual disease for the given case, to determine the judged extent of apparent cuing. A series of ordered categories was drawn up to cover all possibilities.

Each of the reports from the cue judges was classified by an outside person who of course knew the actual disease. Most of the reports were classified by two persons working independently. When a very high degree of agreement was found between them (the correlations falling between .88 and .98), the remaining cases were classified by just one person. For the reports classified by two persons, the few discrepancies were resolved by reexamination and discussion.

To simplify the statistical treatment, a longer list of categories was reduced to just three broad classes with respect to the extent of cuing for the actual disease: strongly cued, slightly cued, and not cued. The "strongly cued" class included cases judged to be definitely cued for the actual disease and also cases with cues for the actual disease and one other, the actual disease being judged equally or more likely. The "slightly cued" class included cases judged to be slightly cued for the actual disease and no other, cases seen as cued for several diseases including the actual one, and cases reported as cued for the actual one and one other, the latter being favored over the actual one. The "not cued" class included cases seen as cued against the actual disease, and cases where no cues were found. Illustrations of the three classes are given below.

Strongly cued: "There seems to be a general tendency to focus on the topics that would have more meaning for the neurodermatitis diagnosis, like closeness, contact, limelight, attention, performance, etc." (Actual disease: neurodermatitis.)

"A very thorough and exhaustive interview covering all areas. But it seemed that asthma and neurodermatitis were cued most often and significantly." (Actual disease: neurodermatitis.)

Slightly cued: "Weak cues for arthritis and ulcer. Several fairly strong cues for asthma make it the most likely diagnosis." (Actual disease: ulcer.)

"General tenor of the interview suggests hypertension but no direct cues." (Actual disease: hypertension.)

Not cued: "Minimal cues. Two fairly strong cues suggest either colitis or ulcer. . . . Thyrotoxicosis is suggested by two allusions to fear of death." (Actual disease: hypertension.)

"Failure to question in the areas of arthritis and neurodermatitis would tend to rule them out. There was but one cue and it suggested colitis." (Actual disease: thyrotoxicosis.)

These three classes can be viewed in terms of the effect of the judged cuing on the odds for making a correct diagnosis on the basis of chance. The original odds were one out of seven. The "strongly cued" cases were ones for which the cue judge felt the odds were better than one out of seven. The "slightly cued" cases had odds a little larger than one out of seven. The odds for the "not cued" cases ranged from less than one out of seven (for cases cued against the actual disease) to about chance. (In a few instances where the actual disease was not mentioned, the odds might be a bit larger than chance if the cues were seen as being against some other disease.)

The Judgments of the Cue Detection Judges

Table 25 shows how the cue judges' reports were distributed among the three classes outlined above. On the average, about one-fifth of the cases were seen as strongly cued and one-fifth as slightly cued. The distributions differ from judge to judge, however. For example, Judge IV saw only 13% of his cases as strongly cued whereas Judge I placed 31% of his in this category. It must be recalled that Judge I was a member of the analytic group. He recognized most of the cases he had seen previously in his role of analytic diagnostician and usually recalled the actual disease, both recollections occurring ordinarily in the first part of the first interview. Hence he alone knew the actual disease in many cases. On the other hand, his view that more cases were cued for the actual disease may have resulted from his more intimate knowledge of the formulations for the diseases and from his acquaintance with views about the seven psychological constellations held by some but not all of the group and not included in written descriptions.

Each judge saw more than one-seventh of the cases as cued for the actual disease. Were the same cases identified by the several judges? The

Table 25

Distribution of Overall Judgments on Cuing For Actual Disease (Per Cent)

	Cases judged not cued	Cases judged slightly cued	Cases judged strongly cued
Judge I	42	26	31
Judge II	58	26	16
Judge III	59	15	25
Judge IV	68	18	13
Mean for the four judges	57	21	21

agreements between the judges are recorded in Table 26. The cases are divided into those reviewed by three judges and those reviewed by all four and are also taken as a total group. Consider the next to the last column of Table 26. Here we find that 15 cases were judged as strongly cued by two or more judges and 26 so judged by just one judge, making a total of 41 cases seen as strongly cued by at least one judge. Although these frequencies are by no means negligible, it is important to determine whether the judges agreed in their impressions of extent of cuing.

Some agreement between the cue judges would be expected on the basis of chance. Thus if one judge considered 40% of the cases to be strongly cued and another judge felt that 30% were, we would expect them both to say strongly cued for 12% of those cases they both saw (12% being the product of the two separate values). Only if they agreed on significantly more than 12% of the cases could we conclude that there was real consensus on which cases were cued.

For this statistical analysis, we used the proportions for each judge as given in Table 25. From these values, the expected frequency was determined for each of the several classes given at the left of each row in Table 26: two or more judges say strongly cued, one says strongly cued, and so on. These expected values are listed in the columns headed "Expected Number" and provide us with a baseline permitting us to compare the agreement actually obtained with the agreement to be expected on the basis of chance, that is, what would be expected if each judge's impressions were independent of and unrelated to those for any other judge.

The full procedure involved several steps. Consider the expected value (6) for Set B ("Cases Seen by Only Three Judges") in the first row ("Two or more say strongly cued") of Table 26. There were two groups of cases, each seen by the same three judges. For the set seen by Judges I, II, and

Table 26

Agreement Among Cue Judges on Overall Judgments

Grouping by Cue Judgments	Set A: Cases Seen by Four Judges		Set B: Cases Seen by Only Three Judges		All Cases (Sets A and B)	
	Actual Number	Expected Number	Actual Number	Expected Number	Actual Number	Expected Number
Two or more judges say strongly cued for actual disease	11	7	4	6	15	13
Only one judge says strongly cued for actual disease	11	15	15	19	26	34
Total of above two rows	22	22	19	25	41	47
Two or three judges say slightly cued for actual disease	4	5	10	5	14	10
All others	10	9	18	17	28	26
Total of above two rows	14	14	28	22	42	36

NOTE: Expected values are based on the proportions of cases that each cue judge called strongly cued, slightly cued, or not cued (as given in Table 25), and the proportions of combinations of such judgments by the three or the four judges which would be expected if the judgments of each judge were independent of (i.e., unrelated to) those of every other judge.

IV, seven outcomes fall into this category. One is, of course, the instance in which all three say strongly cued. Then there can be three pairings of two judges saying strongly cued (I and II, I and IV, II and IV). But for each such pair, there are two possibilities: the third judge may say either slightly cued or not cued.

Assuming that the judgment of each judge is independent of the judgment of each of the other two events, the expected probability of each of these seven events can be calculated by multiplying the appropriate proportions of judgments which the judges made of each type as given in Table 25. Thus, for the outcome that the first two judges say the case is strongly cued and the third (Judge IV) says it is not cued, we multiply .31 times .16 times .68, and obtain .0337. The sum of these seven expected probabilities is .0969. Multiplying the number of cases seen by three judges (24) by this value, we obtain 2.3 as the expected frequency in which two or more of these three judges say the case is strongly cued. The corresponding value for the other combination of three judges is 3.3. The sum of these frequencies is 5.6, which is rounded off to six in Table 26.

Comparisons between these expected values and the actual, observed ones reveal rather small discrepancies: the actual frequencies are very similar to those expected on a chance basis. The table strongly suggests the conclusion that the cue judges did not agree with each other on the extent of cuing of the various cases.

Another way to examine the degree of agreement between the judges is to see how well each pair of judges agree with each other. A representative picture is shown in Table 27. There is no relation between the impression of Judge II and that of Judge III. Even in the cell of most importance, cases judged as strongly cued by both judges, the frequency observed (2) is almost identical with the frequency expected on a chance basis (1.7). The tables for the other pairings of judges show the same lack of relationship, with very little variation from table to table.

Table 27

Comparison of Overall Judgments Made by Judges II and III

Judgment of Judge II	Judgment of Judge III		
	Not cued	Slightly cued	Strongly cued
Not cued	15	2	6
Slightly cued	6	4	0
Strongly cued	4	3	2

Turning now to the specific cues identified by the cue judges, we find in Table 28 that, on the average, each judge found fewer than four cues in the protocol for each case. In some instances, no cues were found. Although one judge found 16 cues on one case, it was rare that more than six were noted. When it is recalled that a cue might be for or against one or more of the seven diseases, it will be evident that in the typical case, a single judge would not find more than one or two cues favoring the actual diagnosis.

The extent to which the judges agreed on the cues they noted is depicted in Table 29. The second row shows that in fewer than one-fourth of the cases did any pair of judges typically find one or more identical cues. In only about half these cases with identical cues was there agreement that the cue favored the actual disease. In a majority of the remaining cases, the judges agreed that the cue favored some other disease.

Table 28

Mean Frequency of Specific Cues per Case

Cue Detection Judges	Means
Judge I	2.8
Judge II	3.6
Judge III	3.9
Judge IV	3.6
Mean of four judges	3.5

When the judges are taken three at a time, the frequencies of cases with identical cues drop. For Judge I, II, and IV there are no such cases. For the other trio compared there are a few. Finally, it will be seen that there was no instance in which the same cue was noted by all four judges.

No attempt was made to estimate the frequency of identical cues expected on a chance basis because of the impossibility of determining the number of things that might be called cues. We may add, however, that of all the cues noted by a given judge, only about 4% to 15% were noted by the second judge in each pair. Even identical cues were often seen as favoring other diseases as well as the actual one: less than 6% were seen as favoring the actual disease by both judges in any pair. We must conclude that judges specifically oriented toward searching for possible cues could only rarely find instances in the protocols on which two of them could agree that the actual disease might have been suggested illegitimately to the diagnosticians.

Table 29

Agreement Among Cue Judges on Specific Cues

	Two Judges Compared					Three Judges Compared		All Four Judges Compared
	I,II	I,III	I,IV	II,III	II,IV	I,II,III	I,II,IV	
Number of cases seen by all judges in the set	83	59	60	59	60	59	60	36
Percentage of cases with identical cues	23%	34%	12%	29%	10%	14%	0%	0%
Percentage of cases with at least one identical cue judged for the actual disease by all judges in set	12%	15%	10%	15%	5%	10%	0%	0%
Percentage of cases with at least one identical cue judged for some other disease by all judges in set	4%	15%	2%	15%	5%	5%	0%	0%
Percentage of cases with identical cues of other kinds[a]	7%	7%	0%	3%	0%	5%	0%	0%

[a] This group includes a variety of cases in which the cue judges disagreed about the disease the cue was for or against. The percentages in the last three rows may add to more than the percentage in the second row because the same case fell into more than one group.

Was the presence of identical cues related to the composite judgment of cuing? To answer this question, we classified the cases according to the number of cue judges saying the case was strongly cued, and then we determined the number of cases with identical cues within each class. This tabulation is presented in Table 30. It will be seen that identical cues were found in most cases considered strongly cued by two or three judges, whereas such cues were noted in only a minority of the other cases. This relationship was statistically significant. Hence, when an identical cue was found, it was more likely to be a case which more than one cue judge felt was strongly cued.

Table 30

Association Between Presence of Identical Cues and Number of Cue Judges Seeing the Case as Strongly Cued

	Number of Judges			
	Three	Two	One	None
At least one pair of judges found an identical cue for the actual disease	5	7	7	6
No identical cues found	1	2	19	36
Total number of cases	6	9	26	42

To make more concrete the matter of agreement between cue judges, three cases have been selected at random: one from the cases deemed strongly cued by two judges, one from those seen as strongly cued by only one judge, and one from those seen as slightly cued by one judge. (As it happens, each case was seen by only three judges.) The general impressions of the judges on the first case (a case of arthritis) can be paraphrased as follows: Judge I—the cues for arthritis are obvious; Judge II—no interviewer cues; Judge IV—numerous cues for arthritis. Judge I found four cues and Judge IV found five. Of these, one cue was identified by both: Judge I saw it as favoring arthritis and Judge IV felt it favored either hypertension or arthritis.

The impressions on the second case (the actual disease being asthma) were these: Judge I—asthma; Judge II—"The strongest suggestions are for ulcer"; Judge III—no positive cues. No identical cues were found.

Neurodermatitis was the disease in the third of these examples: Judge I—no cues of any kind; Judge II—"Three illnesses are favored . . .: ulcer (strongest possibility), neurodermatitis, asthma"; Judge IV—"The overall record is generally free of interviewer cuing. There is a mild hint in the direction of asthma." Again no common cues were found.

The Overall Impressions of the Cue Judges and the Success of the Diagnostic Groups

Was there any relationship between the overall judgments of the cue judges on extent of cuing and the correctness of the initial diagnoses of analytic and internist groups? Table 31 gives the relevant findings. In the second column of this table it can be seen that there is no consistent relationship between the success of the internist group and the findings of each judge on degree of cuing. On the other hand, the first column shows that for each judge, the cases he felt were strongly cued were more successfully diagnosed by the analytic group than were the other cases. For three of the four judges, however, the cases judged as not cued were more correctly diagnosed by the analytic group than those seen as slightly cued. (The other judge—Judge I—it will be recalled, was a member of the analytic group and therefore recognized many of the cases.) We do not find a consistent, regular association between success and judged extent of cuing.

Table 31

Correctness of Initial Diagnoses by Analytic and Internist Groups and Overall Judgment of Cuing by Each Cue Judge

	Mean Percentage Correct Initial Diagnoses		Mean of Difference (%)	Median of Difference (%)	Number of Cases
	Analytic Group	Internist Group			
Judge I					
Strongly cued	54	22	32	28	20
Slightly cued	44	26	18	9	18
Not cued	31	26	5	0	32
Judge II					
Strongly cued	63	32	31	23	11
Slightly cued	29	30	−1	1	18
Not cued	39	20	19	12	41
Judge III					
Strongly cued	51	25	26	14	11
Slightly cued	27	29	−2	8	6
Not cued	42	24	18	18	29
Judge IV					
Strongly cued	56	35	21	13	7
Slightly cued	33	18	15	8	11
Not cued	42	22	20	21	41

The differences between the success rates of the two groups are given in the third and fourth columns of Table 31. The analytic group was relatively more successful on cases judged as strongly cued, but of course we again find that the trend changes direction from the slightly cued cases to the not cued ones. The medians (middle values) are generally lower than the means, the latter being raised by a few extreme cases: since the distribution of differences is very broad and is stretched out toward the high end, the medians are probably the better indications of the general trends. The sets of medians show relationships to judged degree of cuing for two judges (I and II) but not for the other two (III and IV).

Two specific points should be noted. First, no one of these values should be given much weight by itself, since these percentages are based on groups of as few as six cases. Second, although these data are derived from the 70 cases seen by the internist group, the general picture suggested in the first column is essentially the same for the whole group of 83 cases.

In addition to these studies comparing the relative success of the analytic group with the judgments of each cue judge taken independently, studies were made on the basis of the combined judgments of the several cue judges. This composite impression about cuing can be viewed as a more reliable index than the judgments of any one judge: a single judge might fail to note cues that were picked up by the other judges, and, presumably, the more judges who felt a case was cued the more obvious the cuing. The cases were grouped primarily by greatest degree of judged cuing and secondarily by the number of judges reporting the given degree.

Table 32 analyzes the same comparisons as the preceding table, but here the cases are classified by the pattern of impressions from the several judges taken together. The first row shows that for the four cases that at least three judges felt were strongly cued, the analytic group had a mean of 57% correct diagnoses, about twice that of the internist group. The picture is about the same for the next three rows. In contrast, the level of success for the analysts and the average differences tend to be lower for the last three rows. In general, the internist group did about equally well on each of the seven groups of cases.

Some clarification of the groupings of cases seems desirable. The classification was made as indicated, the judges not mentioned seeing the cases as less cued in each instance. For example, the second row includes all cases that just two judges considered to be strongly cued, the other one or two seeing the cases as slightly cued or not cued. Also, once again, the reader should keep in mind the very small frequency in each group and the consequent comparative unreliability of any one figure.

The general picture reveals that for those cases that at least one judge felt were strongly cued, the analytic group did well, and considerably

Table 32

Correctness of Initial Diagnoses by Analytic and Internist Groups and Combined Overall Judgments by Cue Judges for Cases Seen by Both Groups

Grouping of Overall Judgments	Mean Percentage Correct Initial Diagnoses		Mean of Difference (%)	Median of Difference (%)	Number of Cases
	Analytic Group	Internist Group			
Three (or four) judges say strongly cued	57	29	28	20	4
Two judges say strongly cued	59	26	33	20	9
One judge says strongly cued, one or two say slightly cued	42	22	20	12	9
One judge says strongly cued, other judges say not cued	61	30	31	24	10
Two or three judges say slightly cued	27	31	−4	0	11
One judge says slightly cued	35	20	15	0	13
All judges say not cued	23	18	5	−3	14

better than the internist group: the first four categories of cases contrast sharply with the last three. This pattern is congruent with that in the preceding table. One point deserves marked emphasis, however: the analytic group had the same relative success when several judges called the case strongly cued as when only one did. For all cases labeled strongly cued by at least one judge, success was not a function of the number of judges viewing the case as strongly cued. Hence the interpretation of these findings must account for two facts: (*a*) the analytic group was relatively more successful on cases that at least one cue detection judge saw as strongly cued; (*b*) the judgments on extent of cuing made by one judge are essentially independent of those made by any other judge—even for judges looking for cues, there was no consensus that some cases were more cued than others. In other words, whatever one detection judge saw as strong cuing was typically not seen this way by any other judge. The implications of these results will be discussed below after presentation of some further findings.

One small additional study is of interest. Since Judge I had served as a member of the analytic group, it was possible to compare his judgments on extent of cuing with the correctness of his initial diagnoses on the same cases when he functioned as an analytic judge. A statistical test indicated no relationship: his judgments as a cue judge were unrelated to the success of his diagnoses as an analytic judge. Although no great weight can be placed upon the findings for just one person, this result does suggest that evidence which he felt indicated cuing for the actual disease did not help him in his diagnostic judgments as an analytic judge. We may look at the data another way: 48% of his initial diagnoses were correct; if he had originally considered not only the psychological picture but had responded (consciously or not) to possible interviewer cues, his performance would have been much better, since he judged 60% of these same cases to be slightly or strongly cued.

Finally, we asked whether the differential success of the analytic group on the several disease-sex categories might be a function of greater cuing in the cases of some categories. Examination revealed no significant association between median judgment of cuing for each category and mean proportion of correct initial diagnoses of the analytic group.

Factors Associated with Judgments of Cuing

Further information about these judgments of cuing was sought by looking for factors to which they were related. One such variable was the temporal position of the case in the total series. Taking the composite judgments of the several cue judges as used in Table 32, we made a study of the dates on which the cases were discussed by the analytic group. A statistically significant relationship was found: there was a tendency for early cases to be judged as cued more frequently than later cases. We may conclude that as the series progressed, the interviewers tightened up their interviewing and their censoring to eliminate material that might be seen as cuing. But comparing the early and late cases in each of the disease-sex categories, we found that the average correctness of the analytic group's initial diagnoses did not change over time.

We also studied the cases grouped in terms of the interviewer. We explored the possibility that certain interviewers might have contributed disproportionately to the relative success of the analytic group by providing more cases judged as cued. This possibility seemed likely, since the success of the analytic group varied from 21% to 65% for the sets of cases grouped by the interviewer. This variation is of course due in part to the small number of cases (5 to 17) interviewed by each person.

We determined the mean difference between the percentage of correct diagnoses by the analyst group and that of the internist group for the set of cases seen by each interviewer. We also determined the median cuing category for each such set of cases. No relationship was found between these two indices: the conclusion must be that the relative success of the analytic group on the several groups was unrelated to the relative degree of cuing seen by the cue judges.

In a separate study, the set of cases for each interviewer was examined. Over the cases in each set, the relative success of the analytic group was compared with the composite judgment of degree of cuing for each case. The median of the correlations for the several sets was .26, a value indicating that for the typical interviewer there was only a slight relationship.

Another possibility was that much of the basis for the cuing judgments resided in the additional interviews requested by the analytic group. It will be recalled that in instances when the group felt that the interview protocol first given to them lacked some essential information, they would ask the interviewer to hold an additional interview with the patient. The request might be made because they felt that the original protocol did not contain material pertinent to some of the standard questions, or that the nature of the onset situation was not clear, or for some other reason. Insofar as the analytic group was oriented toward the actual disease and asked for material relevant to it, there was the possibility that the nature of the second interview might offer more opportunities for apparent cuing than would the standard first interview. If this were the case, cue detection judges might find more apparent cues in the second interview, but such "cues" would not be legitimate.

This matter was investigated in two ways. First, for the two cue judges (I and II) who reviewed all cases, counts were made of the specific cues found in the first interview and in later ones (for cases with such additional interviews). There was no difference; there was no tendency for a judge to find more cues in second interviews than in original ones. Second, a rough attempt was made to determine the extent to which the overall impression was influenced by the subsequent interviews. Since the judge did not record his opinion after examining each interview in turn, it was necessary to estimate what his impression would be after the first interview, using his list of documented specific cues and his general comments as evidence. It was the opinion of an outside reviewer who was not one of the original cue judges that the additional interviews definitely contributed to the judgment of cuing in some cases: thus a judgment that a case was cued might be based largely on the material in the second interview, or primarily on the first interview but confirmed or strengthened by the additional interview. Although the second interviews with their directed content clearly contributed to the cuing judgments, they were by no means mainly responsible for the overall impression, since first interviews and sole interviews were frequently seen as cued.

An Examination of the Puzzle

As noted in the opening part of this section, we obtained two basic findings that seem incompatible with each other. The cue detection judges showed little or no agreement among themselves, especially on their general impressions of extent of cuing. Yet there is clearly a greater degree of success on cases which at least one judge felt were strongly cued.

Two sorts of interpretations suggest themselves. The findings can be viewed as demonstrating that potential interviewer cues were present in the protocols and could be detected by judges who were looking for such cues. On the average, 21% of the cases were seen by each cue detection judge as strongly cued and an additional 21% were seen as slightly cued. If this potential cuing is accepted as illegitimate, it might be argued that such cuing could be utilized by the analytic group: in cases considered by at least one cue detection judge to be strongly cued these potential cues might well have oriented members of the analytic group to the actual disease, the members following up such leads by noting other aspects of the protocol consistent with the personality pattern expected in such cases. Thus, according to this interpretation, 66% of the cases were judged as strongly cued by at least one judge or were judged as slightly cued by two or more judges. Therefore it is not surprising that the mean of correct initial diagnoses was 41%. The proponent of this view would probably say that the group did not reach 66% correct because the analyst diagnosticians missed some of the cues.

Let us examine this view. Just what is a cued case? What is the criterion? The category "strongly cued" included some cases the cue judges felt were cued both for the actual disease and for another disease. For the four cue judges, the judgments in this subcategory were 2%, 16%, 8%, and 5%, respectively. A diagnostic judge influenced by the reported cues in these cases would be wrong almost as often as he would be right.

More telling is the result of carrying the reasoning of this viewpoint to the extreme. It will be recalled that (for the four judges) the mean percentage of cases judged strongly cued was 21%, and hence that the mean percentage of cases judged not strongly cued was 79%. Let us suppose that we had ten cue judges instead of four and that the judgments of each of these judges were unrelated to those of each of the other nine, just as the judgments of each of the four were unrelated to those of each of the other three. From these assumptions, probability theory tells us that the proportion of cases that would be judged *not* strongly cued by *any* of the ten judges is 79% raised to the tenth power, or 9%. Stated conversely, 91% of the cases would have been judged strongly cued for the actual disease by at least one of the ten judges. (The computations can be done directly in terms of the percentage of cases seen as strongly cued. They are much more laborious, however, since all combinations of one or more judgments of strongly cued have to be included. The result will be the same.)

Carrying the argument even further, we see that if we had 20 judges, 99% of the cases would have been judged strongly cued by at least one judge and only 1% would not. Finally, consider the matter of judgments of strongly cued for diseases other than the actual one. Following the same logic, we could demonstrate that with a sufficiently large number of judges, not only would almost all cases be judged strongly cued for the actual disease by at least one judge but, in addition, almost every case would have been judged at least once as strongly cued for some wrong disease.

This discussion highlights the vital importance of the finding that the judges who were specifically oriented toward detecting potential cues did not agree with each other on their judgments of extent of cuing. In other terms, there is no one obvious way to define a case as strongly cued from the reports of the cue judges. Although the definition used in the statistical analyses reported above was reasonable, it was arbitrary and broad. For instance, we could have utilized a rigorous criterion and said that a case was strongly cued only when *all* judges judged it so. There was one case in which all three judges who examined it considered it to be strongly cued; there was no such case among those seen by four judges.

Consider the related viewpoint that the presence of just one cue for the actual disease might be sufficient to orient one or more of the analytic judges toward the correct disease. This situation is entirely possible. Fortunately, the data indicate that it would occur only rarely, for several reasons. First, the number of instances in which a judge found just one cue was very small. Second, such a single cue was often seen as relevant to more than one disease. Moreover, when a judge found potential cues, more than one disease was generally seen as favored or opposed by the set of cues as a whole.

The most telling point against this view of the role of cues is the lack of agreement among the judges on what constituted a cue. For any one case, the several judges might note several cues, with almost no overlap among the four sets of cues. When the sets of cues from the four judges are all taken together, there are generally cues for several diseases, the correct one and others.

Finally, following the reasoning used above for cued cases, consider what would have been found if we had had many judges, say ten or twenty. Extending our findings, we could safely expect that at least one cue for the correct disease would be found by some judge, and at least one cue for several or all of the other diseases would also be found. For these reasons, it is untenable that, if any of the four judges noted one potential cue for the actual disease, the case was cued by the interviewer and the success of the analytic diagnosticians was aided by it.

Thus far the question "What is a cue that may have helped the diagnosticians?" has been considered only in terms of the lack of agreement among the cue judges in identifying potential cues. The later parts of this chapter will bring out other material relevant to this question: many of the potential cues noted by the cue judges, on subsequent careful examination by the analytic group, were considered not to be illegitimate cues but rather participations by the interviewer quite in keeping with the standard interviewing procedure. Also, when a case was reviewed by a member of the analytic group (a person who knew the actual disease), he would sometimes find potential cues that had not been noted by any of the four cue judges. It is granted that potential cues were present in some cases, but the evidence indicates that such cues were far from obvious, even to judges searching for them. There is also little evidence that such cues were detected even unconsciously by the analysts when they were functioning as diagnosticians.

An alternative interpretation would stress the lack of agreement on specific cues, on just what constituted an illegitimate cue, and on overall impressions concerning the extent of cuing. It can be argued that it was the duty of the interviewer to follow up conscientiously the trends in the patient's material. If the patient's trends corresponded to those postulated in the formulations for the actual disease, it is more likely that one or more of the interviewer's questions would be identified by a detection judge as a potential cue. It would also be more likely that the pattern of emphases on certain types of material and the limited discussion of other topics would be judged illegitimate general cuing. In such cases, however, the emphases of the interviewer's questions should not be considered illegitimate cues since such emphases were determined by the patient's material. The overall distribution of attention to various topics would also be determined by the patient rather than by the interviewer. Hence the correct diagnoses of the analytic group would be based on actual evidence from trends in the patient material rather than on the potential cues, specific or general, noted by the cue detection judges.

Fortunately, the issue need not be resolved solely on the basis of these quantitative analyses of the reports made by the cue detection judges. Highly pertinent information was also obtained in that part of the interviewer cue study that concerned the legitimacy or illegitimacy of the detected potential cues and the extent to which such cues were utilized by members of the analytic group. This work is presented in the following section.

Findings of the Interviewer Cue Detection Study

It was pointed out early in this chapter that we faced three problems in evaluating the diagnostic performance of the analytic judges, the first two of which concern us here. First: Were diagnostically significant interviewer cues present in our protocols? This was the task of the cue detection judges. Second: Had cues, if present, statistically influenced the diagnostic results obtained by the analytic group? To answer this was the task of the statistical analysis just reported.

In a broad way the findings of the cue detection study were that some potential cues were reported in practically all of our cases and many in some cases. Fifteen cases were reported to be strongly cued. A large portion of these was among early cases before our interviewing and censoring techniques had been adequately refined. More potential cues were reported for incorrect than for correct diagnoses. This is not difficult to understand if one remembers that the interviewer was expected to explore in each case the potentials for all seven diseases although there was, of course, only one correct diagnosis. There was little agreement about individual cues or about just what constituted cuing. A typical cue detection report (in summary) might be:

> One judge says: "No cues."
> One judge says: "Three cues" (away from disease).
> One judge says: "One strong cue" (for disease) "one strong cue" (away from disease).

Table 33 offers a simple summary of the total number of interviewer cues reported by each of the four cue detection judges and the distribution reported by each of cuing toward the correct disease and of cuing away from the correct disease. There is also a record of the number of cases in which the individual cue judge, in his overall summary of the cuing in each case, assigned a clear diagnostic primacy to the cues for the actual disease (Col. 11).

We note in Table 33 the imbalance between cues having a diagnostic trend toward the correct disease and cues with a trend away from the correct disease (except for Cue Judge I). In a fair number of instances, individual cues are seen to point both ways (the "equivocal" columns, 6 and 10). This seems to be in accord with what is referred to as the "puzzling findings" of the statistical analysis. If there were extensive unconscious need by the interviewer to "point the way" in our protocols, this probably would not be the case. An interesting finding is the wide disparity between Cue Judge II (an unusually medically sensitive psychoanalyst) and the other cue judges in the way in which he found potential medical cues where the other three judges found almost none. Like other

Table 33

Total Interviewer Cues and Distribution as to Types of Cues—Toward or Away from Correct Disease

			Psychological Cues				Medical Cues				
	Number of Cases Reviewed (1)	Cases with No Cues (2)	Number (3)	Toward Disease (4)	Away[a] (5)	Equivocal[b] (6)	Number (7)	Toward Disease (8)	Away[a] (9)	Equivocal[b] (10)	Actual Disease Identified[c] (11)
Judge I	83	13	234	112	112	10	2	1	1	0	26
Judge II	83	1	120	17	62	41	181	1	130	50	12
Judge III	60	15	231	64	155	12	2	0	1	1	13
Judge IV	62	6	218	51	141	26	3	1	1	1	13
Totals	288	35	803	244	470	69	188	3	133	52	64

[a] Cue was seen as for or against some diagnosis other than actual disease or seen as against the actual disease—i.e., it concerned areas having to do with diagnoses away from the actual disease. In some instances cues placed in this category would lend some inverse weight to the actual diagnosis. Thisis a "wastebasket" category.

[b] The cue was rated for both the actual disease and one or more other diagnoses.

[c] Reported cues led to clear diagnostic primacy for the actual disease in the cue judge summary report.

findings in this study, this points up the importance of the "set" of the researcher: namely, that there is a strong tendency to find either what you are schooling yourself to look for or that in which you are especially interested.

Particularly noteworthy are the differences between the performance of Cue Judge I and that of the other judges (Cols. 4 and 11). Judge I was a member of the analytic team. It is relevant that if the diagnosis of a case is known, the probability of finding cues for the correct disease is greater. This was shown in the cue utilization study when for the most part the cue review judges, reviewing in entirety the case protocols but knowing the diagnoses, easily found many items that could be regarded as possible cues. These items had not been seen as possible cues either by the analytic research judges or by the cue detection judges—who did not know the diagnoses when they reviewed the protocols.

As a cue detection judge, Judge I was reading most of the protocols for the second time. He could be presumed to have at least preconscious awareness of the earlier diagnostic evaluations of many of these protocols. In fact he did correctly recall the actual diagnoses of 30 of the cases. He had an incorrect recall for 2 cases—selecting a related disease instead of the correct one (such as arthritis for hypertension—in both of which hostile aggression is a major conflict) and had for 5 more cases a recall involving two possible diagnoses—one of which was correct. It is thus not surprising that Judge I's record for detecting potential cues for the correct diagnosis is significantly higher than that of the other three cue judges (Col. 4), as is also his score of correct diagnostic primacy in the cue summaries (Col. 11).

It could be expected also that a person who had already made a thorough study of about 100 protocols, such as our series comprised, and had the learning experience of knowing from protocol to protocol how he and his colleagues functioned diagnostically, would perform differently from the other cue detection judges. Of particular significance in this connection is the statistical finding that "cuing for actual disease identified by Cue Judge I, acting as cue detection judge, had not been of help to him in his earlier diagnostic judgments as an analytic research judge." This indicates that his methods of operation as a cue detection judge were significantly different from his earlier modes of operating as an analytic judge. Involved here is the phenomenon of "set." Further evidence of the role of this factor will be found in the next chapter.

The analytic judges in their original efforts at diagnostic evaluation of the protocols were at about the same level of expertness as the outside cue detection judges. Of course they worked with different goals and motivations. For practical purposes both groups represented somewhat of a "constant" in that they possessed the same professional training and roughly similar clinical experience—even with respect to this project. If the analytic judges were to be presumed to have made their diagnostic predictions primarily on the basis of cues rather than on the basis of dynamic formulation, they might be expected to do not much better than Cue Detection Judges II, III, and IV in identifying the actual disease mainly from the trend of the cues (Col. 11)—namely, just slightly better than chance.

Just as Judge II greatly interested himself in residual potential medical cues in the protocols, Judge IV quite seriously interested himself in the form of the interviews and in the interviewing techniques. He wrote long analyses of the interview process, speculated about the interaction between the interviewer and patient, made sharp judgments about the interviewer's motivations, and severely criticized some interviews as "unsuited for research purposes." His comments were of course oriented diagnostically toward the possible cuing effect of the interview material commented on.

It is probably significant that despite Judge IV's careful and often very perceptive analyses of interviewer activity and interaction with the patient, his score for identifying the actual disease from the trends of his reported "potential cuing" is not significantly higher than that of Judge II and Judge III. This again illustrates the difficulty of demonstrating a critical relationship between any particular reported cuing potential and actual cue effect.

Comments of Cue Detection Judges on Their Functioning

Following completion of the cue study, responses to specific inquiry were obtained from three of the cue detection judges about their subjective experiences in making the study. Excerpts from their written comments follow.

Cue Judge II:

> When I was first asked to give my impressions as a cue judge, I felt, initially, somewhat uncertain about my ability to do so.
>
> . . . The first interview I read, and somewhat less so the next two, seemed to present a formidable task . . . trying to put myself in a role to which I was unaccustomed. I went over these first three cases a number of times and rechecked the instructions specifying what I was supposed to do. The task became easier and easier.
>
> . . . The nature of the cues gradually seemed to change from the earlier interviews I received as compared to the later ones I was asked to review. . . . I recall that some of the cues given by the interviewer by the nature of his questioning and interviewing seemed somewhat obvious. I thought I could detect certain catch

phrases and key words that had come to be associated in the public domain with a particular psychosomatic syndrome. Among the later cases which I reviewed, such cues were much less obvious to me and . . . seemed more subtle. . . . I do not recall that there was any notable change in the nature of the medical clues.

. . . The interviewing style was quite varied. Sometimes this appeared to be largely a function of the patient, who I assumed spoke quite freely and spontaneously in some instances so that the interviewer made relatively few comments. In these instances I had paid attention to the content emerging when the interviewer interrupted the patient as a possible source of cues. In other instances, some patients seemed to speak laconically, and repetitions of questions around some specific content suggested themselves to me as possible cues. In still other instances, the personality of the interviewer seemed to be the primary factor characterizing the interviewing style. I found myself trying to guess or phantasying which Institute member might be doing the interviewing. Almost invariably I found such guess work quite inconclusive. . . .

Some additional points on my own mental set and motivations: . . . primary in my decision to participate was a serious curiosity about the role of "specificity" in psychosomatic illness and a wish to participate in this exciting and imaginative study, even in a somewhat peripheral role. . . . The initial tedious aspects of the job decreased as I went on and I found myself making a somewhat playful game out of the work. I also began to discover that the job brought to my attention many, many points of interest relevant to my interests in the psychotherapeutic interview which I hope, sometime in the future, to write about.

Cue Judge IV:

The outstanding feature of this assignment was its novelty: nothing in the professional preparation or experience of a psychoanalyst could serve him as a guidepost to gauge his performance. The knowledge that several colleagues were making judgments on the same material added a competitive element to the task.

Consequently, the personal motivations of this cue judge, at least, impelled him to seek out every possible cue. In practice, however, it was very difficult to determine what constituted an illegitimate cue because gross and unequivocal cues had already been eliminated from the protocols. For the most part, those cues which remained consisted of interviewer activity which did not seem to be the inevitable consequence of the ongoing process. . . . Whenever . . .

the interviewer departed from the conduct of the interview that he felt would have been natural for someone who did not know the medical diagnosis, the cue detection judge had to assume that this departure might have been caused by the interviewer's awareness of the nature of the patient's illness. Thus, the detection of a cue is a highly subjective judgment.

In spite of efforts to concentrate on the job of detecting cues alone, I found it impossible to stop myself from responding to the affective content of the protocols, i.e., to prevent myself from looking at the material in a usual psychoanalytic manner. This was a serious interference with finding cues because I was unable to pay consistent attention to both sets of data simultaneously. This statement may sound implausible in view of the multiple levels of meaning to which an analyst must respond in his daily work. However, the analyst is used to disregarding the cognitive, logical organization of his patient's communications—precisely that aspect which must be studied most systematically in order to pick up many illegitimate cues. Eventually, I found it necessary to read the protocols more than once, trying to satisfy my own need to organize the material in terms of its psychodynamic significance the first time and proceeding to the actual job of detecting cues subsequently.

I am convinced that the cue judge's detection of particular cues was heavily influenced by his preconscious assessment of the psychodynamics and his automatic prediction of the medical diagnosis suggested by them. The cues detected in any specific segment of a protocol would be more likely to be those related to the disease the cue judge thought to be the correct one at that time. Many more cues might have been detected if each record had been surveyed by a separate judge seeking cues for each of the seven diseases, since it was extremely difficult to keep all details of the elaborate hypotheses about each disease explicitly in mind at the same time.

Cue Judge I:

The real difficulty I found was to keep my knowledge of the psychological data from pointing my attention in the direction of the correct diagnosis. Once I had an idea about the diagnosis I had the additional problem of being objective about what I considered proper conduct by the interviewer from what could be evaluated as an improper course of action that would require listing as an interviewer cue.

Judge I, being a member of the research team, naturally did not experience the same kind of initial difficulty in learning how to deal with the massive amount of material in each protocol as did the other judges. A major focus of his comments had to do with his efforts to keep from being influenced in his cue search by his familiarity with the project and his recognition of many of the protocols. He also indicated that his functioning as a cue detection judge could in no way be considered comparable to that of the other cue judges since the cue utilization studies showed clearly that the more familiar one is with the project and especially if one knows the diagnosis, the more cues one tends to find.

These reports from the cue detection judges are interesting in the way in which they confirm by subjective comment some of the speculations made by the analytic research group and some of their observations from the cue utilization studies. They also constitute an important statement at a subjective level of some of the factors contributing to the phenomenon of psychological "set" referred to in several places in this study.

Summary

A panel of three outside psychoanalysts of approximately equal training, experience, and sophistication about psychosomatic disease as the analytic judge team was asked to go over all the case protocols and examine them minutely for evidence of possible interviewer cuing. They did not know the diagnoses of the cases. (One analyst from the analytic research team joined this panel.) They were asked to search out and to document anything with the slightest potential for interviewer communication for any of the seven diseases and to make a summarizing judgment as to the dominant diagnostic trend or trends represented in the cues reported. They were asked not to make dynamic formulations and not to "diagnose the case," but to give only the diagnostic trends of the individual cues.

An overall average of something more than three "potential interviewer cues" was reported per judge per case. (Case protocols ran from 40 to 100 or more pages in length.) More than half the reported cues were "away" from the actual disease.

The accuracy of the overall judgments identifying the actual disease from reported "potential cuing" made by the three outside cue detection judges was a little better than chance expectation.

A careful statistical analysis was made of the results of the cue detection study and has been reported.

CHAPTER SIX

The Interviewer Cue Utilization Study

The final task of our interviewer cue study was to find out whether and how interviewer cues, when present, were used by the analytic judges. To a considerable degree we were dealing with minor cues or only apparent cues, serious and gross cuing having been largely censored out. We realized that in addition to the anticipated statistical results from the formal cue detection study, we had an important source of possible information about "cue utilization" in the recorded transcripts of the analytic judges' meetings. In these transcripts were the analytic judges' dynamic formulations of the cases, each reported and defended by the judge who brought it to the meeting; discussions and arguments over conflicting points of view about these dynamics; recorded bits of evidence that one "item" or another might have achieved prominence in determining choice of diagnosis by an analytic judge—and on occasion such an item might well prove to have been judged as a cue item in the cue detection study. There were of course no uncontested claims of cuing in our analytic judge discussions as such cases would have been eliminated from the series. How much influence the cuing present exerted was obscured largely by the difficulties of demonstrating it with certainty.

The analytic research group's cathexis centered from the beginning on the group ideal of the correct dynamic formulation. Each member was strongly motivated toward finding for each protocol a personally convincing and diagnostically significant global dynamic formulation of the case. This may have played an important role in the judges' apparent obliviousness to obvious cuing in some protocols. But neither singlemindedness of purpose nor lack of demonstrable gross cuing can vitiate the argument that subtle cues may on occasion have alerted an analytic judge's thinking in the direction of the correct diagnosis at preconscious levels, and that he would then proceed from that point to reconstruct from the protocol material a comprehensive dynamic formulation in the diagnostic direction to which he had been unconsciously alerted. We believe that our careful cue utilization studies (to follow) furnish a considerable body of evidence of both the use of cues in some of our intensively studied, "judged cued" cases and of the failure to use cues in others.

To the question whether any of the analytic judges could with conviction claim immunity to possible cuing, the answer is: Probably not. We cannot study this question, however, beyond the "judged cued" items openly reported or showing some sort of prominence in the formulations and analytic group discussions. One must regard the statistical cue study as the method of evaluating in summation the effect of cuing at unconscious levels. Study of the formulations and meeting transcripts furnishes us with evidence of cue utilization or lack of it at conscious levels.

Methodology of the Interviewer Cue Utilization Study

Following completion of the cue detection study our statistician selected 30 cases for intensive study of cue utilization at the clinical level, as supplemental to the statistical studies. Each of the six analytic judges then comprising the Chicago group was assigned his share of the 30 cases for this study. Each thus became the "cue utilization judge" of the particular case, and had the task of going over all the records of the case: the original recorded but censored interview; the analytic judge's formulations; the cue detection judges' reports; the medical control group reports; and the transcribed recordings of the analytic judges' meetings. The cue utilization judge was expected from this review to contribute findings of his own about cues he felt were missed by the cue detection judges or to criticize material designated by them—in his opinion, mistakenly—as cuing. He was expected to scrutinize very carefully the transcribed meeting reports to evaluate the consistency and the explanatory accuracy of the dynamic formulations, especially those for the correct diagnoses. He was expected to ferret out as far as possible evidence that material judged as cued by the cue detection judges had or had not figured significantly in the diagnoses made by the analytic judges. He was also to report any passing references in these discussions to material described by the analytic judges as possibly representing cue material, medical or psychological. Following this he was expected to make a résumé expressing his evaluation of cue utilization in each case studied. This résumé was then reported to the analytic research group where again every detail was carefully discussed by the group as a whole, with the discussions recorded and transcribed for later study.

The 30 cases selected by the statistical consultant for intensive study by the analytic team were grouped and studied under three broad categories of criteria for their selection. Each case has been assigned its own cue study case number (1 to 30) for easy reference.

Group I. Ten from among the "strongly cued" cases, i.e., "judged strongly cued" for the correct diagnosis by the cue detection judges. Cases were chosen in which the analytic group were relatively successful in their diagnoses (Cases 1 to 10).

Group II. Ten "slightly cued" cases—cases in which the analytic group diagnosed the disease relatively accurately but the majority of the cue judges found minimal or insignificant cuing for the disease (Cases 11 to 20).

Group III. Ten cases presenting a variety of cue phenomena, including some cases strongly cued for the wrong diagnosis and some virtually non-cued cases (Cases 21 to 30).

Table 34

Comparison of Intensively Studied Cue Cases with Total Cases

	Frequency		Column 2/ Column 1 (Per Cent)
	In Total Group	In Intensively Studied Group	
Marked Cuing			
Three or four judges say strongly cued	6	6	100
Two judges say strongly cued	9	4	44
Total this category	15	10	67
Some Cuing			
One judge says strongly cued, one or two say slightly	12	1	8
One judge says strongly cued, others say not cued for actual disease	14	3	21
Total this category	26	4	15
Minimal Cuing			
Two or three judges say slightly cued	14	1	7
One judge says slightly, others say not cued for actual disease	15	5	33
Total this category	29	6	21
Not Cued for Actual Disease			
Cued for another disease or not cued	7	4	57
One or more judges say cued against	6	6	100
Total this category	13	10	77
Totals	83	30	36

Thirty cases from our series were selected as a sample for intensive study by the research team. These represented varying degrees of potential cuing as judged by the cue detection judges. Among them were 10 of the 15 cases judged as strongly cued. Most of these 10 cases were processed very early in the project, highlighting our still imperfect interviewing and censoring techniques.

Table 34 shows the distribution of the different degrees and directions of cuing as reported by the cue detection judges in the 30 intensively studied cases and in the entire series.

Findings of the Interviewer Cue Utilization Study

To determine the validity and influence of reported potential cues is a complex task. The fact that an analytic judge did not mention that certain material, later judged as cue material, had entered into his diagnostic formulation might have nothing to do with whether he had been influenced by it. Neither did his mentioning such material prove that his diagnostic results depended in any substantial degree upon that particular material. There was perhaps no final way in many instances to determine whether specific cues were used by the analytic judges in making their formulations, since cues never were used manifestly as the bases for these formulations.

Clinical diagnostic activity usually involves complex patterns of intuitive, empathic, preconscious and conscious gestalt perceptions that do not lend themselves easily to accurate description. The analytic research judges had not been asked to report their diagnostic formulations in terms of the use of particular items which might later prove to be seen as potential cues. There remained then only the method of examining these formulations and discussions of the analytic judges, to find and evaluate material subsequently judged as having cue potential and spontaneous references to possible cuing.

On the whole, efforts to tie judged strong cuing to manifest items in the transcripts were unsatisfactory. Even after the analytic research judges began seriously to interest themselves in the possible factor of interviewer cuing in the protocols, it was difficult for them to keep on the lookout for subtle cue material. The clinical evidence from these transcripts suggests that the analytic judges did not easily sustain interest in the intangibles of cue searching—in the face of the more difficult and primary task of making dynamic formulations. From time to time one or another analytic judge would interest himself more or less casually in potential cuing in a case he had just finished studying, but only one judge kept this up over a fair period of time. Spontaneous references by the other judges to possible cuing seemed mostly to occur when something "hit them in the face." Thus evidences of cue utilization from these transcripts are usually sketchy or anecdotal.

It is important to remember that the 30 cases intensively studied include a large number of the definitively judged cued cases as reported by the cue detection judges. Among them are cases we have since recognized as demonstrably interviewer-cued, with the diagnosis (right or wrong) stemming at least in part from that cuing. Included also are judged "strongly cued" cases—in which, however, there was much doubt at the clinical level whether such cuing exerted any influence. Half (15) of all these cases were early cases dating from 1956 or before, when our techniques were less refined. Eight of the 10 strongly cued cases were in this early category. Although interviewing and censoring techniques were relatively crude in a number of the early cases (and occasionally in later ones), clinical evidence of influence upon the analytic judges varied greatly.

As might be expected in this group of 30 cases, constituting a large proportion of our strongly cued cases, analytic group diagnostic performance was relatively successful. Twenty of the cases had been selected because of relative diagnostic success: 10 from the strongly cued cases and 10 from the slightly cued cases. Nineteen of the 30 had been for the most part correctly diagnosed, in contrast to 17 mostly incorrectly diagnosed by the medical control group.

We have already discussed various interviewer intrusions that could lead to suspicions of inadvertent and unconscious cuing. Retrospectively we realized that we had included in our series an occasional patient who was psychotic or too ill to furnish satisfactory interview material or too unintelligent, constricted, uncommunicative, or unmotivated. The efforts of the interviewer to overcome such obstacles sometimes resulted in high levels of judged cuing. On close examination such cuing sometimes proved to be real and sometimes only apparent.

It is understandably difficult to claim convincingly that a given item of interviewer behavior becomes an apparent cue only when it points toward the actual diagnosis. There is no question that interviewer activity reported by a cue judge as a "strong cue for disease *X*" is not a cue (namely, by our definition of an "interviewer cue" as an item of inadvertent interviewer behavior determined by unconscious need to "send a message" to the analytic judge group to help them achieve a particular diagnosis) but only an apparent cue if the actual disease is *Y*. We were forced, however, to regard every reported and confirmed strong cue for the actual disease as a real cue—having perhaps influenced the analytic group's diagnostic formulations. This possibility existed even though the analytic judges apparently did not consciously perceive or use the cue and even though there was evidence in the formulations that apparent cuing for the wrong disease was more striking than real cuing for the correct disease.

We now offer some brief clinical material illustrating some of the cue problems as we found them in the 30 intensively studied cases.

Strong Cuing: Correct Diagnoses—Cues Probably Used

Case 1 (thyrotoxicosis) showed serious problems, with strong cuing and evidence that the cuing influenced the analytic judges. It was an early case and a moribund patient. The interviewer had become very uneasy, had overexplored and overreacted to the diagnostically significant material centering on death, and had omitted all the standard questions. He was clearly motivated to get the dynamic material for the correct disease and to get out of the situation as quickly as possible. One analytic judge had expressed his opinion at the analytic group discussion that the case was cued and should be rejected but he was overruled. He was right—the diagnosis was too easy to make. Although the diagnosis could have been made from the protocol on psychological grounds, data for thyrotoxicosis were mainly present. In this case the problem was not so much that of specific interviewer cuing as overall deviant interviewing in a difficult situation.

In several instances grossly deviant interviewer behavior, subsequently explained by the interviewer, served demonstrably to cue or to miscue a case. One such example was Case 2 (hypertension), admittedly strongly cued and correctly diagnosed. The interviewer, thinking the unusually clear dynamics for the correct diagnosis had been quite spontaneously and adequately revealed, allowed himself to make an exploration of the effect in hypertension to satisfy some of his own curiosity and in so doing grossly and demonstrably cued the case.

Case 6 (neurodermatitis) was strongly cued for the actual disease and had the largest score of any of our cases for two or more cue judges identifying the same cue (two different items were recognized as cue items by the three cue judges and two others were recognized by two cue judges). The transcripts gave good reason to conclude that cuing had directly influenced some of the analytic judges' opinions. The interviewer too emphatically explored exhibitionism and masochistic fantasies. There were other technical errors leading to unanimous agreement at the cue utilization discussion that the case should have been rejected from our series. The most serious cuing clearly resulted from excessive interviewer need to bring out the dynamics for the correct diagnosis. In spite of this, one analytic judge stuck to his wrong diagnosis, apparently not seeing, or disregarding, the neurodermatitis cues that were there.

Strong Cuing: Correct Diagnoses—Use of Cues Doubtful or Inconclusive

Case 3 (ulcer) presented a difficult cuing problem. This very willingly communicative patient spontaneously gave such a dynamically rich picture of the "onset situation" that the interviewer needed to ask few questions about the onset of the disease. This behavior was seen by Cue Detection Judge IV as a "major cue for this diagnosis." This was one of our best diagnosed cases. Two cue judges reported it as not cued for the actual disease; the other two reported strong cuing, although there was no clear evidence of use by the analytic judges of the reported cue material. In the cue review discussion there was agreement that the interview was dynamically very clear and that clinically there was much basis for doubt that cuing had played a significant role in the results obtained. There was no inclination to deny the validity of the material judged as cued by the two cue judges; the only question lay in whether it was needed or significantly used for the correct diagnosis. We cannot, of course, repudiate possible claims that this was a defensive position of the analytic review judges. That there were some residual interviewer indiscretions in this excellent record cannot be denied. Those reported and others perhaps not detected might lend themselves to many different evaluations and interpretations. The cue review discussion of this case led to an undeveloped proposition that there are probably "hierarchies" of cues in all cases, but almost no consensus about the influence of the cuing in this particular case.

By contrast, in Case 5 (neurodermatitis) not one of the very large number of potential cues was noted by more than one cue detection judge. One judge found no cues for the actual disease; the other three each found their examples of interviewer cuing for the disease in separate sections of the ninety-page protocol. In the original discussion of this case, one analytic judge made a casual reference to some possible cuing for the disease but discounted it: no one else mentioned cues. The analytic group was unable to arrive at diagnostic consensus after considering a number of different diagnoses. Even those who leaned strongly toward neurodermatitis were uncertain and tended to make *B* and *C* diagnoses. In spite of medical cues later identified by the analytic judges at the cue review discussion, only one internist diagnosed the case correctly. Even the cue detection judge who usually found medical cues did not find them "for the disease" in this case. Altogether, the analytic judges more or less seriously considered six of the seven diseases in the course of their deliberations. Being unable to arrive at closure after the first discussion, they asked for another interview. This could not be obtained and the case was restudied a year later, when four of the seven judges participating still had a fair amount of diagnostic uncertainty.

This case was discussed in cue review at great length. It was the consensus of the group at that time—although this in no way constitutes proof—that although the case was clearly cued by excessive interviewer activity toward the correct disease, for some reason the analytic judges did not perceive that cuing, even unconsciously. The much more diffuse character of the cuing as compared with that in Case 6, as well as a fair amount of subtle cuing for other diagnoses through the same excessive interviewer activity, perhaps would account for this. Comparative clinical evaluation of Cases 5 and 6 suggested that in Case 6 the interviewer probably was unconsciously interested only in bringing out the neurodermatitis material, whereas in Case 5 the interviewer was overconscientiously trying to bring out differential diagnostic material for all the diagnoses, resulting in a scrambling of the material. This sort of overactivity in the service of differential diagnosis occurred several times in our series, largely with deleterious influence upon our diagnostic results.

Strong Miscuing: False Cues, Wrong Diagnoses—Cues Probably Used

On several occasions some unexplained (and probably unconscious) preoccupation of the interviewer led to misleading cuing, or "miscuing." In Case 27 (thyrotoxicosis) the interviewer became involved in the anxious and inhibited sexuality of a young patient and became inadvertently psychotherapeutic. There resulted an excessive exploration of the patient's sexual life, which served to tip the scale toward an incorrect asthma diagnosis. In Case 25 (hypertension) the interviewer so actively questioned the patient about sex that the patient became resistant to the procedure. This seriously obscured the material. The group was miscued toward an asthma diagnosis. Case 10 presented the same problem: overexploration in the sexual area with an incorrect diagnosis of asthma. Examination of the analytic judges' formulations and discussions in all three cases, however, revealed little direct evidence of specific use of this material, and it is difficult to state definitely that particular items resulting from these distorting interviewer patterns were directly used as cues toward a wrong diagnosis. One can only say that the too profuse sexual material that was elicited did appear in the diagnostic formulations of the analytic judges, and infer that the analytic judges had thus been misled.

Perhaps cases strongly cued for the wrong diagnosis—with that wrong diagnosis made—offer the strongest evidence that the analytic judges can be influenced by cues. Interviewer behavior resulting in cues that really miscue offers more impressive evidence of cuing than we can get from correctly diagnosed cases. One can always speculate in the latter instance (especially in the absence of direct evidence of cue utilization) that after all the analytic judge may not have perceived or used the cue but made his diagnosis from the available dynamics in the protocol. By contrast, in the miscued, misdiagnosed case the dynamics for the diagnosed disease presumably (at least according to our hypothesis) are not present.

Interviewing Difficulties Leading to Incorrect Diagnoses

In Case 28 (ulcerative colitis) the interviewer scrambled the interview material by an excessive curiosity about separation, with the result that the case was not understood and was misdiagnosed. A somewhat different interviewer activity led to a miscuing of Case 24 (thyrotoxicosis). Here an onset situation that was genuinely puzzling to the interviewer led to an excessive exploration of this area, while at the same time a hypersensitivity about possible cuing led to his leaning over backwards to avoid the standard thyrotoxicosis questions. There were so very many deaths in this patient's life history, spontaneously and persistently brought up by him, that it never occurred to the interviewer that anyone could miss these data. The onset was not, however, manifestly related to a death. This puzzled the interviewer and led to the excessive exploration of onset material, with the apparent result of confusing the analytic judges and influencing their formulations and diagnoses.

Cases 25, 26, 27, and 28 were specifically studied for strong cuing for the wrong diagnosis with that same wrong diagnosis being made by the analytic judges. Case 26 (ulcerative colitis) was misdiagnosed as asthma. This was an early case and the interviewer felt that the patient had been so uncommunicative that the case should be rejected. The analytic group did not understand the patient's uncommunicativeness, misinterpreting it as secrecy and thus seeing it as part of the asthma pattern. At the cue utilization discussion of this case, the phenomenon of the "set" of the researcher came into view. The analytic judge who served as review judge (and knew the diagnosis) proceeded to shower the group with cues he had found for colitis, to the point that Judge I protested that as a cue detection judge he had found only two cues, one for ulcer and one for neurodermatitis. This again illustrates the extent to which one's finding of cues may depend upon knowledge of the diagnosis. The other cue judges had detected some colitis cues, to which they did not give much weight.

Case 8 (hypertension) was a seriously ill patient whose just younger brother had very recently died of malignant hypertension (the cause of his death was of course omitted from the record). One analytic judge reported several medical cues for hypertension but chose the wrong diagnosis of colitis. This was based on his impression of the dynamics of the case: he was considerably influenced by the hopelessness and depression of this seriously ill man. At the same time, this judge overlooked a medical cue for colitis (a reference to a hemorrhoidectomy which should have been omitted). There were many cues reported by the cue judges for a variety of diagnoses. Nevertheless, the impression from the analytic group discussion was that the diagnoses made by the analytic judges, both correct and incorrect, were made upon dynamic bases and not from cues. A complex cuing problem may occur, as in this case, when an interviewer in order to get material has been forced to intrude upon a patient's unconscious determination to use the interview for his own purpose to discharge affect. Here the interviewer did not emphasize questions about the onset of the illness, but the patient took over and told him what had brought it on—which was taken by one cue judge to be a "major cue for hypertension." It is difficult to decide whether this should have been considered invalid interviewer communication (because the interviewer did not press the inquiry) or valid patient communication since it was the patient's spontaneous verbal activity. No analytic judge made any reference to this supposed major cue in connection with any diagnosis.

Correct Diagnoses in Spite of Judged "Strong" Miscuing

Case 15 (asthma) was very successfully diagnosed. At the original discussion of this case, four of the eight analytic judges had opinions of varying strength that the case was cued for asthma. Two of them felt definitely that it was cued, although they made very convincing diagnoses for asthma based on dynamic formulations and were only half-heartedly inclined to reject the case because of probable cuing. One of the analytic judges came in with no formulation but saw evidence for five of the seven diagnoses, including asthma, and wanted another interview. He also felt the case to be cued for asthma and that it perhaps should be rejected. One judge, who made a firm diagnosis for arthritis, considered that the interviewer "made a diagnosis of asthma with both negative and positive bias cues." One of the cues he noted (a clear "out of context" question about separation from husband) was the same cue that was noted by Cue Detection Judge I at the time of the initial analytic group discussion of the case, but was not noted by him when he functioned as a cue detection judge. The analytic judge who diagnosed arthritis felt the case should be rejected if it proved to be asthma. The most interesting thing about the case was the way in which the analytic judges in 1957 "out-cued" the cue detection judges who worked on the same case three or four years later. A case such as this can lead to doubt about the ultimate reliability of any particular cue search: with all this activity by eleven psychoanalysts to find cues on two widely separated occasions, the one really strong statement about cuing in this case was made by Cue Detection Judge IV to the effect that the case was "painfully cued for neurodermatitis," "painful" because he was convinced that this cuing had clearly betrayed the actual diagnosis.

The analytic judges had engaged in an unusual amount of discussion whether this case was really cued or just distorted by overemphasis on sexual material, but no one took a strong stand against accepting the case. The impression gained from the recorded discussion was that the analytic judges were trying to work out something among themselves about cuing in general rather than about cuing in this particular case.

It was not unusual during the original processing of a case for an analytic judge to report that he had found one or more potential cues for a given diagnosis and then go on to ignore his own reported cues and make another diagnosis from his dynamic formulation for the case. Case 4 (thyrotoxicosis) and the just-discussed Case 15 are examples of this. In Case 4 one analytic judge reported the record strongly cued for arthritis, but went on to choose the correct thyrotoxicosis diagnosis because of the convincing dynamics of the case.

Results of Excessive Concern with Cues

In Case 10 (asthma) the analytic judges did very well on diagnosis, and the cue detection judges reported very few cues, none of them for asthma. One of the analytic judges, who was then experimentally searching for cues, turned in the results of this search with his formulation. It might be of interest to quote from his formulation in view of the fact that this case was so unusually clear dynamically. "This is a 100% definite diagnosis. The onset is clearly related to patient's mounting guilt over concealment of his secret correspondence with the absent lover, his need to confess to his wife, and his fear of the consequences." The rest of his formulation of this case is in this tone and is accurate and complete for his asthma diagnosis. Following his formulation and diagnosis, this analytic judge stated that he found very few cues, listing only three: (1) what he considered overemphasis in repeating a question about liking to talk in front of people; (2) an abrupt lack of interest in the patient's discussion of confession and joining the church; and (3) a misstated repetition of something said by the patient about being anxious over being away from his wife. "All three of these are definite cues for asthma," he stated. "There are no cues for anything else."

Although this analytic judge found cues for the correct diagnosis, he did not at the time rate them as having influenced his "100% diagnosis." The tenor of this report throughout is: "The dynamics are clear; there may be some slight cuing for the diagnosis, but it is not important." The report is quoted here partly as a contrast to the later reports of the cue detection judges in this same case—that it was a virtually uncued case with a nearly 100% correct diagnosis. The two reports illustrate the difficulties encountered in drawing hard-line conclusions about what is a cue and what is not a cue, and whether or not it was used. Subjectively in reading this analytic judge's report, one feels that he was able to find these potential cues because the diagnosis of the case had become clear in his mind from the dynamics. The cue detection judges did not find these same cues, perhaps because they did not know the diagnosis. They were not studying the material with a motivation to determine the diagnosis but with a motivation to find cues.

Returning to the three potential cues reported by this analytic judge at his original processing of the case, we might feel that the first cue is as much a cue for neurodermatitis as for asthma. Whether the second cue is actually a cue or not might hinge on the word "abruptly": only listening to the original recording would indicate whether the interviewer was really abrupt. The third potential cue does represent an active interviewer effort to go back after some intervening material to a topic presented somewhat incoherently by the patient. The patient had been talking about being in military service, how his (craftsman) employment and sports activity had affected him: "It kept me busy. It kept me from one day to another—it gave me a diversion; however, broken up our lives about being away from her and I did suffer a lot of anxiety—to a great extent, but I—had an honorable discharge and I was complimented and I made a couple of grades." It would seem entirely reasonable for an interviewer subsequently to pick up out of this incoherent statement the patient's spontaneously expressed feeling about being away from his wife, regardless of diagnosis. In terms of microscopic analysis, the interviewer's choice of the term "leaving" instead of the patient's term "being away" might be regarded as unconscious interviewer communication in the form of the use of a more "loaded" word for the asthma diagnosis. There is no evidence, however, in this analytic judge's formulation that he used this potential cue, nor is there any evidence that it assumed any significance in the diagnostic performance of any of the other analytic judges. It seems much too subtle to be taken seriously into account as effective interviewer cuing influence.

Cue Detection Judges' Misinterpretations of Instructions

Evaluation of interviewer behavior with respect to the onset inquiry as a source of possible cuing presented a particularly difficult problem. It was stated in chapter 2 that one consideration basic to the theory of this project was the importance of the emotional situation at the time of onset of the disease. In most cases there was active interviewer exploration of the onset of the illness. This exploration varied widely, both as to interviewer behavior and patient responsiveness. Consequently there was a corresponding variation in the way in which the different cue detection judges evaluated this interviewer activity, as can be seen in the protocols of the cue detection judge reports. In the instructions to the cue detection judges, there was no reference whatever to procedures concerning the "onset inquiry." Thus there was no guide to how or whether it should be evaluated.

Cue Study Case 9 (hypertension) provides an example. Cue Detection Judge IV considered that the interviewer's "omission of the onset inquiry" betrayed the interviewer's conviction that the data spontaneously brought by the patient sufficed, and this "constituted a major cue for ulcer or hypertension." This type of interpretation of interviewer activity (or lack of it) as invalid or cuing behavior raises several difficult points. First an experienced and sensitive interviewer would tend to feel he had behaved crudely if he ignored spontaneous and rich dynamic material brought by a patient in some particular area—turning around and asking many questions about the same area as though the patient had said nothing at all. Such behavior might lead to patient resistance and ultimate sterilization of the interview material. It is reasonable to assume that on many occasions interviewers quite unconsciously omitted formal exploration of many areas, feeling that these had already been covered adequately. But on a few occasions, as noted in this case (and Case 8), this was interpreted by a cue detection judge as major interviewer cuing. This despite the instructions to the cue detection judges: "If [such] information had been elicited in full in the earlier part of the interview the question would ordinarily be omitted." Other factors too might lead sometimes to the cutting short of exploration of a particular area—unnoted and unforeseeable time limitations, and patient problems of various kinds. To evaluate judgments based on such omissions is difficult. Although the problem was not actively explored, it seems safe to suggest that this type of interviewer behavior was probably not used as cue assistance by the analytic judges in their diagnostic operations.

A second aspect of this same problem lies in the fact that a cue detection judge might report, as did the judge above, that he was diagnosing the direction of the supposed cue from the spontaneously produced patient material in addition to detecting the cue. This he had been specifically requested not to do.

Interpreting the Results

We have presented an overview of some of the variety of problems incurred in evaluating the use, or the non-use, by the analytic research team of the "potential interviewer cues" reported by the cue detection judges after their study of our research protocols.

The analytic research group came to feel that one of the long-range results of these studies would be a contribution to the methodology of a validation study in the psychological field. In going over our protocols for the cue studies it had become increasingly clear how difficult it was totally to exclude illegitimate interviewer communication despite careful technical precautions. The uncertainty about many individual cues and their influence was equaled only by the paradoxical quality of the statistical results concerning the possible role of cuing in the overall diagnostic results obtained. In some of our "flagrantly cued" cases (for the correct diagnosis) there was little or no internal evidence in the transcribed records that such cuing determined diagnostic success of the analytic judges. In other "flagrantly cued" cases the internal evidence did point up such influence. Also there were cases cued for the wrong diagnoses and both correctly and incorrectly diagnosed, and both with and without internal evidence that the cuing was effective.

It became clear that important sources of complexity lay in little-understood perceptual and motivational phenomena of the investigators, the so-called "set" of the researcher. The evidence suggests that when we were studying the interview material in an effort to understand the dynamics of a case, we tended to ignore potential cues to a considerable degree, but when we studied the same material looking only for cues and with little regard for the dynamics of a case, we had no difficulty in finding many possible cues, some very subtle. Further, when one is looking for cues and knows the diagnosis, one finds more cuing than when studying a "blind" protocol with an unknown diagnosis. There was evidence from the cue utilization study that the phenomenon of the psychological "set" of the researcher influenced each of the different research groups in this project: the analytic judges, the cue detection judges, the medical control group, and the cue utilization judges.

It seems reasonable to conclude from the internal evidence of our restudied experimental protocols that the majority of cases were not responded to by the analytic research group as cued while in the process of initially studying them. The rare case definitively perceived as cued after the double censorship of the protocol was eliminated from the study. Potential cues were not referred to in most of the diagnostic formulations. Had the analytic group, at the time of the original discussion of the case interview material, been intensively focused on detecting and evaluating subtle potential interviewer cues, it might have effectively interfered with their diagnostic performance.

Despite careful editing of our interview protocols, many items with more or less subtle potential for "interviewer cue communication" slipped through. In a few instances gross cuing escaped the censoring. Reported cues averaged somewhat over three per cue detection judge per case. Potential cues for the actual disease were exceeded in number by potential cues for other diseases.

Intensive study of most of our "judged cued" protocols led to much doubt about which items were really cues and what was cued for what. In only a minority of cases was any individual cue identified by more than one cue judge. Occasional cues, however, revealed sufficient evidence of unconscious interviewer need to communicate information pointing toward the actual diagnosis.

In addition to evidence that judged cues had relatively little overall influence upon the diagnostic activities of the analytic judges or tended to cancel each other out, there was internal evidence in the individual protocols that in most cases the analytic judges depended little upon cuing in the diagnostic operations. Where cuing seemed relatively effective in our protocols, "cuing out" toward the wrong diagnosis appeared to be nearly as important as "cuing in" to the actual diagnosis. Of course, the possibility of further cuing at preconscious or unconscious levels cannot be excluded. There was evidence that in a few cases major lapses in interviewing technique, which were not identified as such originally did influence the analytic group toward a right or a wrong diagnosis.

Our final conclusions then are these. Potential cues do indeed exist in our interviews, and they are of varying subtlety and direction—lying along a spectrum from grossly invalid interviewer communication to the subtle, almost undetectable interviewer influences upon the patient's responses and the patterning of the interview. These potential interviewer cues, however, seem to bear little or no consistent relationship to the patient's actual disease and seem to have contributed little or nothing to the overall success of the analytic research group's diagnostic activities.

Sample Interviewer Cue Detection and Utilization Project Report

PROTOCOL: Cue Study Case 14

CASE: 1958/130. Mrs. B. P. Age 24. Diagnosis: asthma

DATES: Patient interviewed: 3–15–58, 11–5–58
Interview processed by analytic judges: 6–10–58, 1–13–59
Cue utilization discussion by analytic judges: 3–13–62

Diagnoses of Analytic Judges

Interview No. 1

JUDGE	INITIAL DIAGNOSIS	FINAL DIAGNOSIS
A	Neurodermatitis	No diagnosis
B	Asthma	Asthma
C	Ulcer—4 Arthritis—2 Neurodermatitis—1	No diagnosis
D	Ulcer	Asthma—4 Ulcer—2 Colitis—1
E	Colitis	No diagnosis
F	Asthma—5 Ulcer—1 Arthritis—1	No diagnosis
G	Ulcer—4 Colitis—3	No diagnosis
H	Interviewer	
I	Arthritis—5 Ulcer—2	Asthma

Interview No. 2

JUDGE	INITIAL DIAGNOSIS	FINAL DIAGNOSIS
A	Ulcer—5 Neurodermatitis—2	Ulcer—5 Neurodermatitis—2
B	Asthma	Asthma
C	Asthma	Asthma
D	Asthma	Asthma
E	Asthma	Asthma
F	Asthma	Asthma—6 Ulcer—1
G	Colitis	Asthma
H	Interviewer	
I	Asthma	Asthma

Reports of Cue Detection Judges

JUDGE I

Processed: 8–3–60

Total cues listed: Four

Three cues in the first interview. All cues "undue emphasis" (*re* pride and separation), two seen for ulcer, two for neurodermatitis.

General impression: "These were not very satisfactory interviews because the patient was not very cooperative. The attempt was made to be associative and complete but because of patient's attitude it was necessary to be too obvious and leading in some areas."

JUDGE II

Processed: 2–28–61

Total cues listed: Three

One medical cue (age of onset) seen against asthma, hypertension, neurodermatitis. One medical cue (illness interferes with physical activities) seen for arthritis and colitis. One "omission of questioning" cue (*re* dead bodies, etc.) seen against thyrotoxicosis.

General impression: "No general cues noted. Very few of any kind noted. Medical cues and one interviewer cue are against neurodermatitis, asthma, thyrotoxicosis, and hypertension. One medical cue weakly favors arthritis first, and secondly colitis."

JUDGE IV

Processed: 12–2–61

Total cues listed: Ten

All cues in first interview. All cues listed involve some form of "unwarranted emphasis" and were seen variously for asthma, hypertension, neurodermatitis, thyrotoxicosis, ulcer, and colitis.

General impression: "As to the cues of the first interview, there had been cues for all of the diagnoses except arthritis. However, there were many more cues for thyrotoxicosis than for any of the other diseases. The presence of so many scattered cues is probably accounted for by a peculiarity of the interviewer's style about which I will comment after completing the record.

"I detect no cues in the second interview where interviewer sticks to the questions requested by the group. He has apparently recognized that in the prior interview the patient had been consistently mousetrapping him (to use a football analogy). His style in the first session was characterized by a need to find an answer—a rage to understand. Thus the patient was allowed not to explain herself; usually the interviewer's guesses at the patient's emotions were wide of the mark and gave indiscriminate cues for various diagnoses."*

* The interview was held in a university hospital and the patient was asked to "cooperate in a research interview." She chose, for unconscious and transference reasons, to assume that the interviewer was a Ph.D. student working on a thesis. She did not reveal this to the interviewer. In accord with her assumption the patient was provocative, flip, a little condescending, and felt smugly justified in concealing any information that she found stressful to deal with. Between the first and second interviews the patient learned that the interviewer was a practicing psychoanalyst. She made a

Summary of Medical Control Group Findings

Five out of eight correct on initial diagnosis.
Six out of seven correct on final diagnosis.

Summary of the Cue Situation in This Case

A total of 17 cues were listed by three cue detection judges. In no instance was the same cue identified by any two of the three judges. No consistent diagnostic pattern could be derived from a composite view of all the judged potential cues, and out of this mass of "cue" material asthma was mentioned only once as one of three diagnoses suggested by some material centering on sexual guilt. One judge considered the interview virtually non-cued, one was equivocal, and one, though severely critical of the interview, was equivocal about the direction of the supposed cuing. Thyrotoxicosis was the most strongly suggested, with six of the seven diseases being mentioned. With one exception all the "judged cues" were in the first interview. Judge I reported one cue for neurodermatitis in the second interview.

Special Cue Problems Raised by This Case

The cue detection judges did not find the information used by the medical control group, who found data in the first interview for making the correct diagnosis on medical grounds. The analytic team did poorly on the first interview, and it was only after the second interview that they found the necessary psychological data to make a convincing formulation for the correct diagnosis. Yet two cue detection judges agreed that there were no cues in the second interview. Cue Detection Judge I found one diagnostically incorrect cue.

This case presents an example of how easy it is to misinterpret the statistical presence of a large number of "potential cues" as definite evidence of illegitimate cuing. One must go into the actual details and problems of the particular case. The inability of the analytic judges to formulate the case after the first discussion led five of the eight judges who had previously come in with a diagnosis to switch to "no diagnosis." This led the

---

full confession and apology for her behavior and was cooperative in the second interview. Additionally the patient's husband had seen four or five analysts in the city diagnostically, but the patient did not know who they were. This may have led the interviewer to overedit the first interview in the thought that a member of the analytic team might have been consulted by the husband and would recognize the wife's disease pattern, which had easily recognizable features. At the second interview, eight months later, the patient brought in the names of the analysts who had seen her husband. None were members of the analytic group and so there was no further editing problem [EDITOR'S NOTE].

group to ask the interviewer for a second interview even though three analytic judges did diagnose asthma. After this second interview, with directed questions, seven of eight members of the analytic group arrived at a diagnosis of asthma. The fact that the medical control group had a high percentage of correct diagnoses based upon the first interview, where they found their medical cues, constitutes negative evidence of the analytic group's having consciously or unconsciously used medical cues to arrive at a diagnosis in this case.

In summary, 16 of the total of 17 potential interviewer cues reported by the three cue dectection judges in the first interview were diagnostically inconclusive, covering all seven diseases. All the cues were derived from the interviewer's attempts to deal with an uncooperative patient. The single interviewer cue noted in the second interview (the interview which led most of the analytic judges to arrive at a correct diagnosis of asthma) was judged as moderately strong for neurodermatitis.

CHAPTER SEVEN

A Look Back and a Look Forward

As we review the history of this research to date, various questions and problems with which we struggled come back into focus. We attempted to deal with them by selecting what seemed the best alternatives available to us. In retrospect, some of the solutions might have been better if we had chosen different approaches or procedures. On the other hand, we decided on what we believed to be the best techniques of study that were possible for us at the time we undertook this research.

Our initial project began by asking a simple question: Was it possible to distinguish diagnostically between seven different organic diseases through study of psychological anamnestic protocols and subsequent formulation and construction of the psychodynamic, psychogenetic and characterologic patterns derived from interview data on patients suffering from the disease? Could a "prediction" of the medical diagnosis be made, using these data, with a significant degree of accuracy which would permit valid conclusions to be drawn?

The project started out modestly; it grew in size, however, as we became aware of methodological problems that had to be dealt with before we could formally undertake the research. We had to consider carefully the question of what we were investigating and how we would do it. These decisions involved discussion of what we were and were not going to study. Choices had to be made and interesting ideas had to be discarded or deferred for later investigation. Once we decided on what we were going to test, we required some general agreement about the basic formulations associated with the diseases we were studying. We had to consider the question of criteria for the cases we were to interview—medical criteria for the disease and psychological criteria as they related to the age, sex, and mental integrity of the patient. We had to devise a method of getting relevant data which could be obtained in a standardized fashion, and in such form as not to interfere with or bias the results. The question of control measures as they related to the acquisition of the raw or first-order data had to be answered. We had to decide upon techniques of interviewing, including the form of the interview, the use of standardized questions, and who was to interview the patient. Next we had to decide upon methods of editing the recorded and transcribed interviews so as to present the pertinent psychological information without including medical items that might illegitimately favor or exclude certain diagnoses. A control on the medical background of the analytic judges was needed and resulted in setting up a parallel project involving a team of internists who would study the same protocols that were studied by the analytic judges. We had to design several standardized procedures and forms: for the initial psychological formulation prepared by each analytic judge before the first group meeting; for the group meeting itself; for the quantitative weighting of the diagnosis arrived at from the formulation of the case; for the final diagnosis; and for obtaining additional interviews.

The fact that the analytic predictive team acted also as the research-directing group resulted in group dynamic processes that aided the evolution of our research design but also at times impaired its efficiency. Perhaps the role of administering and directing the research should have been assigned to individuals who were not also participating as predictive judges in the project. In retrospect, there probably should have been four separate teams: a research administration team; a primary data-collecting team (interviewers); a predictive team (analytic and medical); and an actual research evaluation team. Because of our inexperience and the smallness of our core group, and because team research by psychoanalysts is a relatively new methodological approach, this was not done. Although the combination of roles may have complicated our later work we do not feel it has interfered with the validity of our findings.

After obtaining the second-order data, the quantitatively weighted diagnoses, we required the services of a statistical consultant to assess these data and further reduce them to meaningful third-order data that could be used to demonstrate the accuracy of the test of our hypotheses.

Once we obtained our third-order data, the statistical results, we were confronted with the problem of interpreting these findings in ways that were meaningful, useful, and communicable. Questions of reliability and validity had to be considered. In some instances the answers we obtained seemed perplexing, paradoxical, and inconclusive. Nonetheless, we were able to obtain meaningful conclusions that related to our initial hypotheses. We became aware of the importance of the problem of interviewer cue detection and utilization late in our work—a problem requiring further discussions by the group and additional studies.

In the preparation of our material for publication we again used our analytic group as authors. Here too we ran into various difficulties. Individuals entrusted with the responsibility for preparing particular chapters might lose perspective in their written material. Some writers overvalued or undervalued certain items, others presented the material in a form that reflected their personal viewpoints. The group then had to act as an external audience, criticizing and studying each document as it was prepared. At times the discussions about the elimination or inclusion of some material, the means of expression or emphasis, and the integration of the various chapters sorely taxed group coherence. These differences were dealt with democratically, and the finished product reflects the agreement of all the participants.

Various theoretical questions, unrelated to the psychosomatic specificity theory, were discussed at different times. For example, we spent much time and energy debating the question of cues and clues. What constitutes evidence, direct and indirect? How does psychological "set" influence the interviewer and also the diagnostic judges? How far do inductive and deductive processes go in the process of formulation and explanation? What constitutes adequate and minimally sufficient data to arrive at a differentially considered formulation and diagnosis?

We had to make as explicit as we could what our individual internal reference points were. Did all the judges use the same general formulations as a base in the preparation of their initial reports and diagnoses? Were all the judges equally adept at interpreting the available clinical information and then matching their interpretations with the previously agreed-upon general basic formulations?

The values and the problems of team research and group process warrant a full report of their own. In general, the use of the group as a collective critical body proved helpful in correcting individual misinterpretations and blind spots. On the other hand, the administrative coordinator was at times faced with the responsibility of keeping the group working effectively in the face of emotionally charged differences of opinion.

The role of the project secretary, working with the medical case selectors, interviewers, analytic and internist judges, and protocol editors, and yet maintaining anonymity and objectivity, cannot be underestimated. She had to be aware of all records and results and yet remain discreet so as not to reveal information at inappropriate times. The statistical consultant too was required to undertake his technical analyses and present his findings in a form that did not confuse or otherwise disturb the various research groups.

The individual and collective motivations and narcissistic investments of all who participated in this extensive study cannot be neglected but will not be discussed here. Despite the many problems and questions we encountered, we all found the gratifications and rewards involved in working on this project of sufficient magnitude to spur us onward to its completion.

What are the implications of our study thus far? We made careful statistical analyses of our diagnostic successes and failures. We tried to check our statistical results by determining to what extent our diagnoses could be attributed to medical or other illegitimate cues inadvertently present in the interview material.

Our findings seem to justify the conclusion that even after allowing for the possible use of such cues, our percentage of correct diagnoses was well above what could have been expected on the basis of chance alone. On the whole, our extended statistical analysis seems to indicate that one can indeed differentiate between the seven specific diseases on the basis of the psychological patterns associated with each of them. We assume, however, that the typical psychological configuration seemingly characteristic of the specific physical disorder is not exclusively unique to it. We have not, in this volume, discussed the theoretical implications of our research for "specificity" theory. We hope to do this in a future work.

Our evidence speaks for differentiation between the diseases and not for the establishment of specific formulations for the individual diseases. The correctness of each psychological formulation as a whole cannot be directly determined by our statistical method. Such an investigation involves the intensive study of the formulations of the successful judges and careful review of the initial clinical material from which these formulations were derived. This research will be undertaken by us next. We hope to find out if and how these formulations and correct diagnoses relate to the basic patterns or gestalten that we initially started with. We also hope to discover what implicit as well as explicit patterns the successful judges used in arriving at their diagnoses and whether some of these may turn out to be at variance with the initial formulations.

We realize that the psychological patterns are not unique to the patients having the disease, as several conditions apparently must be present for the disease to make itself manifest. These are: a presumed innate or constitutional predisposition and sensitivity; an early life situation in which a core psychological configuration developed, rendering the individual particularly vulnerable to certain types of conflicts; and a disease onset situation precipitating an exacerbation of the basic conflict to which the individual is susceptible. If any one of these is not present, the disease may not appear even though one or both of the other factors are there. It is for this reason that the characteristic psychological patterns may exist in persons not showing the organic disease. Because each of the seven psychological patterns may be present at a minimum non-conflictual level in everyone, we decided to exclude individuals not having any one of the diseases in the present study.

What about future studies? In general there seems to be sufficient evidence to indicate that the hypotheses explicitly stated and used by the successful analytic judges bear some relationship to those presented at the start of our work. A full-scale study and review of the already collected clinical protocols and of the correct predictive formulations will be undertaken with the intention of revising and updating the formulations for the seven diseases. These revised formulations may then become hypotheses that will require further testing with fresh data derived from new studies—one of which has already begun. This study involves the collection of data from the intensive psychoanalytic treatment of patients having one of the diseases we have studied. The analysis, conducted by a graduate psychoanalyst who has not been involved with the psychosomatic research, provides the primary data to be used in checking existing or revised formulations. In this way we may have come full circle, for our initial formulations were derived from individual treatment situations and now we return again to the clinical situation for verification and possible newer hypotheses.

Appendix

Sample Case Protocol

Case: Mr. A. O.
Interview Date: February 20, 1959
Meeting Date, Analytic Judges: May 19, 1959
Diagnosis: Rheumatoid Arthritis
Interviewer: Judge H

All analytic judges participated, with the exception of the interviewer

Brief Sample of Edited Case As Given to Judges

Mr. A. O.

Interview Date: February 20, 1959

Patient is a somewhat small, quite neat, very poised, colored man. He is open, responsive, and cooperative in the interview. He is obviously quite intelligent and his command of the English language is remarkable for a person of his education and background.

Patient was so soft-spoken that the secretary complained there were many places in the record where she could not understand what was said.

A: You understood about our recording this?

P: Yes.
[*omission*]

A: When [*omission*: was disease discovered?]

P: [*Omission*: over a year ago.]

A: About a year.

P: Yes, I have had some trouble [*omission*] maybe five or six years before but . . . ah . . . it passed without my even trying to find out what caused it [*omission*].

A. [*Omission*] [MED. ED.: possibly prodromal symptoms mentioned as long as five to six years ago.]

P: [*Omission*]

A: [*Omission*: best to date disease discovery] about two years ago?

P: That's right.

A. We'll try to pinpoint those dates a little better later on. How old a man are you?

P: Forty-three.

A: Forty-three. What kind of work do you do?

P: I'm a janitor *[*patient speaks quite softly*]*.

A: What?

P: A janitor.

A: Has this been what you've done all the time?

P: Yes . . . for the last . . . say since '39. I had other jobs, but since coming out . . . before going into service in '43 I started doing this

Edited material is indicated as follows: A, analyst; P, patient; MED. ED., medical editor; [ ], material omitted, substituted, or added; *[ ]*, comment by secretary on transcription of the record.

Most of the material "omitted" was removed by the medical editor. Some of the material "omitted" (such as interviewer questions) was edited out by the interviewing analyst because of possible cuing significance.

At the final editing, all identifying references to persons in the research project or otherwise were removed or altered.

work regularly, and then after coming out of the service in '45 I went back to this work *[speaks very softly]*.

A: You were a janitor before you went into the service?

P: Yes.

A: Since '39 you said?

P: Well I'd say since '39—I started learning the work, living with my uncle, I helped him. But working on another job, in a laundry, at a warehouse, bus motor supplies, and then into this.

A: Then you went in the service and you went back into it—janitor work—after you came out of the service.

P: Yes *[clears throat]*.

A: Were you brought up in Chicago?

P: No . . . I was born and raised in Oklahoma.

A: When did you come here?

P: I came here in 1937.

A: In '37, so that was shortly before you started the janitor work.

P: Yes, it was.

A: How old were you then?

P: I would say I was about 22.

A: Twenty-two. What was your reason for coming here?

P: Well . . . I had a brother here and . . . ah . . . to look for work really. I had a brother living here and . . . ah . . . it was easier to come where you have somebody . . . to help you, until you could find work and help you to find it . . . you know.

A: Were times hard down there or did you just want to find something different?

P: Times were hard more or less everywhere, and they were no different there; however, I came from the CC Camp to Chicago. I had finished high school, I went in the CC Camp that same summer and stayed there about 22 months, and then . . . ah . . . you couldn't stay there forever, and I had gone as far as I felt I could go there, I thought I could do better if I left, so I did.

A: Did you have any trouble finding work when you got here?

P: No . . . I didn't have any trouble finding work. . . . I more or less had a job waiting for me.

A: So after you came here things were all right?

P: Yeah. They were all right.

A: But you finished high school down there?

P: Yes.

A: Do you think you can pinpoint [*omission*: disease discovery] a little better than to say five or six years ago? Could you tell me exactly?

P: That won't be easy, but let me think . . . I would say 1951 as near as I can remember it.

A: 1951.

P: Yeah.

[*omission*]

A: Do you know what was going on in your life at that time?

P: Nothing unusual. I was married . . . enjoying what I thought for me was a full life.

A: You had no troubles that you are aware of at that time?

P: No, I didn't.

A: Looking back on it now do you think of anything that might have been causing you emotional strain?

P: As far as emotional strain is concerned I have never been able to pinpoint any emotional strains although I know I have had them down through the years because of different other things that have happened; for instance, there was a period wherein I couldn't sleep . . . after a certain time of night, that is, if I'm due up at five o'clock and I wake up at four o'clock, and then maybe after a few weeks I'd wake up at three o'clock—and it moved back. It didn't matter how early I went to bed. If I went to bed at eight o'clock, I could sleep until three o'clock the next morning and then I'd wake up. If I'd go to bed at twelve o'clock, I'd still just sleep until three and wake up. Well . . . ah . . . I went to a doctor and he couldn't pinpoint it either. I didn't have anything organically wrong that he could find and . . . ah . . . the questions he asked about finance and marital troubles . . . I didn't have because my salary was good for me at the time, that is, I hadn't known anything better. So . . . ah . . . I didn't have any worries along those lines. My wife was, as far as I knew and as far as I cared, loyal, so I didn't have any of those worries. My children were in good health, and I just couldn't find anything that could cause this condition, and neither could he.

A: That trouble about sleeping occurred when?

P: That occurred, maybe a year after [*omission*: prodromal and/or disease discovery].

A: Oh, a year after [*omission*].

P: Yeah, and then about the same time [*omission*: of prodromal and/or disease discovery] maybe the next year this sleepless period came.

A: Oh, I see [*omission*: a year later—symptoms].

P: At about the same time a year later. Of course I . . . didn't then and still don't connect them. If they are connected, then I have no way of knowing. Speaking of the mental strain—*that* I know that I must have been under and yet I couldn't then and can't now pinpoint it.

[*omission*]

P: That's right.
[*omission*]
A: When did you get married?
P: I've been married twice [*omission*].
[*omission*]
P: Mmmhmm.
A: Which marriage was it when [*omission*: disease discovered]?
P: The second.
A: That was the second. How long had you been married at that time?
P: I had been married at that time about three years.
A: About three years. Was there anything bothering you in the marriage at that time?
P: No, not that I recall.
[*omission*] [MED. ED.: analyst questions patient about the possible prodromata and whether they led at that time to a diagnosis. The dates of the questionable prodromata appear to stretch on back for more than a decade and become more questionable the further back they go. They did not lead to a diagnosis.]
[*omission*]
A: [*Omission*] when would you yourself say that you would feel [*omission*: disease discovered]?
P: Well, looking back . . . I would think . . . looking back to the period [*omission*].
A: Which would have been that period [*omission*]—a little over two years ago?
P: Right.
A: Although you [*omission*] [MED. ED.: mentioned prior phenomena as possible prodromata].
P: Yes.
A: But you wouldn't be too sure [*omission*] [MED. ED.: about their interpretation as prodromata]?
P: [*Omission*: is not sure. About the two-year-ago period patient says] there is no question. If there is any question at all [*omission*: it relates to interpretation of prior phenomena].
[*omission*]
A: You say you have been married twice. When was the first time?
P: The first time was . . . ah . . . 20 years ago.
A: You would have been about 23, is that right?
P: Twenty-three.
A: How long did that marriage last?
P: It didn't last very long. About a year.
A: About a year. Any children?

P: One.

A: What happened to the marriage?

P: Just dissolved itself.

A: What went wrong—who didn't like whom?

P: I think the thing that went wrong was . . . ah . . . we were both young. I was perhaps 35 instead of 23, and my wife was perhaps 15 at 18, and the age difference, although there was actually just five . . . ah . . . numerical years there were perhaps 20 years in our thinking. I was thinking too old for a man my age, and she was thinking the age that she was, and so we just never . . . we didn't have . . . maybe the intelligence to reconcile this difference.

A: How did you get to be thinking so old?

P: Now that's a *[slight laugh]* question. I actually don't know. I was really a boy.

A: Did other people notice this?

P: Yes, they did. I was a boy until I was 19 and then I became a man overnight, and I became an older man than I should have become. When I was a boy I was a prankster more than anything else. I played football until I was 19, then overnight I became a man and accepted the responsibilities of the world. It was on my shoulders to carry. That's the way I conducted myself.

A: Did anything happen to make you change that suddenly?

P: *[Clears throat.]* I can't recall anything that happened that made me change that suddenly. I have always had my share of family responsibilities. . . . I mean from a kid . . . if I made 20 cents a dime had to go into the family till. If I made a dime a nickel had to go in, so . . . ah . . . I don't think anything happened to cause this abrupt change except . . . ah . . . maybe one day I woke up and decided I was old enough to not be a boy any longer.

A: Anyway nothing disturbing happened?

P: No.

A: Was there a connection with meeting anybody who made a big impression on you or anything of that sort, that you identified with?

P: Ah . . . looking back I would say about this time I went in the CC Camp, and . . . ah . . . naturally there was . . . army discipline . . . and I had, I . . . ah . . . was given jobs of responsibility . . . just thought I should conduct myself in the same way to merit these jobs.

A: Did you like the CC Camp?

P: Oh, yes I did, very much.

A: Were you happy to be there?

P: Yes, I was.

A: You wanted to live up to the responsibility of it, is that right?

P: Yes.
A: You think this might have been . . .*[patient talks]*.
P: Might have been a factor, a big factor.
A: Your first wife, did she ask for a divorce or did you?
P: . . . I think it was one of those things that was just sort of understood after so long a time.
A: You agreed you wouldn't get along, is that it?
P: We decided that . . . ah . . . maybe we weren't going to get back together. . . .
A: You separated after about a year, is that right?
P: Yes.

Unedited Case with Edited Material Indicated

Mr. A. O.

Interview Date: February 20, 1959

Patient is a somewhat small, quite neat, very poised, colored man. He is open, responsive, and cooperative in the interview. He is obviously quite intelligent and his command of the English language is remarkable for a person of his education and background.

Patient was so soft-spoken that the secretary complained there were many places in the record where she could not understand what was said.

A: You understood about our recording this?
P: Yes.
[A: When were you here?]
[P: I am a patient.]
[A: Oh, you are a patient now. I thought maybe you were coming in from the outside.]
[P: No, no.]
[A: When did you come to the hospital?]
[P: Ah . . . a little better than a year ago.]
[A: You've been here all that time?]
[P: Yes, my visits are from four to six months apart.]
[A: Oh, you're not living in the hospital now.]
[P: No, I'm not living here now.]
[A: That's what I meant. Did you at any time come in as an in-patient, a bed-patient?]
[P: No, no.]
[A: You've been a clinic patient or private patient or what is it?]
[P: As a clinic patient.]
[A: Clinic patient. That's what you've been right along.]
[P: Right.]
[A: You haven't been a bed-patient?]
P: No.]
A: When [did your trouble start]? [Med. Ed.: was disease discovered?]
P: [I would say the current flare-up . . . started about a . . . year prior to my coming in.] [Med. Ed.: over a year ago.]
A: About a year.
P: Yes, I have had some trouble [in these quarters, the shoulders] maybe five or six years before but . . . ah . . . it passed without my even trying to find out what caused it. [To me it was just some things in the

shoulder . . . bothered me at night and early in the morning. It was gone during the day so I didn't do anything about it. But then when it came back . . . ah . . . say two years ago, it has never left—stayed and after so long a time I thought I'd better find out what it was.]

[A: So the first time was five or six years ago.] [MED. ED.: possibly prodromal symptoms mentioned as long as five to six years ago.]

[P: Yes.]

[A: And then you didn't have any trouble then until] [MED. ED.: Best to date disease discovery] about two years ago?

P: That's right.

A: We'll try to pinpoint those dates a little better later on. How old a man are you?

P: Forty-three.

A: Forty-three. What kind of work do you do?

P: I'm a janitor *[patient speaks quite softly]*.

A: What?

P: A janitor.

A: Has this been what you've done all the time?

P: Yes . . . for the last . . . say since '39. I had other jobs, but since coming out . . . before going into service in '43 I started doing this work regularly, and then after coming out of the service in '45 I went back to this work *[speaks very softly]*.

A: You were a janitor before you went into the service?

P: Yes.

A: Since '39, you said?

P: Well I'd say '39—I started learning the work, living with my uncle, I helped him. But working on another job, in a laundry, at a warehouse, bus motor supplies, and then into this.

A: Then you went in the service and you went back into it—janitor work —after you came out of the service.

P: Yes *[clears throat]*.

A: Were you brought up in Chicago?

P: No . . . I was born and raised in Oklahoma.

A: When did you come here?

P: I came here in 1937.

A: In '37, so that was shortly before you started the janitor work.

P: Yes, it was.

A: How old were you then?

P: I would say I was about . . . 22.

A: Twenty-two. What was your reason for coming here?

P: Well . . . I had a brother here and . . . ah . . . to look for work really. I had a brother living here so . . . ah . . . it was easier to come where you have somebody ... to help you ... until you could find work and help you to find it ... you know.

A: Were times hard down there or did you just want to find something different?

P: Times were hard more or less everywhere, and they were no different there; however, I came from the CC Camp to Chicago. I had finished high school, I went to the CC Camp that same summer and I stayed there about 22 months, and then ... ah ... you couldn't stay there forever, and I had gone as far as I felt I could go there, I thought I could do better if I left, so I did.

A: Did you have any trouble finding work when you got here?

P: No ... I didn't have any trouble finding work. ... I more or less had a job waiting for me.

A: So after you came here things were all right?

P: Yeah. They were all right.

A: But you finished high school down there.

P: Yes.

A: Do you think you can pinpoint [the first time you had this trouble] [MED. ED.: disease discovery] a little better than to say five or six years ago? Could you tell me exactly [when it started]?

P: That won't be easy, but let me think. ... I would say in 1951 as near as I can remember it.

A: 1951.

P: Yeah.

[A: Do you remember what time of year?]

[P: Yeah, it was during the late fall and winter months.]

A: Do you know what was going on in your life at that time?

P: Nothing unusual. I was married ... enjoying what I thought for me was a full life.

A: You had no troubles that you are aware of at that time?

P: No, I didn't.

A: Looking back on it now do you think of anything that might have been causing you emotional strain?

P: As far as emotional strain is concerned I have never been able to pinpoint any emotional strains although I know I have had them down through the years because of different other things that have happened; for instance, there was a period wherein I couldn't sleep ... after a certain time of night, that is, if I'm due up at five o'clock and I wake up at four o'clock, and then maybe after a few weeks I'd wake up at three o'clock—and it moved back. It didn't matter how early I went to bed. If I went to bed at eight o'clock, I could sleep until three o'clock the next morning and then I'd wake up. If I'd go to bed at twelve o'clock I'd still just sleep until three and wake up. Well . . . ah . . . I went to a doctor and he couldn't pinpoint it either. I didn't have anything organically wrong that he could find and . . . ah . . . the questions he asked about finance and marital troubles . . . I didn't have because my salary was good for me at the time, that is, I hadn't known anything better. So . . . ah . . . I didn't have any worries along those lines. My wife was, as far as I knew and as far as I cared, loyal, so I didn't have any of those worries. My children were in good health, and I just couldn't find anything that could cause this condition, and neither could he.

A: That trouble about sleeping occurred when?

P: That occurred, maybe a year after . . . [this arthritis attack] [MED. ED.: prodromal and/or disease discovery.]

A: Oh, a year after [an attack].

P: Yeah, and then about the same time [that the arthritis came on that year, [MED. ED.: of prodromal and/or disease discovery] maybe the next year this sleepless period came.

A: Oh, I see [as though it were the first anniversary of the first attack] [MED. ED.: a year later] */patient talking/*.

P: At about the same time a year later. Of course I . . . didn't then and still don't connect them. If they are connected, then I have no way of knowing. Speaking of the mental strain—*that* I know that I must have been under and yet I couldn't then and can't now pinpoint it.

[A: But you do remember that the first arthritis started in the fall and the first period of sleeplessness started in the fall?]

P: That's right.

[A: Has anything else happened in the fall to you?]

[P: No, not that I could recall except that I got married in the fall.] */slight laugh/* [I don't think this had anything to do with it.]

A: When did you get married?

P: I've been married twice. [Married in November and in October, both times.]

[A: Both times—you got married in the fall.]

P: Mmmhmm.

A: Which marriage was it when [you had the first attack of arthritis]? [MED. ED.: disease discovered.]

P: The second.

A: That was the second. How long had you been married at that time?

P: I had been married at that time about three years.

A: About three years. Was there anything bothering you in the marriage at that time?

P: No, not that I recall.

A: The first [attack that you had, what part of your body did it involve and how long did it last?]

[P: The shoulders and it left, I would say, through the winter . . . maybe from the first of November until the first of March *[mumbling]*.]

[A: Then it went away?]

[P: It went away.]

[A: Did you have any treatment for it?]

[P: No, I had no treatment at all.]

[A: You didn't see a doctor for it?]

[P: No.]

[A: So the diagnosis was not made at that time.]

[P: No, it wasn't made at that time.]

[A: Are you sure it was the same thing?]

[P: I can't be sure but when it came back the second time, the symptoms, as far as I was concerned, were the same, except at this time it didn't go away.]

[MED. ED.: Omission in which analyst questions patient of the possible prodromata, and whether they led at that time to a diagnosis. The dates of the questionable prodromata appear to stretch on back for more than a decade and become more questionable the further back they go. They did not lead to a diagnosis.]

[A: Did you ever discuss with your doctors whether they thought that first attack had been an attack of arthritis?]

[P: No, I didn't discuss whether or not they thought that. I did tell them about this.]

[A: And they didn't make any comment.]

[P: No, they didn't make any comment *[mumbling]*.]

[A: Now the first attack that you had that you know was arthritis, that was when?]

[P: The first that I know about was about two years ago.]

[A: That's the one that was two years ago.]

[P: Yeah, that's the one that is current. I had been under treatment for a year and it went on for about a year before I came in.]

[A: I see, you had it for about a year before you came in here.]

[P: Assuming that it would go away the way it did before, but this time it didn't.]

[A: Apparently then it was rather mild.]

[P: Yes, I would say mild according to the doctor's standpoint.]

[A: What about yours?]

[P: If the doctor said it was mild it was mild, I mean in that he had seen so much more than I think I have seen and to me the pain was terrific but then to him as long as there isn't some other damage that he probably would know it isn't there, it is mild. As far as the pain is concerned . . . I don't know how it could have been much worse *[not sure of this; he speaks too softly]*.]

[A: Did they tell you it was damaged? Did they see it on X-ray or things of that sort?]

[P: They took X-rays and I am sure they saw some damage—in the region of my back.]

[A: Did they tell you that they saw some damage?]

[P: Well, when I asked about what it was he told me that . . . ah . . . I definitely had rheumatoid arthritis, that he was pretty well convinced from the examination, and they got the report from the various tests, X-rays, and he could give me a definite diagnosis. I asked him what he thought it came from and he said in your case I would guess that it came from the injury in your back, although he gave me a number of other reasons where you could have arthritis. He didn't actually pinpoint it to the injury but knowing that I had had this injury for some time, well I accepted it as sort of stemming from that.]

[A: When I mentioned mild, what I meant was it seemed to me that if you could go a whole year without going to a doctor, that it probably wasn't too excruciating. Maybe I'm wrong about that.]

[P: I think maybe you are because one of my shortcomings is not giving in to pain. I know that . . . there is a cause for anything you get that isn't caused by an obvious injury, but . . . ah . . . I might, if I had had . . . I don't, but if I had had it I might have had it for a long period of time before I went to see about it, because I have always felt that my body was in good condition *[can't get this]*. Colds, I have seldom ever taken anything for them.]

[A: During that year that you didn't go to the doctor the pain was pretty severe—did it get worse during the second year or did it start getting better?]

[P: No, it didn't get any worse, it just got to the point where . . . I knew that I couldn't handle it any longer. I had . . . used lamps and things like that . . . you get . . . relief to an extent, but tomorrow it is the same thing, and I knew that if the rubbing and the heat didn't drive it away for a period of time . . . then you needed help. I was convinced that heat alone, home remedies wouldn't take care of it . . . then I went to see a doctor.]

[A: When did you first go to the doctor, what month?]

[P: February.]

[A: February would be just about a . . . *[patient talks]*

[P: Year ago.]

[A: About a year ago.]

[P: Mmhmm.]

[A: Would you say that your pain had come back in the fall a year before that or a little more than a year?]

[P: It was a little more than a year because it actually came in the spring but . . . ah . . . the summer months it lightened up to an extent, maybe because of the warm weather or something like that.]

[A: It began in the spring almost two years . . . *[patient interrupts]*]

[P: About two years, I'd say around March or April, in the spring, but it was just one of those things where you had pain today and tomorrow and then you didn't have any more until about two or three weeks—maybe a little in the shoulder or something like that. It would go and come but then in the fall it came and it didn't leave through the winter.]

[A: It was in February then that you went to the doctor and he diagnosed it?]

[P: Yes.]

[A: Did it go away this past summer?]

[P: No, it didn't.]

[A: It stayed through.]

[P: Through the summer, yes.]

[A: You spoke of something about an accident. Did you have an accident to your back or anything?]

[P: Not an accident, an injury.]

[A: An injury rather.]

[P: Yes.]

[A: What was the injury?]

[P: Well, I think . . . ah . . . not being sure but I think I had . . . ah . . . you might call a progressive injury to my back—this work that I do, and pulling the garbage, you carry a heavy can on your back, because I was young and . . . ah . . . that perhaps what I considered strong, I carried heavier loads than I should have carried . . . little by little each day I did damage in that same area. It didn't show up. I mean if it had been something that snapped like that you wouldn't have done it any more, because it went on from one day to another, then . . . ah . . . I know that after going in the service, a posture change, and when I came out of service the change was so obvious, and so I came in for a check on that. They examined me for *[cannot get this; voice unclear at times]* at that time, and they couldn't find any damage, but . . . ah . . .]

[A: This was when?]

[P: This was about . . . '47, I would say.]

[A: '47.]

[P: Yeah—this posture change but they couldn't find anything that caused it and they assumed that my posture was normal for me, and . . . ah . . . we left it at that.]

[A: Do you think it was normal for you?]

[P: No, I knew that it wasn't. But inasmuch as they couldn't find anything that was causing, there wasn't very much that I could do about it. I could have gone to other doctors but when you go to what you consider competent doctors—there is no use to run all over creation—if they can't find it, maybe it can be found some place else—but they say pretty much the same thing *[not certain of this; voice fades away]*.]

[A: Which joints have you had it in?]

[P: I have had it in both shoulders, this wrist, the knee, and this foot and this joint in the back—the lower part of the back.]

[A: Both shoulders, your left wrist, is that right?]

[P: Right.]

[A: And your right knee and foot.]

[P: Right knee and foot.]

[A: And in the back? The lower part of the back?]

[P: The lower part of the back.]

[A: Which has been the worst?]

[P: I would say the worst has been the shoulders . . . the shoulders have been the worst. When I say they have been the worst, they have caused me more trouble—I have to use them more and perhaps they are more painful, but the foot, I have had swelling in the foot for about—since August, but it doesn't restrict my motion, my movement.]

[A: Do you have much pain there?]

[P: No, in the beginning there was *[clears throat]* pain in the left and the right three or four weeks and there was no pain but there was constant swelling there.]

[A: Judging by the pain and the swelling and so forth, since you know the symptoms pretty well now,] when would you yourself say that you would feel [that it was pretty certain that the thing was well started?] [MED. ED.: that disease was discovered.]

[P: . . . Well, looking back . . . I would think *[clears throat]* looking back to the period before the diagnosis, and taking the diagnosis into consideration I would say that it was well started a year before I came in and had a diagnosis.]

A: Which would have been that period [in the fall] a little over two years ago?

P: Right *[clears throat]*.

A: Although you [said you had some symptoms the previous spring?] [MED. ED.: mentioned prior phenomena as possible prodromata.]

P: Yes.

A: But you wouldn't be too sure [that these symptoms . . . */patient talks/*] [MED. ED.: about their interpretation as prodromata?]

[P: I would say definitely that it was the same thing, but what I mean . . . ah . . . two . . . ah . . . say a year previous to the time that I came in] [MED. ED.: is not sure. About the two-year-ago period patient says] there is no question. If there is any question at all, [it's in that period a few months before then */clears throat./*] [MED. ED.: it relates to interpretation of prior phenomena.]

[A: Yes, I see. What is this about a posture change that was studied in 1947?]

[P: Well, ah . . .]

[A: What was the change in your posture?]

[P: . . . Ah . . . I . . . ah . . . began to . . . ah . . ., sway, my back began to sway in, say you were giving in to a tenderness in your back, you were saving a certain portion of your body . . . and then . . . ah . . . although there was no apparent pain there, but something was causing you to favor that particular portion of your body and you just give in to it, it just seemed to sway. When I came in and they couldn't, they didn't find any damage in the area, they assumed it was normal for me. One of the doctors remarked that . . . ah . . . they were mostly checking for TB. They could tell before they were through with the examination that I didn't have TB—if I had I would probably sway forward rather than back, and so . . . ah . . .]

[A: Looking back on it, do you yourself think that it had anything to do with the kind of work you were doing? Did that favor the kind of work you were doing or not?]

[P: I think that it . . . ah . . . definitely had something to do with the kind of work that I was doing. You are speaking of the posture change now, aren't you?]

[A: Yes.]

[P: Well, I would definitely say it had something to do with the kind of work I was doing . . . not at the time that I noticed the change . . . at the period before I went in service . . .]

[A: You didn't have any of the posture change before you went into the service?]

[P: Not that I noticed. I did notice while I was in service, this . . . ah . . . change began to take place. I mean it was obvious.]

[A: You noticed it during the service?]

[P: I noticed it during the service. I mean it was called to my attention during the service—say, the fellows would say he walks like he owns 47th Street because I reared back. You knew this wasn't normal for you but you didn't pay too much attention to it because fellows say anything.]

[A: You had no pain at that time?]

[P: No, I didn't have any pain. When I came out of the service it just continued, I would say, became more obvious. It had become so obvious that I could detect it . . . without being reminded by somebody. So then I thought I should check it and find out what was wrong.]

[A: So getting it checked in '47 didn't mean that it came on in '47, it had been coming on slowly.]

[P: It had been coming on perhaps since '39.]

A: You say you have been married twice. When was the first time?

P: The first time was . . . ah . . . 20 years ago.

A: You would have been about 23, is that right?

P: Twenty-three.

A: How long did that marriage last?

P: It didn't last very long. About a year.

A: About a year. Any children?

P: One.

A: What happened to the marriage?

P: Just dissolved itself.

A: What went wrong—who didn't like whom?

P: I think the thing that went wrong was . . . ah . . . we were both young. I was perhaps 35 instead of 23, and my wife was perhaps 15 at 18, and the age difference, although there was actually just five . . . ah . . . numerical years, there were perhaps 20 years in our thinking. I was thinking too old for a man of my age, and she was thinking the age that she was, and so we never . . . we didn't have . . . maybe the intelligence to reconcile this difference.

A: How did you get to be thinking so old?

P: Now that's a *[slight laugh]* question. I actually don't know. I was really a boy.

A: Did other people notice this?

P: Yes, they did. I was a boy until I was 19 and then I became a man overnight, and I became an older man than I should have become. When I was a boy I was a prankster more than anything else. I played football until I was 19, then overnight I became a man and accepted the responsibilities of the world. It was on my shoulders to carry. That's the way I conducted myself.

A: Did anything happen to make you change that suddenly?

P: *[Clears throat]*. I can't recall anything that happened that made me change that suddenly. I have always had my share of family responsibilities. . . . I mean from a kid . . . if I made 20 cents a dime had to go into the family till. If I made a dime a nickel had to go in, so . . . ah . . . I don't think anything happened to cause this abrupt change except . . . ah . . . maybe one day I woke up and decided I was old enough to not be a boy any longer.

A: Anyway nothing disturbing happened?

P: No.

A: Was there a connection with meeting anybody who made a big impression on you or anything of that sort, that you identified with?

P: Ah . . . looking back I would say about this time I went in the CC Camp, and . . . ah . . . naturally there was . . . army discipline . . . and I had, I . . . ah . . . was given jobs of responsibility . . . just thought I should conduct myself in the same way to merit these jobs.

A: Did you like the CC Camp?

P: Oh, yes I did, very much.

A: You were happy to be there?

P: Yes, I was.

A: You wanted to live up to the responsibility of it, is that right?

P: Yes.

A: You think this might have been . . . *[patient talks]*

P: Might have been a factor, a big factor.

A: Your first wife, did she ask for a divorce or did you?

P: . . . I think it was one of those things that was just sort of understood after so long a time.

A: You agreed you wouldn't get along, is that it?

P: We decided that . . . ah . . . maybe we weren't going to get back together. . . .

A: You separated after about a year, is that right?

P: Yes.

A: How long before you got a divorce?

P: Probably about eight or nine years.

A: That's a long time.

P: It is.

A: Did you see each other a lot?

P: Well . . . we saw each other, I would say frequently, not a lot but . . . ah . . . enough. . . .

A: But you didn't try to live together again?

P: No, we didn't try to live together, we did talk about it from time to time, but conditions . . . where she was concerned . . . really not, I would say not conducive to . . . ah . . . for one reason or another we just did never get back together until after so long a time we decided that . . . ah . . . too much water had gone over the dam and it was useless to try.

A: Who did she live with?

P: She lived with her mother.

A: She went back to live with her mother then?

P: Mmmhmm.

A: She was perhaps a mama's girl and preferred being with her mother instead of you?

P: No, I don't think that. As I said I think it was just . . . ah . . . I think it was a lack of patience more than anything else on my part. If I had been a more patient man, time would have taken care of the little things that . . . caused my irritation.

A: You got pretty irritated with her?

P: Well . . . yes, . . . ah . . . not to the extent where you would become violent or anything like that, but as I said I was pretty stiff. I thought things should be done a certain way . . . well that's the way they should be done. Since I didn't think . . . I thought it was base for a woman to smoke, or take a drink, or anything like that, and . . . ah . . . I was just as set in that as though I was 90, and there was no bending . . . "you either don't smoke or you are a bad woman." And so . . . ah . . . time, as I said, wasn't taking care of that because . . . ah . . . now at a time when I should—if I was going to be set in my ways—I should be set in that way of thinking, now I don't feel that way.

A: So you ground down on her pretty hard, is that it?

P: I think so. She had already had this from her father and so . . . .

[A: You mean she had had too much grinding down on her from her father?]

[P: Yes.]

A: She got too rebellious about this, is that the . . . *[patient talks too]*.

P: No, she didn't want to take that any longer. She made that clear in the beginning. She had no intentions of going through that any longer *[voice fades]*.

A: The child you had was it a boy or a girl?

P: A girl.

A: Have you kept a relationship with the child?

P: Yes.

A: You supported the child and kept up with it?

P: Yes.

A: How old is she now, she must be about 20, isn't she?

P: Nineteen. She will be 20 in June.
A: What is she doing?
P: She's in college.
A: How do you and she get along?
P: Oh, swell.
A: You are pretty fond of her?
P: Yes, indeed *[slight laugh]* *[voice scarcely audible at times]*.
A: And has her mother remarried?
P: Yes, she remarried. Her husband *[voice too low, cannot get it]*. [A: is deceased.]
A: Did she have other children?
P: No.
A: Just the one child. When did you get married again?
P: In 1946.
A: In 1946, so that originally you got married in what year?
P: In '39.
A: '39. You must have gotten your divorce shortly before you got remarried, is that right?
P: Yes, I did.
A: It was in order for you to get remarried or was it in order for her?
P: Yes, for her.
A: She found someone else to get married to first, is that it?
P: Yes.
A: Tell me about your second wife. What sort of person is she?
P: Well, she is a nice person, more fanatic, like I was once. We should have gotten together first *[laughing]*.
A: You say she's fanatic the way you were?
P: Yes—more fanatic.
A: What is she fanatic about? *[both talking]*
P: Religion. She is very much opposed to drinking and smoking, having parties.
A: You've gotten much more relaxed about things.
P: I'm one of the boys now *[laughs]* *[both laughing]*.
A: How does she get along with that?
[So far on this side of the record the patient is speaking so softly that it is almost impossible to hear what he is saying.] [A: nothing especially significant was missed.]
P: That is one of the things that caused the separation.
A: You got separated from your second wife? Did you go back to her or are you still separated?
P: I'm separated.
A: When did you separate?

P: . . . I separated from her in 1950, and we remarried in . . . '55. We were first married in 1946 *[voice scarcely audible]*.
A: So the second time was no go at all?
P: We decided it was no use dragging it out.
A: Did you have any children by her?
P: No.
A: Did you try not to?
P: No . . . shortly after we were married she had to have an operation . . . *[can't get this]*.
A: Had she been married before?
P: No.
A: She had not been married. So she had no children.
P: No.
A: What is she doing now?
P: I don't know really.
A: You don't keep track of her?
P: No.
A: Are you not too friendly with each other?
P: I suppose if we meet each other we would be friendly, sure. I don't do anything like that, not people who have been dear to me. I mean it's hard for me to destroy. I may destroy the ability to live with them.
A: So you don't feel any bitterness or anger toward her?
P: No.
A: Does she toward you?
P: I don't know—I doubt it. *[can't understand him]* I think if ever I needed her I could call on her.
A: She hasn't remarried?
P: Not that I know of, no.
A: When you remarried the last time—when you remarried her, was it mostly she who couldn't get along with you or you who couldn't get along with her?
P: I think a combination of the two.
A: It was pretty much on both sides then?
P: *[Can't understand him.]*
A: How do you feel about not being married to anybody?
P: . . . Well, ah . . . I think I would prefer being married to living alone, but at the same time I would prefer living alone than to being married and unhappy.
A: Are you living alone now?
P: Yes, I am.
A: Entirely alone?
P: Yes.

A: Not with any other family or with any other man or anything? You have your own apartment, is that it?
P: That's right.
A: Do you look forward to getting married again or not?
P: I am not looking forward to it with any great enthusiasm *[can't get it]*.
A: So that you are not too fond of being alone but you also don't find marriage too easy, is that it?
P: . . . I'm not too fond of being alone and . . . ah . . . I am not too skeptical to try marriage again but I'm not too anxious . . . to try without first exploring it a little deeper than I have in my previous marriages. I don't relish the idea of getting in it and out of it again for frivolous reasons.
A: Now, let's see if there is any connection between this second marriage and your illness. You say that you first married your second wife in 1946, is that it?
P: Right.
A: Then it was in '47 [that you began to be concerned about this postural change and had it examined, and then] [MED. ED.: that potential but uncertain prodromal phenomena were noted] you and she broke up in 1950?
P: That's right.
A: Did you get a divorce that same year?
P: No . . . it was about a year before I remarried her.
A: You broke up in 1950. You first said it was five or six years ago [that this started.] [MED. ED.: that phenomena of uncertain prodromal significance were noted.]
P: Yeah.
[A: That would have put your first symptoms in your shoulder within two or three years after you and she broke up, was that it?]
P: . . . Two or three years after we broke up—no, [the symptoms that came back stayed] . . . I may be confused on the dates because [when I first had the symptoms we were together. I mean had this trouble] [MED. ED.: phenomena noted when we were together.]
[A: Your first symptoms were when you and she were together.]
[P: Yes.]
A: So that was before 1950.
P: Before 1950.
A: Because you are sure of the date when you and she broke up.
P: I am sure it was 1950, yeah.
[A: Was it in the fall of 1950 by any chance?]
[P: No, it was in the spring *[both laughing]*. We finally got away from fall.]

A: So that would [really put these first symptoms that we don't know whether they were arthritis or not] would put [them] [MED. ED.: dubious prodromal phenomena] back to really more than eight years.
P: Yeah.
A: Then you and she got remarried in '56.
P: Right.
A: And that would have been not too long before [you had the serious recurrence,] [MED. ED.: what has not thus far been established as date of disease discovery or date of an exacerbation] is that right?
P: *[Clears throat]* Yes, it would be. But she didn't [bring it back] [MED. ED.: bring psychosomatic condition] *[laughs]*.
A: Maybe not but nevertheless the timing is fairly close.
P: Mmmhmm.
[A: When did you and she get remarried in 1956?]
[P: . . . .]
[A: What month?]
[P: . . . This is kind of difficult . . . ah . . . I'd say about—it was in the spring of '56.]
[A: In the spring of '56 and didn't you say you thought it was in the spring of '56 that the symptoms began to worry you again.]
[P: Yes.]
[A: So it would have been about a year. You didn't notice any before that?]
[P: No, not enough to be . . . .]
[A: Then by fall of '57 it was fairly serious, is that it?]
[P: Right.]
[A: Then by spring of '58 is when you had them diagnosed. Is that the right sequence?]
[P: Yes, that's the right sequence.]
[A: Early in February '58, roughly, didn't you say is when it was diagnosed?]
[P: That's right.]
A: So that would have meant [that this came on] [MED. ED.: disease discovery or exacerbation was] within a year after you remarried. You said you got remarried and unmarried all in the same year, didn't you?
P: Yes.
[A: In 1956? You got married to her in the fall?]
[P: In the spring, and separated in the fall.]
[A: Oh, I see, that's right. You were married in the spring and separated in the fall.]
P: Right.

A: '56. So that really [the symptoms actually came on not too long] [MED. ED.: time of discovery or exacerbation was not too long] after you separated then.

P: Yes.

A: Do you think that had anything to do with it? How did you feel about the separation?

P: Ah . . . well I felt that the separation was a necessary thing.

A: You might have thought it was necessary but were you unhappy about it? Angry about it?

P: Naturally I was unhappy about it—angry, no.

A: You were not angry?

P: No, I was not angry. I was unhappy, yes. I don't like to feel that *[cannot get this]*. [A: couldn't make a go of anything as important as marriage.]

A: So that you might very well have been under a good deal of strain, emotional strain? [even though you thought you had this under control, is that it?]

P: That's possible, except as I said I know from time to time down through the years . . . [A: have had] worries but I haven't always been able to distinguish between worries and . . . minor anxieties as far as leaving any scars, I mean any apparent scars.

A: Can you tell me anything else that was going on around that time that might have contributed to having more emotional tension than you otherwise had had?

P: No, I can't. As I said most of all my adult life has been pretty well controlled . . . I have my ups and downs the same as anybody else, but to . . . ah . . . contributing emotional upheavals which might cause me to have prolonged periods of worries, I don't recall it.

[A: You can't think of any? Let me get something else straight. It was February '58 that you had the diagnosis, fall of '57 that you had pretty severe symptoms, spring of '57 that you had milder symptoms, is that right?]

[P: Yes.]

[A: When did you see the doctor about the sleeplessness?]

[P: . . . It could have been '48.]

[MED. ED.: In further exploring the uncertainties thus far attached to dated discovery there comes into discussion a period of "sleeplessness."]

A: '48 or '58? [You said about a year before this came on.]

P: Oh, [about a year before my first]—this was back in the 40's.

A: In the 40's. That was while you were still with your first wife.

P: Yes, while I was with my first wife [that I had these pains and] I also had this sleepless period.

A: That is what I wanted to get straight. So the sleepless period was while you were still with your first wife, [and after the first pains had started] before you left her. Do you ever have any interest in your first wife—you say she is free now?

P: Do I have any interest? How do you mean?

A: Do you like her as a person? Do you ever see her? Do you feel friendly toward her? Do you ever think maybe you and she might get along together?

P: No, I never think that we might get along together. We have always been friends.

A: You are good friends?

P: Yes.

A: You see her in a friendly way.

P: I see her in a friendly way.

A: You and she have no interest in each other?

P: No.

A: Nothing along that line is bothering you?

P: No.

A: Would you tell me sort of step by step, in your second marriage, how the relationship began to deteriorate? What would happen? What sort of things would your wife do? What sort of things would you do? What kind of quarrels would you have? and so on . . . .

P: Frankly, we didn't have quarrels. That might have been one of the difficulties. If we had had quarrels we would have been able to straighten out things that build up. Things build up down through the years—I am not given to outbreaks unless, let's say unless I'm *[can't get it]* [triggered]. If you say the wrong thing then I will go out and express myself in no uncertain terms. But if you don't do anything to trigger it, I won't ever go off. I'll go back to my first wife to try to explain this. She said to me one time, "You don't fuss. I like to fuss sometimes." *[Can't understand him, speaking too softly.]* That has been my pattern down through the years.

A: You don't fuss.

P: I don't fuss. But . . . ah . . . if something comes up where you trigger me then I express myself in no uncertain terms and *I think* I'm through with you, whether I actually am or not, I don't know but I think I'm through with you.

A: By that you mean, if I did something to trigger your anger you would have an explosive attack of anger, is that what you mean? Then you would feel you are through with me for good?

P: No.
A: You don't mean it that way?
P: No. I don't mean it that way. Not an explosive attack of anger but I mean if you triggered me enough for me to tell you, maybe in a calm manner, what is on my mind, tell you what is on my mind and what I think about the thing that has caused you to trigger me—I'll tell you off and then I'm through with it as far as I'm concerned.
A: Oh, you are through with it.
P: I am willing to forget it and we go on from there.
A: I see—you are not through . . . *[patient talks]*
P: Sort of clearing the air—not through with you.
A: You are not through with the individual, you are just through with the subject.
P: That's it.
[A: Do you get triggered about things, except things that make you angry?]
[P: Do I get triggered about things, except things that make me angry? I am not sure I follow you.]
[A: Say if someone were to trigger you, you say what you had to say and that would be that. Is that right?]
[P: Yeah.]
A: Would you react that way about anything that didn't make you angry?
P: Sure . . . as far as discussion is concerned, I am always open to discussion. I don't talk too much, but I guess it's a method of controlling my emotions to discuss any and all subjects. I mean if you don't open a panel—say this is an open discussion—if you don't open a panel first, I probably won't. For instance, I took my wife with me, my second wife, wherever I went. I almost never went out [A: i.e., alone] except to go to work. I started out asking her where would you like to go? What do you want to do? She would say, "I leave that up to you, wherever you want to go, anything you want to do." Then you get in a habit of saying, "Well, we'll go to such and such a place today, we'll do this, we'll do that." Because you have been more or less charged with the responsibility of doing this and you probably forget to ask what she would like to do. And then after a period of time, she finds that she is only doing the things that you want to do and you are not conscious of this. In this particular case it went on for about three and a half years of my doing this, and finally she said, "I'm not going to go any further, the things I've been doing I did them because you want me to, I just won't do them any more. I'm not going to do them any more." Then is where I blow up, and . . . ah . . . express my thoughts in the matter because, "if you had told me anywhere along the line that you didn't like to go to this thing or you didn't like to do

that, I'm sure I would have considered your feelings in the matter, and when I point out to you [A: i.e., ask] so many times where you want to go and what you want to do, and you never know where you want to go, you never knew what you wanted to do, well I just assumed you were happy doing the things I wanted to do. Now I find I have wasted four years. I have been trying to please you for four years and I find that I've failed." And it's almost too much for you to take. You have to be pretty big not to feel pretty burned up about it then and maybe for some time after. I just sort of gave up. What the heck. I'd done the best I knew how, what can I do different?

A: Did that make any sense to her when you told her that? Could she understand what you were saying?

P: . . . I'm not sure she did.

A: Did she defend herself at all?

P: She continued to say nothing I can do *[can't understand him]*. I know one case in particular where we had decided to go to a New Year's Eve party, and . . . ah . . . this is the only thing I have talked about. Now after this thing happened, I recall I thought we were talking about it, but I was the one who was talking about this New Year's Eve party. Well, that New Year's Eve Jack Benny was on television, and we were going to go from there to the place where the party was to be held. Well, after Jack Benny went off I said, "Well, you'd better start getting dressed, Baby" *[something about 9 o'clock]* and she said, "I'm not going." And then I naturally hit the ceiling because I had assumed that we had discussed this all the time, and . . . ah . . . I naturally blew up and dressed and stormed out. When I came back, as far as I was concerned it was all over and told her so. Just all over and done—I just didn't see how she could do a thing like that to me, and then after a couple of days I realized that . . . ah . . . I was the only one who had ever talked about the party, and the party itself wasn't important enough, even to me, to break up my home. So I went and got her and apologized for my conduct and still tried to show her the place where she was wrong and not letting me know before this particular time. If she wasn't going at least I could have . . . sort of prepared myself for it, and . . . ah . . . but . . . things still didn't improve too much. Underneath the calm I think things were still as disturbed as they were *[mumbling]*.

A: When you finally got to the point of separating, who brought up the question of separating—she or you?

P: Ah . . . she brought up the question of separating. Now I might have brought it on, but she brought it up. I was concerned about it, and I have a friend, John, and he lived at one time in Chicago and we discussed our problems, you know, with each other. Well, because the things were going the way they were going, I had received a letter from him telling me that if I was here in Chicago that summer, he expected to stay with us. And this gave me an opening to . . . ah . . . discuss my problem with him. So I wrote him one Sunday evening and told him that by the time that he got here in the summer I might be a bachelor, not meaning that I was going away but meaning that my wife might be going away by the time he got here. Well . . . I don't ever remember her reading the letter, but . . . ah . . . I did write the letter and we had dinner. I finished it after dinner, sealed it, and the next she said, "Do you want me to mail this letter?" I said yes. She said, "Are you sure you want me to mail this letter?" I said, "Sure, go ahead." Well, she went out and mailed the letter, I went to work, and when I came back she said, "I'm going home."

A: Home being where?

P: Oklahoma. So I wasn't too surprised although I didn't . . . ah . . know exactly what had brought it on . . . the thing that triggered this, it never dawned on me that it was the letter, if it was the letter she never . . . .

A: You don't know?

P: I don't know for sure. But the only thing that might have caused her to . . . ah . . . make the final decision was the letter, if she read it, and if she read it without understanding . . . but . . . ah . . . as I say . . . .

A: You didn't ask her what made her . . . *[patient talks]*.

P: Yes, I asked her, but I told you she was a noncommittal person.

A: She wouldn't say?

P: We didn't discuss it—anything about it.

A: And she wouldn't say what she had against you?

P: Never did.

A: Never did?

P: Never did. She was always writing me she would like to come back and be the kind of wife she should have been, made me think that maybe I should remarry her. After so long a time maybe, maybe she has realized that . . . ah . . . this thing that caused the separation—whatever it is—was just a figment of her imagination. And so like the average individual, I suppose I exonerated myself of any blame in the separation, well, we are going to try it again. Because except you tell me where I'm wrong or what I'm doing that you don't like, then I can't change because within myself I feel I am right, what I am doing is all right, and so, if you don't tell me I will probably go and do the same thing.

A: This business about the letter was the first time you separated?

P: Yes.

A: During that year, less than a year that you were remarried, would you tell me something about that situation. How that deteriorated?

P: Well, after it started I don't think it got off the ground.

A: What happened first?

P: . . . I really don't know how the matter came up but we hadn't been married two weeks before . . . *[sighs]* one night she severely criticized the things I had done since we were married. [A: the first time.] The fact that I had bought carpeting, bought new drapes, the different things that I had done in the house, you know, when she was away.

A: You had done these things while she was gone?

P: Yes. And that . . . ah . . . I always said that I wanted *[can't get it]* this, that, and the other.

A: You wanted to what?

P: *[I think he said "to build"]* [A: They had planned to buy or build a building.] If I had saved the money, rather than buying this stuff, new ties and things like that I could have my building. She said she didn't come back to help me build a bank account . . . so that . . . ah . . . she can be driven off—to leave it with me. Well . . . it was a little disturbing but I figured that . . . ah . . . I can handle this. So I told her that maybe what you should do now, while you feel this way, is get up and in the bottom dresser drawer, there is a little strong box, take it out, take my bonds, take my Post Office book, my bank book, and my checking account, savings and checking account, you check them, and you will see that I don't need anybody to save my money. You wanted to come back here to help me save money. I have been saving ever since you have been gone, and . . . ah . . . it's there for you to see. Whether she checked it or not I don't know, but . . . ah . . . I felt that . . . ah . . . if that was bothering her—it shouldn't bother her any at all, that she should know that I either had her come back for herself, or I had some other motive, other than the one she had figured out. So . . . ah . . . *[mumbling]* one of those things I had done in the marriage before. I never paid $800 for anything to wear—I simply never would have done it—she was talking about a fur coat that I had bought her, and I thought that . . . ah . . . to pay $800 for a fur coat for your wife was just what a man should do . . . but I did realize as I was told by my sister-in-law, some time later, "You got the things that *you* wanted for her, you gave her what *you* wanted her to have instead of waiting until she asked for it. Maybe later she would have wanted a fur coat, but she would have wanted it then. She resented your giving it to her without her asking for it." Well, how do you know?

A: You know as you quote your sister-in-law, [trying to tell you what your wife objected to] it sounds as though your sister-in-law thought [or your wife had told her that] you were [either] too dominating [or too controlling].

P: That's barely possible—I am dominating, not purposely but it's just my nature.

A: Can you tell me some more about that?

P: My nature to . . . ah . . . ?

A: Yes.

P: Maybe I'm just what I call a too controlled guy.

A: A too controlled guy?

P: Yeah. I feel if I have a responsibility, I assume that responsibility and that's it, maybe I . . . ah—maybe it's the way it's supposed to go, and I don't call an account *[can't get this]*.

A: Can you tell me any other examples of difficulties you've gotten into along those lines?

P: Well, no.

A: How about people you work with?

P: I have had very few difficulties with people I work with, and as a rule, the jobs or positions I have been in, I was in sort of a dominant position . . . there just wasn't too much opposition to encounter from the individual that might be, let's say irritated or disturbed about your manner, and I didn't antagonize the individuals that were over me, and probably didn't tolerate any antagonism from those that were under me.

A: So that you would take a strong position with the people who were under you.

P: I think maybe.

A: And not with the people over you, is that it?

P: Except that . . . ah . . . I am . . . ah . . . pretty vocal with the people over me . . . when I think it's necessary.

A: You are pretty vocal?

P: Yeah. If they become rough and I think they should be told about it in no uncertain terms, the fact that you are over me—it means nothing —I'll tell you about it, but I never lost the respect of anybody by having done so.

[A: But you don't take control?]

[P: No, I don't try to take over where—in an area where I don't belong.]

[A: So that when it's with somebody who has the right to control, you may be vocal but you don't try to take over, is that it?]

[P: Yes.]

[A: Do you ever take over a little too much especially if you figure you have the right to—is that right?]

[P: Well, I don't know . . . I consider myself considerate, and if you have a problem, regardless how small it is . . . I consider it.]

A: You want to be considerate.

P: I am as considerate as I know how to be.

A: This is a desire of yours—to be considerate.

P: To be considerate, yeah.

A: Would you tell me about your family? Your background, your childhood, your parents, your brothers and sisters, and those things. You were raised in Oklahoma you say. Your parents living?

P: My mother is.

A: Your mother is living. How long since your father died?

P: 1937.

A: Your mother lived down there. Had either of them been married to anybody else?

P: No.

A: How many children were there?

P: Eleven.

A: That's a big family.

P: Yeah *[I think he said "a pretty big crowd"]*. *[both laughing]*

A: Where did you come in?

P: Seventh.

A: You were seventh of eleven. Did all of them live?

P: One sister died in infancy and one died in 1935.

A: So that 11 was the total number of pregnancies that your mother had?

P: Right.

A: One died in infancy and one died—this was an older sister?

P: Yeah.

A: How old were you when she died?

P: I was 19 when she died.

A: She was how much older than you?

P: . . . Let's see, oh about six years.

A: The rest are all living?

P: She was four years older.

A: Four years older. Where do they live?

P: They live scattered all over the country, from lower California to up the coast *[can't get it]* and here.

A: Many of them here?

P: Just two—my brother and myself.

A: One brother—younger or older?

P: Older.

A: How much older?
P: Well, he's the first.
A: The oldest brother lives here.
P: Yes.
A: Married?
P: Yes, he's married.
A: Children?
P: One.
A: He is how much older than you?
P: Well, let's see—he's about 14 years older.
A: Then he's about 57—you are 43, didn't you say?
P: Right.
A: What does he do?
P: He's a cleaner and presser.
A: Do you see much of him?
P: Yes, I see him about once a week.
A: You feel pretty close to him?
P: Yeah, I do.
A: Do you like his wife?
P: Oh, yes.
A: So that you are close to them. That's the only family you have here?
P: That's the only family, except my own family, my daughter.
A: Your daughter, she is going to school here?
P: Yes, she is going to school here, and incidentally before we get too far —I do have a son—this is a son born out of wedlock.
A: Would you tell me about that?
P: Well, he's just—I'm not passing him off lightly.
A: You are close to him?
P: Yes, I would say close . . . ah . . . what do you call it, you are not as close as you would like to be . . . you would like to embrace him but he won't put his arms around you—so, as far as I'm concerned I can understand it. I am biding my time until such time he does come to me, in the hope.
A: How old is the boy?
P: He's 24.
A: So this was before your daughter?
P: Before my daughter, yes.
A: What does he do?
P: He's in the army now. He was decorating before going in.
A: Did his mother get married to somebody else?
P: Yes.
A: Does she still have a husband?

P: His mother was . . . killed when he was 7. And he was really raised by his aunt.
A: Sister of his mother's or what?
P: Aunt of his mother's—so he grew up . . . more or less on his own—I would say doing more or less what he pleased, whatever he did as far as she was concerned was all right. He came to live with me when he was about 17.
A: I was wondering how come you hadn't taken him when his mother died.
P: Well, he really wasn't mine when his mother died. His mother married before he was born.
A: So that legally he belonged . . . *[patient talks]*
P: He belonged to her husband, but after she died, sometime after she died, everything was changed. His name was changed to mine and everything else, and that's why I say I can understand his antagonism because it was quite a shock . . . I can understand his being shocked. So let's say he is 14—from seven to ten years he had to build up some feeling against me more or less, not knowing that he was going to live with me. When he came to live with me, it was just a question of breaking down this barrier and keeping him disciplined and everything else; one worked against the other. So it . . . wasn't as easy as it might have been, but by the time he went in the service I think we had both . . . begun to realize that we were necessary to each other, even more than he thought he ever would be.
A: Now the man that his mother married, did this man know that the boy wasn't his son?
P: Yes, he knew.
A: But he raised the boy as his son, is that it?
P: Yes.
A: The boy was how old when he found out?
P: He was seven, eight anyway. His mother died when he was seven.
A: After his mother died, did his legal father refuse to have anything more to do with him, was that the idea?
P: I really don't know when or whether he disclaimed the boy; whether he didn't know he had a right to him or whether he didn't want him. That is one of the things I never pried into. If I had it probably might have helped to straighten out the relationship; it was one of the things that I just never bothered to go into and try to find out.
A: So you have no answer.
P: No.
A: How come you didn't marry the girl?
P: . . . That's a good question . . . and I don't have the answer.

A: You must have been about 19.

P: Nineteen, and . . . ah . . . *[can't get this]* . . . her idea was that I should go on and finish school and become a doctor or something else [and I could be out].

A: She didn't try to make an issue of you marrying her?

P: No, in fact she said I needn't worry there wasn't going to be any *[cannot get this]* [A: "shot-gun" wedding]. Looking back on it I just simply *[can't understand]*.

A: Did you have much guilty conscience over it?

P: I think I had some guilty conscience over it down through the years.

A: At that time did you? You said when you got married to your first wife you were a pretty strict guy.

P: Yes, well I guess that might have been one of the things to help discipline me, looking back on it now and talking to you. I had a guilty conscience, yes, either that or I was terrified. At that time I couldn't distinguish between the two. I know I was terrified. *[Both laughing a little.]*

A: [I wonder if you were such a strict person if] [A: Perhaps] this [had] really bothered your conscience a lot?

P: Well, it might have, but . . . ah . . . at 19 what can bother you for long?

A: Well, people are different. *[Both laughing.]* Now tell me, what kind of work did your father do?

P: My father was a man of many trades—he was a plumber and a cook (?) *[mumbling]* *[can't get it]*.

A: Was he a good man?

P: Yeah. He was definitely.

A: A good solid family man?

P: He was a good solid family man—a poor manager, but he did the best he could.

A: His money went for the family?

P: His money went for the family, yes. He didn't have very much for anything else.

A: I mean it didn't go for gambling, drinking, or anything of that sort.

P: He gambled but . . . ah . . . .

A: Much?

P: My dad was [also] a professional gambler—when I say he was a professional gambler, he didn't gamble to gamble as long as he could make a living for himself and his family working, but when the depression came on he was a *[can't get this]* [A: not able to get a job in his line] and where he had been accustomed to . . . ah *[something about stones]* at \$2.75 to \$3.25 an hour, he couldn't reconcile himself to fifty cents or seventy-five cents an hour. So he quit work because he was—his theory was that a man can't both work and gamble. "I will work as long as I can make it working, [MED. ED.: when] I can no longer make it working, I'll gamble," and so he was equally as good a provider while he was gambling professionally as he was when he was working *[can't be sure of this; voice too soft]* [A: correct].

A: That is most unusual. He must have been a smart man also.

P: He was, and I'll say for a man with a limited education he was a smart man.

A: What kind of a personality did he have?

P: It's pretty hard for me to say what kind of a personality my dad had because we weren't close—when I say we weren't close [MED. ED.: I mean] like I am to my daughter. I don't ever remember sitting down to a conversation with my dad. There were orders that came from him and they were obeyed. There were no questions asked. He said, "Do this" and we did it.

A: He was [a pretty] strict [person]?

P: He was strict without your being conscious of the fact he was being strict. He didn't *[something about not using violence]*.

A: He [laid it on the line] told you what to do and it never occurred to you to do it different?

P: Yes, [he laid it on the line].

A: But he was not violent?

P: No, he was fair. When he said something it was to be done.

A: Did he slap you around or beat you up?

P: No.

A: Any of the kids rebel against him?

P: No, never.

A: Nobody rebelled?

P: No.

[A: So he had everybody under control?]

[P: Yes.]

A: What about your mother—what kind of personality?

P: She was sweet and gentle, she had more than her share of troubles down through the years and she never once complained. She has mothered and doctored every child in the community and she is loved for it.

A: She still lives down there?

P: Yes, *[something about her sitting up all night with people]*. She was firm and . . . ah . . . strict as far as right and wrong was concerned. If you strayed from what she said not to do *[cannot get this; something* about she did the disciplining except in extreme cases and then his father did it*]* [A: correct].

A: She did most of the disciplining, is that it? He laid down the laws but she carried them out?

P: Yes.

A: And how would she carry them out?

P: She believed in the rod.

A: She believed in the rod.

P: Yes, she did.

A: What else did she do?

P: That's about it. She didn't cut off privileges because you didn't have too much privileges to begin with—there were the rules and regulations. We were to be in bed by a certain hour, and so to make you go to bed an hour earlier would make you go to bed before dinner. She didn't ever make anybody go to bed before dinner. So . . . ah . . . the greater punishment that she could give out was whipping.

A: Did she do a lot of that?

P: Well, she did if it was necessary *[*can't get this*]* *[*both laughing*]*.

A: If one kid did something bad she would lick them all, would she? [A: Something said made this an appropriate question.]

P: No, she didn't lick them all. I don't think anybody was hardly ever punished unjustly. You might have gotten a licking that you didn't deserve but you made up for it somewhere down the line.

A: How are you about discipline with your own children?

P: I think I am a pretty strict disciplinarian, although I don't never did resort, let's say to corporal punishment. With the girl, as a baby, I discovered the very first time I spanked her that spanking wasn't the way to handle her. She is like myself in that she is stubborn, [but you can't leave them like that]—to an extent she is headstrong *[*can't get this*]* but I've always . . . prevailed upon her to express herself, then I know what she is thinking. As I tell her, I'm not always right, or I may not always be right, you give me your ideas, you see, if you are wrong—be big enough to be corrected, if I'm right—so we have our understanding. That is the thing, as I said, I didn't have, my father—I never knew what he thought except what he told me—[they know my thinking].

A: What kind of a kid were you?

P: I was supposed to be a bad kid, although I can hardly believe it *[*both laughing*]*.

A: Tell me about it.

P: Well, I don't know, when I say I was supposed to be a bad kid *[*something about didn't know how you could consider him a bad kid*]* you always think of people who wind up in reform school, labor farm, or something like that . . . and that never happened to me. But . . . ah . . . I think it was merely because I fought quite a bit. I fought everybody.

A: Quite a scrapper?

P: Yeah, anybody wanted to fight I would fight them, and . . . ah . . . a lot of it came about by the older boys knowing that I was of that temperament—and they'd boast about it—so every day there had to be a fight, and so I fought and I got whipped when I got home, got whipped when I got back to school. So as far as damaging property or stealing or anything like that, I don't ever recall ever having done anything like that, but as far as the community was concerned you were bad.

A: Were you a good enough fighter to lick the boys who were bigger than you?

P: Well, yes, I held my own.

[A: You were a pretty good scrapper.]

A: What were your main hobbies or activities when you were a kid, what did you like to do best—besides fighting?

P: Mmmm, I think I was very active in all sports that we played at the time, but . . . ah . . . when I got old enough to just maybe . . . organized sports—I played football.

A: So you were quite interested in sports?

P: Yes.

A: Tell me about your football history.

P: Well, I played on the high school team and played on the team when I was in CC Camp. I was thought . . . of as being pretty good when I was in high school and respected when I was in Camp.

A: What position did you play?

P: Half and quarter.

A: Did you have any other sports interests?

P: Yes, I played tennis and some baseball, ran track, not much swimming. I like to go in the water but I couldn't swim. We were forbidden to swim. That's where we would kick over the traces and go out to the swimming hole.

A: Why weren't you allowed to swim? A dangerous hole?

P: I don't think it was so much a dangerous hole, it was that my people didn't—sort of had a phobia of kids going near the water, and that was just one of those things they said don't do and we were supposed not to do it.

[A: Did you have any serious illnesses or accidents when you were a kid?]

[P: I had influenza in 1929. That was the only serious illness that I had. I had the usual mumps and measles, things like that, but . . . ah . . .

serious, no. I had an accident. Well, in training football my shoulders and sides were injured—I don't know how severely. I played with them taped up week after week—after the first game they had to be taped every week after that, and . . . ah . . . other than that I didn't have any serious injuries.]

[A: Any accidents?]

P: I had an automobile accident in 1954, but . . . .

A: A bad one?

P: As far as the car was concerned, yes—I didn't get shook too bad—I didn't get any broken bones or anything like that.

A: Was anybody else injured?

P: No—there were some other people in the bus [A: i.e., injured].

A: You hit him or he hit you?

P: He hit me and I hope the court sees it that way *[laughs]*.

A: It is still in litigation, is it?

P: Yes, it is still in litigation *[mumbling]*. I am sure I suffered some emotional shock, but how much I am not able to say.

A: This is the only accident you had?

P: Yes, the only accident.

A: Have you been a more jittery driver since then?

P: Well, for a time, yes, but . . . ah . . . as I say, there was an aftermath of say maybe six to eight months, period of . . . sort of a welling up inside when some individual races up to a corner, and I know he has to stop, the light is green and he races up to the corner, and slams on his brakes. I get irritated to see an individual do that, and I know it stems from the accident that I had because I didn't have that feeling before. It bothers me less and less as time goes on.

A: Was it a head-on collision?

P: He hit me on the side.

A: On the side.

P: I was traveling south and he was traveling west.

A: Did he go through a light?

P: He went through a red light.

A: So he must have hit you on the side where you were driving.

P: Yes.

[A: Didn't do any injury to you?]

[P: Well, no broken bones or anything like that.]

[A: It would show up on X-ray. Have you had any illnesses or operations as an adult?]

[P: No.]

A: Have you kept up any of your sports activities as an adult?

P: No, only spectator.

A: You haven't done anything of that sort since you were in high school, is that it?
P: I have done some since I was in high school.
A: What did you do?
P: I played football in service *[mumbling]*.
A: You played football in service. But you haven't done any athletics since you came out of the service?
P: No, not since I came out of the service.
A: What do you do for exercise or activity?
P: My work.
A: Your work takes care of that, does it?
P: Yes—after you work, you are just a spectator, not much room for activity *[can't get this]*.
A: Before [this started to get bad] [MED. ED.: period of disease discovery or exacerbation] was there any reduction in the amount of your activity?
P: . . . Ah, how do you mean that?
A: Were you on a less strenuous job or did you drop out any activity of any sort?
P: No . . . ah . . . I carried on my work.
A: Your work has been about the same all the time.
P: About the same. I will say this, there was a lessening, yes, because I did a lot of little things extra . . . it isn't actually a hobby with me, making window screens, repairing the window frames and things like that, well I cut that down to the bare minimum because it was an overload [even if this condition hadn't been developing, I would have]. I had decided to cut it down. I was overloaded, and so . . . .
A: Did you cut it down *before* [this started? Do you recall?] [MED. ED.: period of disease discovery or exacerbation?]
P: Yes, I am sure I had started cutting down [when you say before this started,] do you mean [*before*] [the present siege?]
A: It's about two years since [you feel pretty sure this was underway] [MED. ED.: period of disease discovery or exacerbation] isn't that right?
P: I had started cutting it down before then.
A: You had started cutting down—is there anything else you had cut down before that? Any other activities you had eliminated or reduced?
P: No, not consciously.
A: So that there has not been any particular change in your physical activity?
P: No.

A: How did you happen to get into the line of work that you're in? Would you do it over again?

P: I should say not [both laughing]. No, well if I didn't know any more then than I know now I would do it over again . . . if I had the benefit of my present experience, I wouldn't do it over again, and I advised my son against doing it. My wife's uncle—we roomed with him when we were married—and he was in this kind of work, and . . . ah . . . to supplement my earnings I did little jobs for him.

A: This is your first wife?

P: Yes, and from that I got interested in the money and handy in the work.

A: It is pretty well paid, is it?

P: It is as far as I am concerned, and then when the opportunity came to get the building on my own—but would I do it again, no.

A: Why not?

P: Well . . . ah . . . frankly I think it's too hard and . . . ah . . . it . . . when you get in it, it is next to impossible to get out of it—when I say next to impossible to get out of it—it takes a lot of willpower to get out of it; once you get in it and get a family, something like that, well it's pretty hard to break away from it. [My doctor has told me that I should change my work.]

[A: I was wondering about that.]

[P: I have every intention to change it but to what? And when? I mean—if tomorrow you felt you couldn't do it anymore, you would probably resign yourself to the fact that you're out, but] as I said, my daughter is in college—she is in her third year of college.

A: Where is she going to school?

P: She is going to [X college], and as long as she wants to go to school . . . whether it's right or wrong, I feel like I owe it to her to send her, and . . . ah . . . I can't very well change jobs and do it—what job could I change to, with say a limited amount of skill, that would—I don't think pay equal to what I am earning now—but pay enough for me to send her to school and live . . . ah . . . somewhat in the manner I have accustomed myself—you face this problem.

A: I can see it's a problem. Incidentally, what is your daughter studying?

P: Psychology. [And . . . ah . . . when I was advised by my doctor to change the work, I . . . ah . . . said the best thing for me to do is to go to school and take up a trade, but I know enough about myself to know I don't have the energy or I didn't have the energy, say a year ago, to carry on my work and to go to school. I needed the rest because I got terribly tired, and after doing my work, I needed the rest, I probably wouldn't have been able to make it to school anyway. I feel if the condition has improved maybe I will be able to start a course, in the hopes that I can change, but as I say the pay is good and it isn't easy to change.] [MED. ED.: Patient talks of perhaps he should go to school.]

A: You feel very strongly that you owe it to your daughter to send her to college. Can you tell me any other things about your personality that may be along that line? After all nobody sent you to college, did they?

P: No, nobody sent me to college, but I accept the fact that my people did the very best that they could do by me . . . and . . . ah . . . I could have done better by myself than I did.

A: You think you could have?

P: I know I could have. I could have done better by myself than I did, except that . . . ah . . . let's say at 19 or even at 22 . . . who thinks constructively who hasn't been conditioned or trained to think constructively, so I feel that if I haven't trained or conditioned my children to think constructively now, then it's up to me to advise them, even to prod them to . . . ah . . . go on and do better by themselves with or without my help than I did by myself.

A: You understand I thoroughly approve, don't you?

P: I understand.

A: I only wanted to know if there were any other aspects of your personality that might be similar to this. Do you see what I mean?

[P: Yes.]

[A: Can you tell me any other aspects of your personality. You seem to be very conscious about this, and I wondered if you could tell me any other things about yourself along the same lines.]

P: [MED. ED.: Yes.] I don't know anything that I believe in . . . [MED. ED.: more] strongly . . . education for children, for people in general, I think is . . . ah, our salvation and for my people in particular. I feel very strongly about that. That may be the extent of it.

A: You don't sound like a man whose education had ended when he graduated from high school, what have you been doing since?

P: My education didn't end, my formal education did.

A: What do you do? Do you read? Have you taken any more—do you get interested in community activities? What sort of things do you do now?

P: . . . I read mostly . . . I take no active part in the community.

A: You have no active part in the community?

P: No. I do read and I'll get up on a soapbox—in a minute.

A: Oh, really [*both laughing slightly*].

P: I mean people that . . . won't listen or won't discuss . . . [do understand], and when I say that I mean the paperboy, when the paperboy comes around and says, "Well, I graduate from high school in June, what are you going to give me?" Well, I'm going to give you a half dozen shirts when you get ready to go to college. Then we'll talk about his going to college, whether he wants to go or not, about whether he should go, or something like that. If I find an individual that lays himself open I'll lecture him about it *[can't be sure; he is speaking too softly]*. [A: generally correct.]

A: You try to guide people in ways that you think will be to their benefit?

P: Yes, I do. I am and have been called on quite a bit—say marriage difficulties *[can't get this]*. [A: i.e., people come to him for their troubles] in spite of the fact that I talk a lot, I am also a good listener. I try to guide them in my way, to do right.

[A: You mean if somebody is worried about a friend of theirs is having a tough time in their marriage they'll ask you, will you talk with them, is that it? Tell me more.]

P: Maybe an individual is having a tough time in his marriage, will call me or come by and talk . . . there are a number of people who do that —they seem to get a certain amount of relief out of it.

[A: Do they think of it that you are a helpful person, is that it?]

[P: I think they do.]

[A: Are there any other ways in which people regard you as a helpful person?] [A: Anything else?]

P: Well . . . I can't really think of any, except that someone will come by to borrow money from me *[laughing]*.

A: You spoke of your mother doing so much for so many people, do you remember?

P: Yes.

A: I wondered if you were like your mother [in any way].

P: Yes, in a sense, except that . . . ah . . . my mother drew no line. If you needed help, you got it . . . I do [A: i.e., draw a line] . . . I don't figure it's right to set myself up as a . . . judge as to whether or not they need help. I don't mean when an individual is sick or something like that, but say they wanted . . . needed a hand-out and I know they used money that they should have saved . . . no. But with her, regardless of why you needed help, what your circumstances were, you got it. She would help.

A: So she would help anybody about anything.

P: . . . About anything and I'm discriminating.

A: How was your father about these things?

P: My father, as far as I know, never—he would help when he had time. My father was very busy, and he didn't have so much time to help, but . . . ah . . . he did whatever he could do and he'd sanctioned Mom in whatever she did.

A: Which one of the parents do you most take after?

P: . . . I would rather say my father . . . as much as I know about him. I would rather say after him.

A: You think you are probably more like him.

P: More like him yes. A certain tenderness, I think, might come from my mother; the ability to control it *[can't get this]*. [A: I think he said this was like his father.]

A: Do you think you were in any way more unhappy about not being closer to your father than the other kids were?

P: No . . . I don't think it bothered me at all. I didn't really realize that I wasn't close to him until . . . ah . . . I had become a father myself.

A: That's when you began to be aware of it.

P: Began to be aware that . . . ah . . . my baby is just a baby. She enjoyed my being there. She seemed to be happy when I was around. She wanted to show me off—"This is my daddy," and I enjoyed it. Then I thought how much my father must have missed in not having me and the other kids do these same things where he was concerned. So . . . because it was a broken home the least that I could do was to try to keep the relationship as close and as warm as I can so that my child don't suffer more emotional scars than is absolutely necessary, and so . . . down through the years I kept the relationship close.

A: You got full cooperation from your ex-wife in that too?

P: Yes.

A: Has she been a good mother to the girl?

P: Yes, she has.

A: Your daughter has done pretty well apparently?

P: Yes, she has.

A: Incidentally, what church did your family belong to?

P: It was split—my father was a Methodist and my mother a Baptist.

A: Were they both good churchgoers, strong church people?

P: They had strong convictions about the church. There was naturally a period when my mother couldn't attend church as much as she wanted to because of the children—my father attended church as much as he could. They both attended church more than I did.

A: Did they bring up you kids to be good churchgoers?

P: Yes, they did.

A: But you are not too strong a churchgoer now?

P: No, I'm not.

A: What's happened?

P: I don't know . . . . Once upon a time I analyzed my—let's call it antagonism—for want of a better word—for the church, but later years I decided that I was looking for excuses . . . and I could find them if I wanted to . . . but . . . ah . . . in spite of my being able to see this thing in myself I still didn't go to church. Once you've started missing, it's easy to miss.

A: Church is not that important to you now? At the time that you [were so strict, that you] made so much difficulty with your wife about things like smoking and drinking and so on, was that based on strict church adherence then, or was it . . . ? *[patient talks]*

P: It wasn't.

A: It was outside of the church?

P: It was outside of the church, because at that time I had begun to develop this . . . ah . . . antagonism—not to the church because I am very much in favor of the church—and I'm possibly more religious than my expressions here might lead you to believe. I mean I have strong convictions where religion is concerned, but as far as the active participation in the church is concerned, well I'm just negligent along those lines, but my feelings run deep. . . . But I have had some experiences that . . . ah . . . that stamp themselves sort of indelible on my mind . . . and it took me quite a while to erase them. If I ever erased them. For instance . . . in the community there wasn't very much to do . . . so the fellows got together and organized a choral club and we practiced—one of the teachers in the town we knew worked with us, and so we got the group going and then . . . ah . . . we decided that we were going to give a concert. We went to my church, our parish, and I had . . . all the faith in the world in the reverend . . . to me he was my idea of the man of God. This is the thing that maybe ——he didn't do it—I built it up myself. I learned later that I have a knack of putting people on a pedestal where they didn't belong, but . . . ah . . . when we went to him, he consented to let us have the concert in his church, and then two days before we were to sing, he called us—asked us if all the boys belong to church . . . and he said, "You can't sing in my pulpit unless you all belong to church." I argued that the only two boys in the club that didn't belong to church had already sung in his pulpit. They came to the town from another little town with a quartet, and they had already sung in this church, "Why then would you examine us, and you didn't examine these fellows that came from out of town?" But . . . he was unyielding . . . it destroyed something in me.

A: I don't wonder, yes.

P: So then the . . . ah . . . the Methodist pastor came to us and told us that we could give our concert in his church, and he didn't care if any of us belonged to church, but my roots were in the Baptist church, and if I had been a more yielding person I might have turned to the

Methodist [and been saved but] . . . instead of that I just rebelled against the Baptist church and started to drift, and then when I went in service, I went to church with a boy one Sunday morning that wanted to join . . . the second best church in Los Angeles . . . and they told him to come back the next week—they would vote on him. I just couldn't understand why they should have to vote in order for him to get into church, and so from there—little things like that . . . .

A: [I think I agree with you.] I want to ask you about your brothers and sisters. On the whole have your brothers and sisters done pretty well?

P: Yes, they have.

A: Are they all good solid citizens like you?

P: Well, thanks *[slight laugh]* I think they are. There are some that are less strict, that is they don't . . . ah . . . discipline themselves as much as I do.

A: How have they done in general about jobs, marriages, and so on, have they been pretty stable workers and fairly successfully married and so forth? They are responsible people?

P: They are responsible people.

A: Have any of them been very successful?

P: . . . Well . . . I don't know how to answer that. Ah . . . I don't know who you would say is the most successful. What would you . . . ah . . . ?

A: Oh, I would think of somebody who was a well-known doctor or lawyer? A public official? Something of that sort?

P: I have a brother who works in the City Hall in my home town but he's not an elected official. I have one that teaches school. This one here has his own business. The one in Los Angeles is *[can't get this]*.

A: A what?

P: *[Can't get this.]* He's a bartender. *[Both laughing.]*

A: That's a new term.

P: That's what he told me.

A: Very good.

P: He's tops in the field. When they opened a well-known nightclub in Los Angeles, he was one of the bartenders who was selected to open it.

A: Does it bother you to have a brother who is a bartender?

P: No, it doesn't bother me, except *[word or two missing]* that "if you want to sit up all night to drink and pay 55c for . . . ah . . . grenadine, I can make them for you."

A: You don't drink?

P: I do drink some now. At that time I didn't drink anything at all. *[Something about the time when he didn't drink and thought everybody who did drink should be penalized.]*

A: Incidentally, the ones that were close to you in age, who was just older than you—a brother or sister?
P: A brother.
A: A brother just older, and what about just next to you—younger?
P: A brother.
A: So that you were in between two boys. Maybe I had better get the order. You say the oldest was a boy?
P: That's right.
A: Next one?
P: A girl.
A: Next one?
P: A boy.
A: Next?
P: A girl, three girls.
A: Three girls, two in a row. Then?
P: Boys.
A: Then boys all the rest of the way?
P: Right.
A: Where was the sister that died?
P: The sister that died was the third.
A: Third sister or the third child?
P: The third sister. *[Can't get this; fifth child?]*
A: Did you kids have a lot of scrapping between you as kids do between brothers and sisters?
P: Yeah we did our amount of scrapping, nothing ever serious. We scrapped.
[A: But you don't think it ever got too far out of line?]
[P: . . . Well, I didn't think it was too far out of line.]
A: Did you get very jealous of each other?
P: No, never, I don't think it ever stemmed from jealousy.
A: I'd like to ask you a few questions about sex. What was your first knowledge of sex when you were a child—or did you have any sexual experiences as a child?
P: . . . Ah . . . I don't know what to say—I don't follow you.
A: Lots of small kids do lots of sexual things, they talk or play sexually with each other, things of that sort.
P: No . . . my first . . . my first knowledge . . . of sex came . . . from one of these discussions . . . lectures that they give in the schools in the spring. I was probably 17 at that time . . . and I was too busy . . . as I say I was a boy until I got to be a man.
A: You certainly must have known something about sex before that?

P: I knew there was a difference between boys and girls but I didn't know what it was. My first encounter with sex was when I was 19.
A: That was when you first had sexual activity?
P: Yes.
A: When did you start having wet dreams? Start masturbating?
P: I never masturbated, and I don't think I ever had any wet dreams until after I was . . . ah . . . oh I must have been 20 or 21.
A: That is rather unusual. Do you think you were pretty scared of sex?
P: No . . . it just never . . . it was just one of the things that was never discussed . . . at home.
A: In a gang of boys?
P: Well . . . now that's another thing . . . I didn't associate with the boys around the alleys.
A: I mean with your brothers.
P: My brothers didn't. We never discussed it.
A: That's very interesting. What happened that you got involved sexually at 19?
P: . . . Well, I was asked to do it.
A: By the girl?
P: I mean it developed to the point where there wasn't anything else . . . . she had been my girl friend for nearly three years.
A: This isn't the one you got pregnant?
P: Yes.
A: This *is* the one you got pregnant.
P: Yes. That was my first experience, and as I say she had been my girl friend for nearly three years—it was somebody I loved in my way.
A: You hadn't made any passes at her?
P: No, because I felt very strongly about her. I felt that nobody should touch her, nobody should do anything wrong where she was concerned and I think I felt at that time that I might kill anybody that did. I didn't think of doing anything wrong where she was concerned, and I couldn't conceive of anybody else doing it. So I guess my being strict went even further back than . . . ah . . . I had told you before.
A: Is this the first girl you went out with much?
P: Yes.
A: The first one you went out with at all?
P: Yes. The first one I went out with.
A: And you had been going with her several years at the time that you began having intercourse with her?
P: Yes.
A: Did this keep up over a period of time?
P: No, it only happened twice and that was it.

A: She asked you?

P: Yes.

A: That's probably why she took the attitude that you weren't responsible, is that right?

P: It's possible if that's the attitude she took [laughs slightly].

A: You said she said she wasn't going to have any forced marriage.

P: I don't think that it was out of . . . I don't think it was a feeling of lack of responsibility on her part for me . . . I think it was . . . she felt that here is . . . ah . . . a good student that shouldn't have his education cut off, and if he doesn't have to marry then he will go on to amount to something and I'll benefit by it later. If she thought anything about herself at all, well she just didn't think that I should, say, get saddled in marriage at this point. I think she loved me too.

A: That was a very decent attitude.

P: Yes, but it's pretty rough for one individual to take [can't get this].

A: But she meant well anyway. What did you do for sex in between that and your getting married?

P: Well . . . I . . . ah . . . had an older woman friend that . . . ah . . . took advantage of—when I say took advantage—she was taking advantage of—I made a statement that I wasn't touching anybody any more until I married, and this . . . two of the boys, I guess, and it got back to this woman, one of the teachers, and . . . ah . . . she called me in and lectured me on this—one of the hazards of life, and you can't close yourself up and what-have-you. I think it started out as one of those "Tea and Sympathy" things, and turned out just like "Tea and Sympathy" and so . . . that relationship lasted maybe a year or longer. Then I went to CC Camp. I had no sexual relationship for the next 22 months, then I came to Chicago and it . . . ah . . . started all over again.

A: With whom this time? With this same woman, you mean?

P: No.

A: With somebody else, other than your first wife?

P: That's right.

A: Was it again someone who took the initiative with you?

P: Yes, it was.

A: Has this been pretty generally a pattern?

P: It has, down through the years.

A: Have you ever taken the initiative with anyone?

P: I'm sure I have . . . yeah, I'm sure I have, but as a rule . . . .

A: In general it's the other way around?

P: In general it's the other way around.

A: After you were married—how about then?

P: Well . . . when I married, I don't fool around.
A: No, I meant when you were married—did you take the initiative then?
P: Yes, indeed.
A: Were you quite actively sexual?
P: Yes.
A: Did you have any conflicts about it or any difficulties?
P: No . . . ah . . . no, not to my . . . knowledge, that is . . . I mean as far as my first wife was concerned, I had to assume that everything was going all right because, as I said, I was boss and that's all there was to it. With my second wife, I had no control *[not sure of this]* . . . she was not too warm or affectionate.
A: Did either of them make any complaints about you sexually?
P: No.
A: They didn't say that you weren't aggressive enough or that you couldn't hold off long enough or anything of that sort?
P: No.
A: You didn't have any troubles of that kind?
P: No.
A: Incidentally do you like it better on top or on the bottom?
P: Well . . . ah . . . I haven't found *[can't get this; something about trying it both ways and not knowing which he prefers]*. [A: Probably indicates not having much preference.]
A: You have done it both ways?
P: Yeah.
A: And you don't have any preference?
P: No.
A: Did you ever have anything to do with boys sexually?
P: No.
A: Did you ever get worried about it?
P: No.
A: Did anybody ever approach you?
P: Yes, I have been approached, not until I was . . . grown and in the Navy. I was approached on the street . . . I passed it off as lightly as I could. In most cases I passed it off lightly. There have been . . . a couple of cases wherein I was sort of violent with him, and expressed myself.
A: You got angry or anxious?
P: I got angry.
A: You got angry?
P: Angry.
A: Since you broke up with your wife this last time, your second wife, what have you been doing since then?

P: Well, I have had girl friends.

A: Do you like any of them particularly well?

P: Yes . . . I have liked a couple of them.

A: So that you are more comfortable about sex now than when you first started out?

P: Yes, I am. If I *was* uncomfortable when I started out.

A: It sounds like it because you were so upset about this first girl.

P: Well it wasn't . . . I don't think it was so much upset, [A: i.e., about sex] it was upset about . . . ah . . . what happened. I mean the second time that you are out with her.

A: You mean the second time you slept with her?

P: That's right.

A: What I had in mind was this, you didn't want to have anything to do with the boys that talked about sex, you said you didn't masturbate as a boy, and you had the wish not to do anything with a girl sexually until you got married. Usually boys who adhere to those ideas are rather uncomfortable when they do start having sex.

P: No, I think that wish came . . . born of fear. To have this thing happen, it was born of fear. It was fear of having this thing happen again rather than fear of having intercourse.

A: So you think when you made up your mind to it you didn't have any trouble?

P: No.

A: It was okay with you once you made up your mind. Incidentally, after you were in the CC Camp or in the Navy, didn't you masturbate then?

P: No.

A: You never masturbated?

P: No.

A: Do you have any idea why? You must know that most of the men do.

P: No . . . I . . . ah . . . it was amazing to me to hear that statement even when I was a boy, it is equally as amazing now. I mean . . . ah . . . the first time I heard the word masturbation was when I was being accused of doing it. I reacted violently.

A: When was that?

P: This was in . . . ah . . . high school, as I say I was about 16 or 17 when we had one of these discussions, and . . . ah . . . I really didn't know what the word meant, and when I was . . . when it was defined . . . I knew that I wasn't guilty, and so down through the years . . . .

A: Do you think your mother would have been very opposed to something like this? Do you think that's where you would have gotten it? Or your father?

P: As far as I knew they never talked about it. The thing about it—we were raised in a pattern where you don't have to put your finger on everything that you were supposed to do or everything that you were not supposed to do . . . I think that it's just the atmosphere that exists in the home channels you're thinking . . . .

A: Very good way of putting it. Do you think of anything important that I haven't asked you about? Any important events of your life?

P: No . . . I don't think . . . .

A: Something may come to you. I have a list of routine questions that I have to go through. There may be some overlapping of things we've talked about so don't be surprised. What is your first memory?

P: . . . I don't know what my very first memory is because up until then . . . ah . . . say 1925, I had a memory of complete recall, as near complete recall as one could possibly have.

A: Is that so? Not back until you were six months old, did you? [Both laughing.] How far back did you remember?

P: I can remember quite a ways back—to point it to a year, I can't very well do that. I do know that before I started to school I could read, write, and I knew all of the . . . poems.

A: Is that so?

P: . . . Yeah.

A: Could you tell me what might seem to be one of your earliest memories?

P: No, I can't say [something about anything important enough].

A: It doesn't have to be important.

P: If an incident was brought up—I mean that happened, way back when, I would doubtless remember it, because, as I said, I do remember . . . quite in detail, so many things that happened when I'm sure I had to be quite young.

A: You say you read before you went to school?

P: Yes.

A: Incidentally, did you think of going to college?

P: . . . I don't think I ever thought seriously of going to college.

A: Would you have wanted to?

P: I would have wanted to but I felt that when . . . ah . . . you see the family came up in sort of a pattern—my brother before me graduated from high school and went to CC Camp. When I graduated from high school he was out of the camp, and I felt that, without being told, "It's your turn now." We graduated from one job into another: you wash dishes until you are so old, then the boy behind me did it, and so we just went that way in sort of a pattern, and before graduating from high school, I suppose that I felt: "Now it's my turn to take over and help the family."

A: But supposing you could have gone to college, supposing you hadn't been brought up in this kind of a pattern, what do you think you would have liked to have gone into?

P: I was always . . . I mean someone would ask me: What are you going to be when you grow up? I would say—a doctor.

A: So you would have liked to be a doctor?

P: I think I would have liked to. My ambitions as a child, without knowing anything about what was required or not, I felt then that I would have liked to have been a doctor.

A: It didn't occur to you really to try to do this for yourself, did it?

P: No . . . ah . . . .

A: You were too routinized in your pattern.

P: Too routinized, yeah—you think of first things first—and now it's your time to take care of the family so you go out and do it.

A: I forgot to ask you about dreams. Do you dream much?

P: . . . Mmmm . . . not much but occasionally.

A: Can you tell me any dreams from recently?

P: Mmmm . . . .

A: Can you remember any nightmare that you had as a child?

P: I had nightmares all the time as a child.

A: Could you tell me what they were?

P: They were of attack—I was being attacked from all sides.

A: Oh, really. By what?

P: By . . . ah . . . ghosts or bigger boys with knives or something like that.

A: Mostly they were dreams of being attacked.

P: Dreams of being attacked, yes. I used to . . . react . . . violently, I would say, in that I would wake up screaming.

A: You say you had quite a few of those?

P: Yes, quite a few.

A: Would you say when they dropped off?

P: I guess I just sort of grew out of them.

A: Grew out of them. Do you remember any dreams since you're grown up?

P: No, I don't remember any dreams since I've grown up, although, like I said, I do have them and then maybe the next morning . . . if I don't relate them to somebody—they've just passed.

A: Have you ever been in the position of bossing anyone—having somebody working under you?

P: Well . . . yes. When I was in the CC Camp and . . . ah . . . in the navy.

A: Let's say you were a boss, you had somebody, people working under you, and so and so wasn't doing what he ought to do, would you show him how, would you do it yourself, or would you fire him?

P: I think first I would . . . ah . . . tell him . . . probably . . . what was expected of him. I would also make it plain to him that I intended to have him do it if he stayed there and failing to do it I'd fire him, but sure I would give him a chance.

A: Give him a warning.

P: Yeah, give him warning. I had a case . . . now that I think about it . . . when I was in the navy . . . like that. I was storekeeper in charge of the *[can't get it]* and I had . . . ah . . . several *[can't get it]* working under me. One that . . . ah . . . with your liaison—you told him what you wanted done *[speaking too low, cannot understand him]* he contacted the other *[one word I cannot get]* [A: if he didn't want to do it] and gave him the work. Well it dawned upon me that this boy would be passing out all of the work, he wasn't doing anything. I'm doing my share of the work, he isn't doing anything, and . . . ah . . . not because I'm not doing my share of the work but because he isn't doing his share of the work. I had him to stay one evening after work hours and I told him that . . . ah . . . there was so much work to be done—Joey was good and the material was good but you and he have to do some work too. Now I notice whenever I give you work you pass it down to *[can't get name]* or one of the girls or something like that to do it. When I give you something and say: "Give this to Joey and have him type it up," I mean I want Joey to type it up, when I say, "Sammy, type this up," I mean Sammy type it up. He wanted to know if there was anything personal in it and I let him know—"No, it is nothing personal in it because if I had anything personal against you, I would have had you locked up when I saw you stealing those shoes out there."

A: That's a good answer. You know everybody gets antagonistic about this and that, could you point out any significant differences between how you would react when you were mad about something? When you were a small child? When you were an adolescent?

P: I think the . . . ah . . . reaction down through the years has been more or less the same—anger—quit the anger—more apt to do something about it, maybe scream or spit as a child and as a boy, and try to control it as a man.

A: You get pretty angry?

P: Ah huh.

A: Do you cry?

P: Very . . . very seldom.

A: Under what circumstances would you?

P: To become emotionally upset, I think . . . ah . . . in family relationships is about the only thing I can recall I might cry.

A: Would you in connection with a death, for instance?

P: . . . Ah . . . maybe, depending on the individual. If it was my mother, my father, yes, but outside of that, probably not.

A: Would you be more likely to cry alone or if somebody were there?

P: Well, when I cry it doesn't matter who is around.

A: It would be a matter of your feeling.

P: It might be.

A: How was your mother about you children crying, how did she act about it?

P: Well if you cried too long, she *[I think he said she let you cry]*.

A: She wasn't too impatient about it?

P: No, not too impatient about it.

A: Incidentally I didn't ask you what your mother died from?

P: My mother is living.

A: Excuse me, I meant your father.

P: My father died as the result of an automobile accident. Now, he wasn't killed in the accident, but he was injured—he was thrown against the windshield, and he had a blood clot or something in this area [points] that moved back *[something about three or four years]*.

A: He was how old when he died?

P: Fifty-four.

A: Did you feel real bad about that?

P: Well . . . ah . . . I felt bad, I mean to the extent that I had lost a good father.

A: Had he been pretty crippled by the accident?

P: No, he had been active.

A: Oh, he had been able to be active?

P: Yes.

A: What sort of scene in the movies would upset you? *[Patient interrupts]*

P: That would depend on my emotional condition at the time. I go to the movies to be entertained, and I select the type of movie I like to see. I don't go to see depressing movies—if *I* have the choice. I don't go to see "I'll Cry Tomorrow," something like that. I select lighter movies that . . . ah . . . well. . . .

A: Let's say you made a mistake, one that wasn't so light. What kind of thing do you think would upset you in the movies?

P: Well, that again would depend on the . . . ah . . . my emotional state, for instance, if I was in any sort of trouble and saw a picture that sort of paralleled the thing I was going through I think it might upset me. Something like "King's Row," for instance that would disturb me, a brutal way of punishing sin where you'd find it—was sort of brought out, that would upset me. I've always felt like that . . . no man should be judge and jury unless *[can't get this]*. *[Both laughing.]*

A: How are you about clothes?

P: Clothes—my taste in clothes has changed right down through the years. At 22, I wore nothing but shirts and ties—no sport clothes in my wardrobe at all, and . . . ah . . . but as the years go by I find my wardrobe varies so much so that you can't type me by the clothes I wear.

A: You are more interested in sport clothes now, is that what you mean? You were more formal then?

P: Yes, I was more formal then in every respect, but now I realize that sport clothes are more comfortable.

A: Have you ever been flashy about clothes?

P: No, I wouldn't say I have been flashy although . . . ah . . . I have worn and do have some flashy clothes now—that's because . . . ah . . . with my children growing up . . . they think that Daddy should have an Ivy League suit so Daddy wears an Ivy League suit.

A: But spontaneously, I take it, you like to be neat and well dressed, is that it?

P: Yes.

A: And fairly conservatively, is that it?

P: Right, ah huh.

A: How do you feel about public speaking?

P: I don't quite follow that question.

A: Would you give a speech in public? Would you get panicky about it? Would you refuse to do it? Have you ever been in a play—things like that, performing in public is what I was wondering about.

P: Yes, I have performed in public, that is, in a dramatic club.

A: Recent years or when you were young?

P: When I was young and then . . . ah . . . I have given a speech, say in recent years, I'll admit that before the end it gets uncomfortable.

A: You get a little worried about it.

P: Mmmm, a little uncomfortable.

A: What kind of things have you given speeches about?

P: This was a banquet when my son was . . . ah . . . was through . . . ah . . . this was a testimonial dinner given my son after he had completed his course in decorating. I gave a little speech—I felt a little welling up—I guess you'd call it sort of fear or something like that.

A: What kind of decorating—interior decorating?

P: Interior decorating.

A: Does he show promise?

P: Yes, he does. He was quite good for the time that he did it. I was trying to encourage him, am trying to encourage him to go on and get off the ladders. [A: I think there is some mistake here] you know *[can't get last two words]*.

A: Do you blush easily?

P: . . . No, except that it . . . ah . . . makes *you* more comfortable.

A: How do you mean?

P: I don't blush for my own . . . relief, but if it will make the other individual . . . .

A: Oh, you blush for the other fellow.

P: If it makes you more comfortable.

A: That's interesting.

A: How are you about pets? Do you like pets or not?

P: Now I am *[can't get word]* [A: unaffected] as far as pets are concerned, we always had them—we always had two or three dogs . . . . I don't suppose I liked them any better than they liked me. They didn't, but I . . . ah . . . tolerated them, and . . . ah . . . since I have been . . . ah . . . grown . . . I haven't had any, and sometimes in the work that I'm in I have an antagonism towards pets, not as such, but the manner in which they are handled by the individuals that have them.

A: They are awful nuisances in city buildings.

P: That's what I mean.

A: But spontaneously you would have liked pets?

P: Yeah.

A: You were used to them as a child? How are you about money? You already told us you are good about saving money.

P: *[Mumbling something and laughing slightly.]*

A: Aren't you any more?

P: Don't seem to be able to save it any more somehow.

A: How are you about spending? Do you have a hard time spending or on occasion spend with a fair amount of comfort?

P: I spend almost always with a fair amount of comfort but . . . ah . . . I'm always mindful of what I spend . . . that is, when I spend something, I don't regret it.

A: You are conservative about spending it?

P: If I don't think I can afford it, I don't think it's worth the money, I don't spend it.

A: How are you about giving money away?

P: I wish I was tight but I'm not. That's one of my difficulties.

A: Whom do you give money to and what?

P: Almost anybody that asks for it.
A: Do you lend them money or give it to them or what?
P: Yeah, I loan money and in instances where you are almost sure you won't get it back.
A: You don't try to get it back?
P: Don't try to get it back by helping this friend . . . .
A: I mean if you lend somebody some money and figure he ought to pay you back, is going to and then he doesn't, do you ask him or do you let it alone?
P: I let it alone. Yes, I let it alone more or less.
A: This is something of a problem then, is it?
P: Yes, it is a problem.
A: Did you have any feeding difficulties when you were a child?
P: Feeding difficulties?
A: Were you a finicky eater?
P: No.
A: Any eating disturbances?
P: The only thing I couldn't eat was fresh pork—I could never eat it. *[I simply cannot get this; something about: I liked it but it didn't like me.]* [A: correct.]
A: That's interesting. Do you know anything about your toilet training? Did you have any trouble along that line? Do you know how old you were when you were completely trained?
P: No, I don't but . . . ah . . . I'm sure my mother didn't have any trouble.
A: She didn't waste any time?
P: She didn't waste any time either.
A: How important is appearance to you?
P: It's very important.
A: How about the appearance of other people—how important is that?
P: Well, it's rather important if I had any relation with them.
A: What do you do if you are afraid?
P: Why I really don't know. . . . When you say what do I do if I'm afraid —I must say I can't pinpoint what you mean there.
A: Let's say if you get frightened.
P: I react calmly until . . . ah . . . the situation is taken care of, then I may faint.
A: You are calm until everything is taken care of? In a dangerous situation is it fight or flee?
P: I would fight, I think.
A: Supposing somebody held you up?

P: Supposing somebody held me up—I've never had the experience, I think I would more or less obey.
A: You're not that much of a fighter—you are not foolish?
P: No, I'm not foolish.
A: Do you consider yourself brave?
P: Well . . . ah . . . I consider myself brave, yes, to an extent. I tremble in the face of fear, I recognize danger as such, but . . . ah . . . I think I'm brave in that I would try to . . . ah . . . ah . . . take control or command of the situation . . . ah . . . even after some risk to my own safety, if it was necessary but I wouldn't do it foolhardily.
A: If the situation calls for bravery you can pull yourself together and mobilize this.
P: Yes.
A: In either of your marriages did you have extra-marital affairs?
P: No.
A: Have you been holding out on anything?
P: Well . . . I don't know *[both laughing]*.
A: You don't think so.
P: I don't know if I understand the question.
A: You know sometimes people think—well I'd rather not answer that.
P: No, I think that I've answered as freely as I know how.
A: There hasn't been something that you haven't wanted to answer?
P: No.
A: Are you inclined to confide in people a lot?
P: *[Can't get one word.]* [A: idea is: certain] people.
A: What people would you confide in?
P: Well, I pick my people, as I said, for instance my sister-in-law, my brother's wife, down through the years I've leaned quite heavily on her, not as much so in the late years, and then . . . ah . . . another relative that sort of married in the family—I talk with and this friend I spoke of in Phoenix I confide, say wholeheartedly, in him.
A: How about with your mother? Did you confide in her?
P: I confided in my mother when I was at home, yes, I felt completely free to talk to her about anything.
A: If you did something bad would you go and confess it to her?
P: No, if she found it out I would confess, but I wouldn't just go and . . . .
A: But you wouldn't volunteer?
P: No.
A: If you could have three wishes satisfied, what would they be?
P: If I could have three wishes satisfied. I would have to study on those. Wishes are important things.

A: You take it pretty seriously?
P: I wouldn't wish for [something] /both talking/ [A: just anything].
A: You couldn't say anything off the top of your head about it?
P: No.
A: How do you feel about people dying?
P: Well . . . ah . . . I feel . . . strongly about people that . . . ah . . . are able to contribute to the well-being of other people—pretty strongly about dying. Now people in general I don't feel too strongly about them dying, except that they are young. Doctors—when I read about a doctor dying, it upsets me. Even though I know they are human like the rest of us, it seems—here is a man, an individual that can do or could do, and has done so much good for so many people, yet he has to die too. But just an ordinary individual that dies—just take it as a course of life.
A: How do you feel about dead bodies?
P: I have no fear.
A: You have no fear of that. You go to funeral parlors when a friend dies and so on?
P: Yes, as a matter of fact I helped do an autopsy once.
A: You did and even that didn't bother you?
P: No.
A: Was there any significant death connected with your illness coming on? Anybody close to you die? Any close friends or—when did your father die?
P: No—father died in '37.
A: '37—that was way back.
P: There wasn't any close death in the family except a nephew died summer before last and that didn't have an effect, I know. It wasn't entirely unexpected.
A: Did you feel you were under any unusual pressures about anything before [you got sick]? [MED. ED.: time of disease discovery or exacerbation.]
P: No.
A: Do you think pressure had anything to do with it? The feeling of pressure to succeed at something, or get ahead, or accomplish a purpose?
P: No, I always felt that I was . . . ah . . . moving ahead . . . at a pretty good rate. When I came out of the service, I set goals for myself . . . and I drove myself too hard trying to reach those goals in that period and then I realized that I wouldn't be able to reach these goals in the period I had set for myself. I didn't change the goals; I just threw away the timetable, and that relieved the pressure.

A: That's fair enough. So that you didn't have any accumulated pressure that you are aware of?

P: No.

A: Were there any deadlines that you had to meet?

P: No.

A: Was there anything about which you felt a sense of failure? Did you get awfully down-at-the-mouth or have a terrific sense of failure about the break-up of your marriage, for instance?

P: No, I never considered my marriages in the sense of personal failures. I know that they are failures, and I regard them as such, but as far as having any strong personal feelings about it, say that if I had done this or if I had done that, things would have been different, no, I don't—never had those feelings.

A: At no time did you feel awfully down-at-the-mouth, that everything is no good or gone to pot?

P: Well no . . . ah . . . you may have . . . ah . . . ah . . . a few . . . ah . . . days or a few hours when you feel . . . .

A: Yes, but I mean a broad sense of failure. Was there any way in which any important relationship was threatened for you shortly before [the illness started?] [MED. ED.: disease discovery or exacerbation.]

P: Any way in which any important relationship was threatened . . . . Well, it's pretty hard to pinpoint the year—I did undergo an emotional strain along this period [when this thing was coming on] . . . but . . . ah . . . with me emotional strains—they are short-lived. Now I . . . there was a woman I was quite interested in—interested in each other; as a matter of fact we had talked about . . . ah . . . getting married, and then the thing sort of—well it broke up.

A: This was after your separation from your second wife?

P: Second . . . .

A: Yes.

A: Did you feel threatened by anything such as loss of job, sickness, or anything of that sort in connection with the onset of your illness?

P: No.

A: We've already gone into the physical activity. Was there anything that stirred you to more anger?

P: *[Can't get this; both laughing.]*

A: This lady friend that you speak of—how long after you separated from your wife?

P: This was in between—the separation of my wife, maybe about a year before we remarried.

A: This lady was in between.

P: Between the two marriages, which might have had something to do with my yielding for the second marriage—this thing broke up.
A: Were you involved with this lady sexually?
P: When you say involved . . . .
A: Were you having intercourse with her?
P: Yes.
A: You didn't have any conflict over it?
P: No . . . ah . . . didn't have any conflict over it. The thing that happened. This lady's sister had died about a year before [with a thyroid condition. She had come here and they had diagnosed her as having a thyroid condition.] [MED. ED.: the unedited text here is ambiguous but suggests that the lady herself was given a diagnosis of a disease comparable to that by which her sister died] and she broke it off.
A: Oh, she broke off with you on account of it?
P: Yes.
A: Oh, I see, and was that [terribly] upsetting to you?
P: It was, yes, it was upsetting.
A: Did that have something to do with your remarrying your second wife, do you think?
P: I think it might have had.
A: You think you might have done better with her?
P: I would hate to think it did but in being fair it might have.
A: Why do you think she would react [to a thyroid condition] [MED. ED.: to her own disease] by breaking it off?
P: This individual was even more emotional than I knew at the time we went together. Her sister had lived with this condition for a number of years without it being discovered and she actually died without them knowing what it was.
A: Oh, she died.
P: Yes, this, I think, had instilled a fear in her that she might suffer with the same thing and come to the same ending.
A: Can you tell me what movie or play in the last—say six months or a year before you got sick, maybe had the most effect upon you?
P: Most effect? Emotionally or how?
A: Emotionally?
P: They just don't affect me.
A: Most effect otherwise then? What most impressed you?
P: Now the picture that most impressed me, say in the last two or three years was the "Ten Commandments," and . . . ah . . . the play was "My Fair Lady." Whether either one of these were prior to the onset of this condition or not is hard to pinpoint.

A: Mostly I think it tells us something about you [both laughing]. I don't have any other questions. Do you have any questions to ask me? [Well, I think we cooked up a few questions] [both laughing]. You have been very good. If we do need to ask you anything, I understand you will be willing to come back. I tried to be very thorough today. I hope we've got all we need today. But if we do need any more Dr. Z will get in touch with you. I want to thank you very much. You have been very good and very cooperative.

P: Thank you.

Analytic Judges' Written Formulations

Diagnoses Submitted by the Judges

Mr. A. O.

	INITIAL DIAGNOSIS		FINAL DIAGNOSIS	
Judge A	Rheumatoid Arthritis	7A	Rheumatoid Arthritis	7A
Judge B	Rheumatoid Arthritis	6	Rheumatoid Arthritis	
	Neurodermatitis	1		
Judge C	Rheumatoid Arthritis	5	Rheumatoid Arthritis	6
	Hypertension	2	Hypertension	1
Judge D	Rheumatoid Arthritis		Rheumatoid Arthritis	
Judge E	Rheumatoid Arthritis		Rheumatoid Arthritis	
Judge F	Rheumatoid Arthritis	7A	Rheumatoid Arthritis	7A
Judge G	Rheumatoid Arthritis		Rheumatoid Arthritis	
Judge H	Interviewer		Interviewer	
Judge I	Neurodermatitis		Neurodermatitis	

Judge A's Formulation

The most impressive feature about patient is the importance of the element of control over himself, over his wife, children, and those under him on the job. There is a family history of strict discipline, with rebellion against it (i.e., swimming hole). He was guilty for years over the consequences (illegitimate pregnancy) of letting himself get out of control. The adult "fanatic" seemed to grow out of this experience. He claims to have become "one of the fellows" yet there is a rigidity in his manner, and one feels that he sticks to his routines with great constancy. There is a lingering dependent-type relationship upon the older brother in Chicago. The dreams are suggestive of possible unconscious homosexual feelings. Onset is problematical. It seems to have begun around two years ago. Final separation from the second wife was one year earlier. He does state that he had cut down on physical activities just prior to onset.

Patient is most ambitious, has pushed his informal education and plans for the children to go to college. He loves to think and is intellectually much higher than a janitor. He is concerned about what people think of him. He is also concerned over the idea that he failed in marriage. I would assume that he also considers himself a failure in life. Something has held him to the janitor job. I would guess that it is his intense feelings of inadequacy and fear of failing by himself.

The chief thing activated would then be the feeling of failure in life and in marriage. There is anger about this since he must blame the family (superego). He has kept himself in a dependent role (janitor) and it has not paid off with success. There must be increasingly strong urges to rebel against the system of control and dependence and to strike out for himself (school). This in turn requires the reconstitution of increased control.

Initial Diagnosis: Arthritis 7A

Judge C's Formulation

This soft-spoken Negro man evokes a feeling of surprise as one reads the history. In view of the degree of intelligence he manifests, and the value he places upon education, one wonders why he remained in the position of a janitor. He manifests other surprising or unexpected reactions. Seemingly totally inhibited sexually until the age of 19, never having masturbated, at 19 he "becomes a man" suddenly. Only late in the interview does he make it clear that this included fathering an illegitimate son by a girl who was very protective toward him and who was anxious to assure his further educational development by sparing him the responsibilities of marriage.

Patient is an opinionated, self-righteous man, exceptionally self-controlled, who builds up resentment until "triggered," at which time he explodes. He then forgets the matter. He was vigorous and fighting as a boy, gave this up about age of 19 years. He has a great sensitivity to injustice—practically carries a chip on his shoulder as manifest in his attitudes toward the intolerance of churches and the undependability of the minister who let him down after promising use of his church for a choral performance.

Patient states he is "as considerate as I know how to be"; he likes to help others as his mother did, but is more discriminating than she was, and uses his ability and interest to help as a device to control; e.g., he will give the newsboy six shirts as a graduation gift when he has decided what college he will attend. He is a good listener as well as talker; he is sought as a marriage counselor.

It is difficult to ascertain significant onset considerations in relation to the illness. Time of discovery of the disease was not long after the second separation from his wife in 1956. It is a question whether the poorly defined prodromata occurred about the time of his first separation from his wife, in 1951.

Impression *Arthritis*. Physical action has always been important to this man; as a boy he was very active in sports, all his life he has remained a janitor, permitting some degree of muscular activity on his job. He indicates that preceding onset of his illness there was some cutting down of the degree of activity on his job. He was an acting-out person, early as a prankster, later in "grinding down" his wife by an indiscriminating imposition of his will and wishes. The combination of responsibility, of wishing to care for others combined with his rigidity, self-control, and control of others, is highly suggestive of arthritis.

Hypertension is a second possibility. He is a chronically irritated man, who conforms essentially to family expectation. Early nightmares were dreams of attack by bigger boys with knives; there is considerable confusion between passive wish to serve and need to control. His dependency in relation to his wives is evident; a divorce was secured only after eight years of separation, and again a remarriage occurred to the same wife five years after a divorce. Strict obedience to the firm yet somewhat distant father was expected and accepted by the patient. Until age of 19, aggression found some expression in the prankster role; sexual aggression was fully inhibited until that time. Resentment builds up and is expressed in an explosion after there is "triggering" by the act of a second party.

Initial Diagnosis: Arthritis 5
Hypertension 2

Judge D's Formulation

Onset of symptoms in this 43-year-old Negro janitor seems rather ambiguous but apparently was connected with feelings at the time his second marriage to the same wife broke up in 1956.

However, there had been some symptoms for many years previously which had not been diagnosed. It is not exactly clear why his two marriages to this woman failed, or why his earlier one at the age of 24 broke up.

It seems to have been a clash of temperaments in which they amicably "agreed to disagree." In his first marriage the patient was much too stern and disapproving of his young wife, who couldn't take his domination. In the second marriage this was somewhat reversed, in which he became much more free and easy—"one of the boys"—and his wife was rigid, sullen, and uncommunicative. He has apparently never been able to establish a flexible give-and-take relationship with one person so that he prefers to live alone and be lonely rather than be married and unhappy. There is also evidence that his wives didn't trust him, were sensitive to rejection, and mastered the situation by leaving him first. E.g., his second wife, on her return, showed an almost paranoid attitude that he had bought drapes and furniture, etc., in order to be independent of her and get rid of her. Underlying this was possibly her resentment that he had deprived her of her female prerogative of doing the decorating. This would be in line with a rather clear feminine identification in this man. He says "I would *rather* be like my father" but actually he is a Baptist like his mother, rejecting his father's Methodism, and resembles his mother in being a benevolent do-gooder, although in a more discriminating way, i.e., that his philanthropy has strings attached in that it depends on the recipient following his advice. E.g., he will give the paper boy half a dozen shirts if he will go to college. He is quite motherly to his children, and curiously his son is a decorator, which patient himself seems to have leanings toward.

The passive bisexual nature is also shown in his sexual pattern, in which he is generally seduced by an aggressive woman. Also he likes the recumbent position in intercourse as well as the superior—which probably means he prefers it.

Patient handles authority in a decisive fashion, gives orders easily and has no hesitation in firing. On the other hand his years in the CC Camp show that he can also be quite submissive to superior authority.

Patient grew up in a large Southern family, which had a very strict religious orientation. Both parents were strict; yet patient, who was a middle child in a long series, was rebellious, pugnacious, and loved to fight. As he grew older he curbed the direct aggression but was extremely active in sports, excelling as a halfback on the football team. Although his job as janitor entails physical activity, he is apparently much less active than formerly.

The one dream reported is a nightmare of childhood in which he is being attacked on all sides by knives. This probably conceals a great deal of passive homosexual feeling in relation to his father and brothers, as well as intense aggression toward them which he directed outward in his fighting and athletics. Self-control and discipline are paramount to this man, as well as conflict and frustration over controlling others. In spite of the overwhelming sexual denial of his youth, which is somewhat suggestive of asthma, I think the great preponderance of evidence points to Rheumatoid Arthritis 7A.

P.S. He was impressed with "King's Row," where a sinner has his *legs cut off*, and "My Fair Lady," where the hero tries to dominate the heroine completely.

Judge's E's Formulation

When asked about his life at the time of onset of his somatic illness, this 43-year-old colored patient immediately mentions his marriage, but states that there was nothing unusual. He was "enjoying what I thought for me was a full life."

Later we learn that he has been married twice. His first marriage, at the age of 23, did not last long. In explanation he says, "it was lack of patience more than anything else on my part. If I had been a more patient man, time would have taken care of the little things that caused my irritation." His irritation did not go to the extent "where you would become violent or anything like that, but as I said, I was pretty stiff. I thought it was base for a woman to smoke or take a drink or anything like that. I was just as set in that as though I was 90 and there was no bending. You either don't smoke or you are a bad woman." He and his wife were separated after about a year, but didn't get a divorce until 8 or 9 years later, when he wanted to marry a second time. This second marriage didn't last too long either. "Frankly, we didn't have quarrels," he says, when asked what led the relationship to deteriorate. "I am not given to outbreaks unless, let's say, unless I'm triggered. If you say the wrong thing then I'll go out and express myself in no uncertain terms. I'll go back to my first wife to try to express this. She said to me sometimes, 'You don't fuss. I like to fuss sometimes.' That has been my pattern down through the years." When he married the second time, he took his wife with him wherever he went. "I almost never went out except to go to work. I started out asking her where would you like to go? She would say, I'll leave that up to you. Then you get in a habit saying, well, we'll go to such-and-such a place today, we'll do this, we'll do that. Then after a time, you'll probably forget to ask what she would like to do. And then after a period of time, she finds that she is only doing the things you would like to do and you are not conscious of this. In this particular case, it went on for about three and a half years of my doing this and finally she said, 'I'm not going to go any further. The things I've been doing, I did them because you want me to. I just won't do them any more.' Then is where I blow up. And . . . uh . . . express my thoughts in the matter because if you had told me anywhere along the line that you didn't like to go to this thing, I'm sure I would have considered your feelings in this matter. And when I ask you so many times where you want to go and what you want to do, and you never knew what you wanted to do, well I just assumed that you were happy doing the things that I wanted to do. I just sort of gave up. What the heck! I'd done the best I knew how. What can I do different?"

For example, one day the wife refused to go to a party which the patient had been taking for granted that they were going to. Then he "realized that . . . uh . . . I was the only one who had ever talked about the party and the party itself was not important enough even to me to break up my home. So I went and got her and apologized for my conduct." The marriage finally broke up after another incident of this kind. But after a time she began to write that "she would like to come back and be the kind of wife she should have been." So they remarried. He thought "maybe she has realized that this thing that caused the separation, whatever it is, was just a figment of her imagination because except you tell me where I'm going or what I'm doing that you don't like, then I can't change." So after the marriage started again "I don't think it got off the ground."

The patient is rather indefinite about when his somatic illness started. He tells of prodromal symptoms dating back five or six years ago (about the time of his marriage to his second wife), but the actual discovery of the disease seems to have occurred about two years ago—about the time of his separation and remarriage.

This pattern of quiet and reasonable domination of both his wives, and the break-up of his marriages as a direct result of it, suggests a somatic diagnosis of rheumatoid arthritis.

His description of his parental home gives an excellent background for these attitudes and tends to confirm the diagnosis. His father was a professional gambler. However, the patient explains that the father did not gamble as long as he could make a living for himself and his family by working. But when, as a result of the depression, he was unable to get a job, he quit working and began to gamble because his theory was that a man can't both work and gamble. "He was equally as good a provider when he was gambling as when he was working." As to discipline, "he was strict without your being conscious of the fact that he was strict." The father never used violence. "There were orders that came from him and they were obeyed. There were no questions asked. He said do this and we did it." The patient's mother was "sweet and gentle. She has mothered and doctored every child in the community and she is loved for it." As to discipline, "she believed in the rod. She didn't cut off privileges because you didn't have too many privileges to begin with. There were rules and regulations. We were to be in bed by a certain hour and so to make you go to bed an hour earlier would make you go to bed before dinner. She didn't ever make anybody go to bed before dinner. So . . . ah . . . the greatest punishment that she could give out was whipping." As to his own attitude about punishing his child (by the first marriage): "I think I'm a pretty strict disciplinarian, although I don't, never did resort, let's say, to corporal punishment. I discovered the very first time I spanked her that spanking was not the way to handle her. She is headstrong. But I have always prevailed upon her to express herself. As I tell her, I'm not always right. You give me your ideas, you see, if you are wrong, be big enough to be corrected."

The patient says that he himself "was supposed to be a bad kid, although I can hardly believe it." (Both the patient and interviewer laugh.) He was always fighting. "I fought everybody." He was so well known as a fighter that the other boys put him up to it. He would fight and then get whipped for it when he got back from school. As a boy he was very fond of sports, especially football, which he played until he came back from the service.

It is of interest to trace the effects of the restrictive atmosphere of parental discipline on the development of the patient's own attitudes. During his childhood, he pictures himself as extremely self-restrictive in relation to sex. So far as he remembers, he never masturbated and did not have wet dreams until he was 20 or 21. Sex was something that was never discussed at home and he did not associate with the boys "around the alleys." He first became involved sexually with a girl at the age of 19. "Well, I was asked to do it," he explains. He had been going with the girl for nearly three years and now had intercourse with her only twice. The immediate result was her pregnancy. But she promptly took the attitude that she wasn't going to have any forced marriage. She felt that the patient was a good student and should not have his education cut off by having to marry her. "She just didn't think that I should, say, get saddled in marriage at this point. I think she loved me, too," he adds. The patient, however, felt extremely guilty and is inclined to attribute his prematurely old and excessively restricted attitude toward his first wife to his guilt about this experience.

My somatic diagnosis is rheumatoid arthritis.

Judge F's Formulation

This intelligent Negro came from a large family of eleven children. The parents were strict, the one a Methodist and the other a Baptist, and the children were raised by iron discipline, against which the patient did not rebel but accepted it as a matter of course. His life followed a prescribed routine pattern. Patient was extremely interested in sports and was for a long time a football player. He married when he was 23 years old, about the time he became a janitor, an occupation which he held up to the present. Before his marriage, when he was 19, patient was seduced by his girl friend to have sexual relations. She gave birth to a boy but did not insist on marriage because she did not want to interfere with the patient's career. Patient developed considerable guilt about this.

His first marriage dissolved after one year, although the actual divorce took place several years later, when patient remarried. The marriage dissolved because patient was intolerant about wife's smoking and drinking, and could not enforce his principles. He thinks he was mentally too old for his immature wife. He married again in 1946 when he was 30. From this marriage (son was illegitimate; daughter was by first marriage) he has a daughter. This marriage was also unsuccessful, but it is difficult to reconstruct the reasons. What appears as fairly certain is that patient was a very domineering person. The wife finally rebelled and left him. They divorced in 1950. Patient remarried in 1955 and separated almost immediately again. Patient appears to be a self-willed, stubborn, and domineering person, who, nevertheless, *tries to be considerate to others*. He seems to have, at the same time, strong dependent needs directed toward men. When he first came to Chicago, he leaned on his older brother. Later, he turned for advice in his marital difficulty to a friend. An SOS letter written to this friend, because of his marital problem, was read by his wife. This seems to have precipitated her leaving patient. Patient's latent homosexual tendencies are further indicated by: (1) his typical dreams: men are attacking him from "all sides" (evidently also from the back) with knives; (2) by his sexual history. He mostly leaves the initiative to women—was for a long time very hesitant to have sexual relations because of extreme sexual inhibitions—was often approached by homosexuals and sometimes reacted with extreme anger. Apparently he likes the bottom position in sexual intercourse.

Dynamic Reconstruction: Over-compensated passive homosexual tendency directed originally to father and older brother. Chronic rebellion against external regimentation at home. Expression of rebellion appears in continuous fighting with peers and physical exercise. Patient tries to regiment his children the same way in which he was controlled by his parents. Patient is irritable, but controls his anger, and in general, controls all his impulses. He reacts with anger if others indulge in those things he forbids to himself. The most central feature is consistent self-control and attempts to control environment. *Onset:* Patient's actual symptoms started two years ago, just about the time of remarrying, and soon after separating from his wife. His wife leaving him frustrated his urge to dominate her.

Initial Diagnosis: Rheumatoid Arthritis 7A

Judge I's Formulation

Patient is a 43-year-old colored male who was one of many siblings. His father was a hard-working and responsible man. The patient learned from him how to control his tender and affectionate traits. He was not as warm or as close to his father as he would have liked. It was from his mother that he learned or acquired his tendency for tenderness. She would mother everybody in the neighborhood.

There appears to be a great deal of emphasis on responsibility, loneliness, domination, and need for closeness, and finally I am struck by this man's narcissism, vanity, and lack of real feeling for others.

At 19 he felt that a change occurred. He was only a boy until then and overnight he changed into a man and assumed adult responsibility. This may have had something to do with the incident of his illegitimate child.

From that time on he accepted his responsibilities except for the child or marrying the girl. He had a very rigid idea of what was right and proper and apparently this led to the floundering and break-up of his first marriage.

The other significant trait is his extreme passivity in the sexual area as well as his generalized inhibition about sexual matters.

The narcissism and emphasis on loneliness and need for closeness and the idea of separation appear to be a central theme. He speaks about the effect of separation and lack of warmth leaving a scar. He felt frustrated in his relationship with his wife. He does not bear a grudge, likes to get his anger out in the open and get it over with because he has this strong desire for reconciliation. Although he failed to get along with his second wife, got a divorce and separated, he still remarried her and tried to make the best of it because he wanted to be reconciled with her, especially after the breaking of his romance.

He makes a contrast between the lack of closeness between father and self and compares this with the great warmth and closeness that exists between himself and daughter. He tells how his daughter was proud of him and always wanted to "show off her daddy." So because the home was a broken one he tried to keep the relationship with her a warm and close one so that she would not suffer any emotional scars.

He volunteers the words that his second wife is "not too warm or affectionate."

It is significant that he remarried his second wife after his love affair of two years ago broke up. His need to be close to someone outweighed his ambivalence toward her and his illness began soon after this marriage —or its reseparation; that is, re-break-up.

The narcissistic and exhibitionistic features are shown by his choice of language, his tendency to lecture, his pride about his memory recall, and his ability to read before he went to school, or the feeling about his failure to make a marriage work. I think we are dealing with a man who is narcissistic, exhibitionistic, and has a great deal of erotization of the skin. He needs a lot of warmth and affection, but is conflictful in being able to get along with love objects.

His attack comes on in connection with the theme of separation.

If the emphasis is on reconciliation the case is made for neurodermatitis. But if the emphasis is on fear of separation then the possibility of asthma must also be considered.

Neurodermatitis 5 Asthma 2

Additional Notes

The somatic language of referring to the scarring effect of emotion. The sense of specialness and importance. God-like, "Ten Commandments." The exhibitionistic traits as pointed out above, plus the significance of the picture and story of "My Fair Lady" and the importance of language.

Data

1. A boy until 19, then became a man overnight.
2. Accepted the responsibilities of the world.
3. Accepted these responsibilities and was happy to live up to them.
4. An impatient man and also an irritable man.
5. Also a rigid ideal image.
6. But now he is changed and his second wife is like his former self.
7. A lack of real warmth for people.
8. Separation plays a role . . . the attacks.
9. Leaving any scars.
10. Insomnia (related to skin).
11. Emphasis about loneliness.
12. Feels frustrated in his relationship with wife.
13. He feels and acts on his anger.
14. He does not bear a grudge, it's out and over with.
15. Also a desire for reconciliation.
16. He bought household furnishing.
17. Is he dominating, opinionated?
18. Yes, he is narcissistic!
19. Emphasis on closeness—in regard to son ambivalent need for each other. Just like with second wife.
20. Lack of feeling for objects. Can be a lacking in feelings.
21. Emphasis on lack of closeness between self and dad, and contrast of closeness between self and daughter.

22. He is stubborn.
23. Quite a scrapper.
24. Quite athletic in youth but now only a spectator.
25. Causes

    Belief in education. Salvation for Negroes.
26. "I'll get up on the soap box in a minute."
27. Tenderness from mother; ability to control tenderness from father.
28. Daughter wanted to show off her daddy. So because the home was broken, he tried to keep the relationship close and warm so the child would not suffer emotional scars.
29. Volunteers such words as second wife "not too warm or affectionate."
30. A memory of complete recall. Narcissistic. Read before school.
31. Dreams of being attacked from all sides.
32. Some trouble in crying . . . but not really.
33. Clothes and appearance.
34. Remarried second wife when his love affair broke up. Needs to have someone close.

Analytic Judges' Meeting Notes

Meeting Date: May 19, 1959

Judge B: I would suggest that we hear one formulation for arthritis, and then the rest of us add to it instead of going through our own formulations, and we spend the time on differential features. If there is so much agreement I am sure that all of us will probably have picked out many of the same points. But if there are differences we should focus on the differences in the formulations, and avoid repetitiousness. Let's discuss specifically the differential which will help us in terms of understanding this case, and in terms of some of our own thinking.

Judge E: I wonder whether this habit of forgetting his anger—which he makes so much of an issue—is typical of arthritis? Of course the fact is he may not forget. He may just have a principle of forgetting, but really hold a grudge predominantly. I would think that would be one of the points that might . . . .

Judge B: I would wonder how many people who hold grudges are willing to talk about the fact that they hold grudges.

Judge E: Of course this man goes further than not talking about it—it's an issue with him. Perhaps the fact that he makes an issue of it is evidence that he does.

Judge B: The fact that he . . . .

Judge E: He has a reaction formation.

Judge B: That's right. But to take a simple thing—because one of the things we have said is that some hypertensive patients hold a grudge—I would say since socially one is not supposed to hold grudges—at least in our culture—how many people would talk about the grudges they hold?

Judge D: Most hypertensives do. From my experience I would say yes.

Judge E: I think arthritics too. They may not say they hold a grudge, but it is very evident from their material that they do. They just never forgive. They are like elephants. At least that is the impression I have of arthritics.

Judge B: Then what type would forgive? Ulcer patients don't forgive.

Judge E: I think ulcer patients do.

Judge D: Very frequently.

Judge B: In the analytic relationship—they try to forgive.

Judge E: I've been going over these ulcer cases—the characteristic feature seems to me with many of them is they blurt out their anger—usually verbally, not muscularly. Blurt out their anger and don't seen to be affected by. . . . It may be two different types of situations.

Judge B: As a result of an ulcer patient I am working with, I began to make inquiry of some people in the field of dentistry. An interesting correlation seems to be possible, although I haven't gotten any specific data. There is a condition called bruxism.

Judge E: Teeth grinding?

Judge B: Teeth grinding at night.

Judge D: There are all kinds of oral symptoms at night. A lot of people wet the pillow.

Judge B: This is a specific instance that came up in the case of this male ulcer patient. He has a severe case of bruxism, and actually grinds his teeth a great deal. Yesterday he came in and told me —he is engaged to be married—that he went out with his girl friend last week, and in the process of necking he began to playfully kiss her with his teeth. As he held on to her shoulder he actually took hold of her triceps with his teeth and for a second he was afraid he wouldn't be able to control himself, and that he was really going to take a mouthful, to bite. Then that night . . . .

Judge E: Even in classical descriptions of sexual behavior . . . behavior in sexual intercourse, biting is one of the . . . .

Judge B: He thought that he wanted to destroy her, and that night the amount of bruxism that occurred was so great that apparently the door to his room was open and his father or somebody passed and said: "Were you dreaming of Spanish dancers, because I thought I heard castanets?" Apparently there was so much movement of the jaw—and this followed his going out with the girl. There came on a tremendous amount of oral sadistic destructive material.

Judge D: When I was an intern I treated any amount of injuries of that type in Negroes.

Judge E: I think it would be very helpful if we would undertake to survey the ways that these different diseases handle aggression. I think this would be an excellent differential diagnostic point.

Judge B: This goes along in some ways with concepts about body language. There might be some correlation. I suggested methodologically that since four of us are for arthritis, what we should now do is have one formulation presented for arthritis and we will all add to the arthritis discussion and spend some time on the differential features. There are two things that suggested themselves for differential—two clusters. One is the hypertension, the other is the neurodermatitis/asthma. So, Judge G, you go ahead and start. Maybe you can present your formulation.

Judge G: I was very much interested in the personality of this 43-year-old, intelligent, and cooperative Negro, with a position only as a janitor. He was much more intelligent.

Judge D: Racial. It's not a bad job considering the . . . it's a very secure job.

Judge G: It is not clear when the disease was discovered. On the first page—the disease started over a year ago, then two years ago, then five or six years ago prodromal symptoms appeared. Then the year 1951 was indicated. Page 164 prodromal symptoms began before 1950. In 1956 an exacerbation occurred not too long after second separation from his wife.

Judge E: First separation.

Judge D: He remarried and separated all in that one year.

Judge E: It wasn't while he was with the wife the second time?

Judge D: It is not clear.

Judge E: It is not clear whether he got sick before the separation or after the separation. He was having an affair with another girl, and this other girl decided not to get married.

Judge I: And during the emotional reaction to the loss of this girl he took back the second wife again. It was taking her back that made him sick, but we don't know whether he got sick after he broke up with her again, or whether just taking her back.

Judge G: One year after the prodromal symptoms patient suffered from insomnia. Patient was born in Oklahoma and came to Chicago in 1937. He comes from a family of eleven children; he is the seventh. His father always set the law; his mother did the disciplining. If the father said something it was to be done. No discussions were permitted. His father forbade the children to swim, and so the patient who indulged in football and all kinds of sports does not know how to swim. His father also functioned as a voluntary counselor for other people. He wanted to guide other people, and enjoyed very much controlling everybody. Also his mother was a controlling woman, who also gave money indiscriminately to people in need. Patient does the same but is more discriminating. Money is a frequent means to control other people, and I have the impression the mother used it to control other people. To make them indebted, grateful.

Judge E: Is there evidence that she used it that way?

Judge G: She was very domineering. This is my inference. He wanted to control his second wife by buying her a fur coat. I come to this later.

Judge E: Is there evidence that he used money to control that way?

Judge I: That is also inference.

Judge D: Well, he does with the boy.

Judge E: Well, I'd like to distinguish what is inference and what is your guess.

Judge D: Give him the shirts provided he goes to college. Put strings on him. He says that very clearly.

Judge G: The patient himself admits that he is of a dominating nature. On page 172 "probably I did not tolerate any antagonism from those that were under me." If someone who worked for him would not do his work properly, first he would explain to him how to do it, then he would fire him. His pleasure to control is also expressed in his desire to be a doctor. We found that many women want to be nurses, and so on. It is very probable that his disease developed from his feeling of uneasiness in his two marital relationships. The patient's attitude toward both his first and second wife is somewhat obscured by the patient's version of his marital difficulties.

Judge E: Is obscured? I think that is one of the most dramatic descriptions by a patient of his attitude that I ever read.

Judge G: He rationalizes. I will explain when I come to it. He is intelligent, makes every action of his appear reasonable, but I consider his attitude as pseudo-tolerant. He depicts himself as being very tolerant, and so on, but he is not.

Judge D: One of the boys.

Judge E: Well, Judge A's phrase fits this case better than any patient I have ever seen—"benevolent tyrant."

Judge I: May I ask a question about this phrase "benevolent tyrant"? This refers to the patients themselves as a rule, or to the mother of the patient?

Judge D: The patients.

Judge E: Especially the patients.

Judge G: He depicts himself as the frustrated victim of his wife, who never let him know what her actual wishes were. Since he could never learn from them what their wishes really were or what they enjoy or to what places to go . . . .

Judge E: Put him in the position where he would have to be a benevolent tyrant without knowing it.

Judge D: He had to take responsibility, and he didn't like it.

Judge G: He himself had to make the decisions in everything—what to do. He was then frustrated and surprised when they complained that they had always to do what pleased him and that he never considered their wishes. Once when he bought his second wife a fur coat, he learned from her sister that he should have asked his wife first before buying the coat. The interviewer asked him then whether his sister-in-law implied that he was dominating. For me this was a clue.

Judge E: Well, the sister-in-law said a very significant phrase there. "You were buying your wife what you thought she ought to have—not what she wanted."

Judge G: As his mother tried to dominate other people through money, so the patient tried to dominate his wife through presents, money, and so on. The dominating, controlling attitude is very clear here. Another important point is his sexual life. He started late. He said that he matured suddenly when he was 19. His sexual life started when he was 20–22. He asserted that he never masturbated. He was always seduced by girls—also by the first one whom he impregnated. He has never taken the initiative. I have the impression that he is somewhat feminine in his manners and in liking nice clothes.

Judge E: I think there is an important clue here—I don't know how important diagnostically, but very important, I think, for understanding this man. He describes himself at the beginning of his first marriage as acting like a 90-year-old man. Extreme rigidity in the sexual attitude. Well, it isn't explained at that time why he should have been that way. Then we learn later that this was caused by his relationship to this other woman. He blames her for seducing him, but he is not critical of her for that reason. He made her pregnant the first or second time they had intercourse. Then she was excessively generous in dealing with him. She said that he shouldn't marry her—that it would spoil his career, and so on. He apparently accepted this, but it left a terrific guilt; and I think his attitude to the first marriage, which occurred shortly afterwards, was a reaction. All the rigidity in his character was intensified by his guilt about this first affair.

Judge G: This is precisely what I wanted now to say. That he felt very, very guilty for his first affair with this girl who was so generous towards him, and he himself says he felt very guilty. I think this is very important.

Judge E: He pictures himself as having really grown up suddenly at the age of 19.

Judge I: How would you fit this in with an arthritis personality organization?

Judge E: I'm not bringing this as an argument for diagnosis.

Judge I: I think what you raise is a very good question, because here you have a beautiful explanation to explain a certain large segment of this man's character structure, without having to resort to the dynamics of arthritis.

Judge D: That fits in very well with arthritis.

Judge E: The reason that he reacted in this particular way is indicative that he had this kind of a character before—this just intensified it. That's my general impression. I'll go into it more in detail after Judge G is finished—if he doesn't bring this out.

Judge D: He was a tremendous fighter as a boy. He used to go out and fight everybody. So one day he decided he couldn't do that any more. So he controlled himself, but it's the same with his sexuality, which is strongly mixed with aggression. What he is saying is: every time I let down the bars something terrible happens.

Judge B: On page 189 the patient makes a statement which I think is in relation to what you say, Judge I. He is talking about this girl—the one that he got pregnant. This is his first experience: "and as I say she has been my girl friend for nearly three years"—which was before 19—"somebody I loved." The interviewer says: "You hadn't made any passes at her?" And he responds: "No, because I felt very strongly about her. I felt that nobody should touch her. Nobody should do anything wrong where she was concerned, and I think I felt at that time that I might kill anybody that did. I didn't think of doing anything wrong where she was concerned, and I couldn't conceive of anybody else doing it. So I guess my being strict went even further back than I told you before." In other words, this history of being strict, he himself reveals is antedating his nineteenth year.

Judge I: That's another reaction to guilt—to impregnating her.

Judge B: I don't think it's a reaction to guilt.

Judge E: He said it intensifies it.

Judge B: But the genesis is not in terms of the impregnation.

Judge E: What I'm saying is that he already had this character, but then when he broke through, when he did impregnate the girl, and had such guilt provoking consequences, then this whole attitude . . . .

Judge I: What did he have guilt about though—that's the point. There is an element here that is completely overlooked, I think, and that is: this man's completely callous attitude toward this woman and toward the child. Why doesn't he marry her? She was so wonderful to him. That's ridiculous. There is a mighty defect in this man's attitude to this woman.

Judge B: But I think what I just read already gives us a clue as to what he is guilty about. I think he is guilty about the fact that he would like to kill somebody. And what he did in this little remark that I just made—he said: "I became the defender of the right."

Judge I: What happens to his guilt though, in terms of this girl being pregnant?

Judge B: This came afterward.

Judge I: What was his guilt? How come he didn't come forward and take care of her?

Judge E: That's the thing that made him guilty—that he didn't come forward.

Judge B: I think he identified with the child. But let's hear Judge G again, or we will end up with nobody hearing anyone's formulation.

Judge G: His wish to wear very nice clothes—I have the impression that this is feminine attitude and not so much exhibitionistic, because he was very passive. He was seduced by the girls. He reacted with anger when he was approached by a homosexual boy. I consider this a reaction formation. In intercourse he enjoys equally both positions.

Judge D: That means he enjoys the bottom one better.

Judge G: Yes. This feminine identification is very consistent with our formulation of arthritis. He has no separation anxiety, and therefore I excluded neurodermatitis.

Judge I: You say he has no separation anxiety? I have a lot of evidence to the contrary.

Judge G: He prefers to live alone, rather than with a woman whom he could not control. In his description, however, the women frustrate and irritate him instead of appreciating his reasonable and considerate attitude toward them. He does not keep resentments, and once the air is cleared after an argument, he is through with his anger. I think that this is not the answer that the hypertensive patient would give. I think this is much more consistent with arthritis. He is also very strict with his illegitimate son, and with his daughter from his first marriage. In his boyhood he fought with everybody.

Judge E: What happened to this need for muscular . . . ?

Judge D: He became an athlete.

Judge E: How long did that last?

Judge D: He was athletic in his adolescence. He became a big athlete, and was in football.

Judge B: He went into the service.

Judge E: I don't know that I tried very hard, but I can't trace the muscular outlet up until he got his disease.

Judge D: He was a janitor.

Judge G: In his nightmares as a child his aggressive drives appeared as men or ghosts who attacked him. I interpret it as a projection of his own aggression. He liked football and other sports.

Judge E: I'd like to make a comment here. Other types of patients also have fears of being attacked by animals. Ulcer cases, colitis cases.

Judge B: Cases without psychosomatic diseases also. But I think right now we should hear the formulation and deal with the specific items later. We want to get a picture of what this man is like psychologically, and not so much the individual items.

Judge G: He played football also when he was in service. But before the onset of the disease he indulged less in muscular activity.

Judge I: May I comment about that? The interviewer says to him: "But you did not decrease your activity before you got sick?"

Judge B: Page 181 if you want the exact reference.

Judge I: Apparently there is concern about our getting the information wrong, so he finally makes a summary remark.

Judge B: He says on page 181 "Before [*omission*] [period of disease discovery or exacerbation] was there any reduction in the amount of your activity?"

"How do you mean that?"

"Were you on a less strenuous job or did you drop any activity of any sort?"

"No . . . ah . . . I carried on my work."

"Your work has been about the same all the time."

"About the same. I will say this, there was a lessening, yes, because I did a lot of little things extra. It isn't a hobby with me, making window screens, repairing the window frames, and things like that, well I cut that down to the bare minimum because it was an overload. [*omission*] I had decided to cut it down. I was overloaded."

"Did you cut it down before [period of disease discovery]?"

"Yes, I am sure I had started cutting down."

"It's about two years since [period of disease discovery] isn't that right?"

"I had started cutting it down before then."

"Is there any other activity you had eliminated or reduced?"
"No, not consciously."
"So there has not been any particular change in your physical activity?"
"No."

Judge I: Now there you are. Let's read that sentence again and again and ask ourselves what this means. This is Judge H saying this now, the interviewer.

Judge B: But that is at variance with what the man had said just above.

Judge I: OK. That makes it even more important. If I read this through for interviewer clues, I would say this is a clue. Don't mistake this for arthritis.

Judge F: I think I would agree with that.

Judge B: I would too, but I do not see where the material led into that.

Judge I: That's even more significant.

Judge D: But we have to go by our formulations.

Judge E: Yes, we shouldn't make our formulations on the basis of interviewer clues.

Judge G: So I come to my formulation now:

1) He was controlled by his father and mother.
2) He himself is of dominating nature.
3) Sexual inhibition related to his passivity.
4) Diminished muscular activity before prodromal symptoms.
5) Irritation and frustration in his relationships with his wives, who accused him of controlling them.
6) Onset seems to be related to these unhappy marital relationships.

I come to the conclusion: Rheumatoid Arthritis.

I considered asthma and hypertension, but I excluded them. I excluded asthma because he didn't have the urge to confess. He cries only when he is very angry. The disease didn't start when he was afraid somebody might be estranged from him. He was quite satisfied to live alone. Also a neurodermatitis patient wants to be close to somebody. The kind of aggression he expressed, and how he deals with it, is not typical of hypertension. So my diagnosis is Rheumatoid Arthritis 7A.

Judge B: Now I would like first of all for us to discuss the arthritis alone, without bringing in the differential features. Are there any particular points that we want to add positively?

Judge D: About the boys with knives. It is older boys with knives—which is much more in the family situation.

Judge G: Did he mention knives?

Judge D: Bigger boys with knives—something like that. So I think that is much more a phallic attack by sibling rivals.

He has a real feminine identification with the mother—which is further shown by his being a Baptist. He says, curiously, when the interviewer asked him: "Are you like your father or mother?" He says: "I would rather be like my father." But then it comes out he is really like the mother. There apparently is an intense religious difference. You know the narcissism of small differences between the Methodists and the Baptists. He is a Baptist like his mother—not a Methodist like his father. He makes that clear later when he got angry at the pastor of the church who wouldn't let him sing. His feelings about plays and movies: The two things that impressed him the most were "King's Row" and "My Fair Lady."

Judge I: He mentions the "Ten Commandments," doesn't he?

Judge D: Well, the "Ten Commandments," I think, could be used for many things. The situation in "King's Row"—the man seduced the doctor's daughter and the doctor later cuts his legs off. The fellow, after seducing the doctor's daughter, is mangled in a train accident and amputation is not necessary, but the doctor cuts both his legs off. The patient says: "That's a terrible way to pay for sin."

Judge I: The patient says that.

Judge D: Very specifically referring to that emphasis. As far as "My Fair Lady" is concerned, the hero tries to dominate the woman. Otherwise my formulation is very much like Judge G's. One of the fights he had with his wife when she came back the second time was—she was angry at him for decorating everything.

Judge E: For having decorated everything while she was gone?

Judge D: While she was away. Now there is another double attitude here. He would make it appear that she is angry on the basis of separation. Also, "you bought all these things so you would be independent, so you could get rid of me." I don't think that is the reason that she left. Actually his son is also a decorator.

Judge E: I'm not satisfied about the onset. In the first place, I don't know when this onset came. Of course the picture is that he had prodromal symptoms going away back ten years—which were doubtful, the medical editor says. Then they got less and less doubtful as he went along. Five or six years ago, which is the date of his second marriage, corresponds to . . . then two years is the point at which he is really sure of the onset. That seems to correspond either to the remarriage or to the separation—both were close together. But now what puzzles me is what would be the dynamics in relationship to the marriage—the second marriage seems clear. What would be the dynamics of either remarrying or stopping being remarried, to the somatic symptoms—assuming it was arthritis? I don't know just how it would work.

Judge B: I have an explanation for it—a tentative one. Maybe I could just bring my comments in because they deal with this. Here we get the picture of a domineering, controlling man, and yet you get an individual who always wants the woman to take the initiative. The women have to take the initiative sexually, but the women also took the initiative to get the separations. This he makes very clear in both instances—the women broke off with him. He never broke off. Immediately the question occurred to me, in terms of formulation, not specifically disease—how do we reconcile the fact that this man has to control everything, but yet the very thing that would be most meaningful to him, he really doesn't control but abrogates the control—the separation from a significant object—and we know how significant this was with one wife, she had always to go with him. This emphasis on wanting to be close. The question occurred to me: Is this domination, is this need to control a defense against disillusionment? As long as he can think that he is controlling everything then he doesn't have to face the fact that he really can be controlled and he can be traumatized and he can be hurt. If we accept this as a premise, and it evokes anger, would she then have to control? And it evokes longing to be held, which he then may well have brought into focus. It may evoke the wish to be close to another person. In other words, the fact that he has as a life theme the idea to defend himself against putting himself into the position where he will be vulnerable, may have accounted for the appearance of this kind of—I would call it a pseudo-control. What does this man control? He can control somebody at work. He can control the picking up of the garbage in the building or something else like that, but in a human relationship, what aspects did this man really control that have been important to him?

Judge D: He even dresses the way the kids want him to dress.

Judge B: Yes, he dresses the way his kids want him to.

Judge D: Seems to me that that first woman rejected him—the one that got pregnant.

Judge B: The first woman became the mother. Now if we stop and think, again dynamically, not diagnostically, we say: what does this mean in terms of this man's homosexuality? It seems pretty clear. We know that he wants very much to be close to the son. He wants to put his arms around him. He feels very bad . . . .

Judge E: The son doesn't take to that.

Judge B: The son doesn't take to that, and understandably. We know that there has been the violence with the homosexual approach. He said "I got violent with a couple of people who have attempted to have intimate relationships"—which I think is an indication of the need to defend himself against it. I don't think that this is at the level, say, of the oedipal type of homosexuality; I think this was a kind of a longing to get from father what he may not have been able to get from mother. Father did not do the beating. Father set the rules, but it was mother who always carried them out. Father never did it. He makes this point.

Judge I: All this is very interesting, but how does this answer the question Judge E raised?

Judge B: I think it does.

Judge E: I think this answers it, and I'd like to supplement what you say. Judge B is saying that the patient is holding on to mother figures. When he can no longer dominate them he is deprived. He is deprived of this relationship. My own impression is that arthritics tend to get their symptoms when their domination fails. Now as long as he is married to this woman—now I'm assuming; we don't even know that this is a fact—I'm assuming that this happened after the separation. As long as he is dominating this woman he has an outlet for his aggression. When she refuses any longer to be dominated then that would correspond to what I recall from other cases.

Judge I: Why didn't he get arthritis with the other separation then?

Judge E: The other separation was the one when he got it. Prodromal symptoms occurred then.

Judge I: No, that is definitely ruled out.

Judge B: (Reads from interview, page 165.)

Judge I: Then later on in the record the medical editor says that none of the material re onset is valid except for the episode two years ago.

Judge B: That's the one. I'm on page 165. I'm using just that one, because the other one is presumptive. I'm using the one that we have most information about.

Judge E: Well what I'd like to know—I'm still in doubt on my own diagnosis. My own diagnosis is arthritis, but, if this failure of his domination—the wife finally breaking away—if this is the thing that produces the arthritis, why didn't he have this when the first marriage broke up?

Judge D: You would expect that.

Judge I: Or when the second marriage broke up the first time.

Judge B: Both times the prodromal symptoms and the onset occurred after a separation. This is in the record. I'll have to find it.

Judge E: Why not after the first marriage?

Judge B: I can't answer that.

Judge D: He was 25 years old then, he was very active.

Judge B: I can't answer that, and that may be the question that Judge D raises. To come back, though—if we think dynamically, not diagnostically, this is important. The onset after a separation could fit in with the skin-allergic diathesis too. I'm attempting to think of what the separation might mean—this apparent paradox between this fellow who talks about how dominating he is (and we know he is dominating in terms of giving money with strings attached), I'll give you the shirts if you go to college, and that kind of thing. And yet when I asked myself the question: Does this man really control? He didn't break up with the women. They broke up with him. He didn't take the sexual initiative, they took the initiative with him. On page 168 he says, for instance: "I took my second wife with me wherever I went. I almost never went out alone except to go to work." This isn't the picture of a man who wants to be so dominant, so controlling, so independent. Instead what comes through to me is somebody who really wants to be close, who wants to be cared for and is needy.

Judge E: You are developing something that I don't think has been discussed by the rest of the group. The point you are making is that you are dealing with the dependence that is *back* of the need to control.

Judge B: That's right.

Judge E: He needs to control a woman. It's either control or be controlled. He needs to have a secure relationship.

Judge I: I think the argument you are making could just as well fit neurodermatitis.

Judge B: I'm not talking diagnostically. I am talking now in terms of the formulation. We can see how the homosexuality comes in—if we think of it in terms of the basic longing of this man. We can see that this wish for closeness, which peppered the record, is not only for physical closeness, but it is for the kind of emotional closeness that he feels he didn't have, and we can see this beautifully illustrated even in terms of the children. He really pushed the son away. He could have taken some interest. It is almost as if some change occurred and now he wants this. Some place he says—I forget exactly how—but the implication is, "I should have done this long ago." Or, "I should have maintained contact with him," or the like. So that this brings in an explanation for the latent homosexuality, and also the conflict about it. The dependency, the control, the homosexuality. Now the question that occurs though, is, what about this anger? This man does have a great deal of anger. I would postulate that the anger again goes back to the early familial situation where we will have to rely a great deal upon inference. There were many, many children in this family.

Judge D: Seventh of eleven.

Judge B: If we accept manifestly what he says—that the parents set certain standards of rigidity, they would not tolerate any kind of hostility; as Judge D brought out, there had to be an externalization of it, and I think basically the feeling of hostility comes from destructive impulses toward the siblings who came after him, and also toward the mother. I would like to have known a little bit more about mother's preference in the familial hierarchy, and also the father's attitude. This is not too clear. So one has to speculate.

Judge E: His position in the family—we don't know why that should have made him get arthritis.

Judge B: Or why he should have been angry about it. Something was there. And that comes out in his talking about the job. The feeling he conveys to us about the job—he can argue with the boss, or he can argue with the person who is under him. When I read that immediately I thought: he would like to argue with the parents and he would like to argue with the siblings.

Judge E: The answer toward the one under him is no argument because he does not permit it. I am in control. He has a reaction formation toward his daughter. He makes it a point that she is free.

Judge I: You don't seem to come to a closure though. I agree with your formulation of the need for closeness, and the formulation of a conflict over passive homosexuality [*all speaking at once*] but you don't answer the first question.

Judge B: But what is your first question?

Judge I: Why did he get sick with arthritis after separation?

Judge D: Because he couldn't control the women. They left him.

Judge B: You don't see this?

Judge I: In the recent case we discussed, that of the policeman, there was the same kind of ability to get angry. The policeman was extremely athletic and active. The policeman had a conflict about his homosexuality, and the policeman turned out to be a case of neurodermatitis.

Judge B: Well, but the group . . . .

Judge I: The group still was uniform for arthritis.

Judge E: I think the difference between you and Judge B now is that Judge B is not discussing diagnosis. You are trying to get the application of all this to the diagnosis.

Judge I: I'm trying to understand why he developed arthritis—on the basis of all this formulation, because of the separation from his wife.

Judge G: Because he could not control.

Judge B: He couldn't control them, and he couldn't control his own anger. He had reached a point where it required internal control and there was an absence of external control. This recapitulated an earlier kind of trauma for him, that he then attempted to master by using sublimated sports activities.

Judge I: To control anger—what did that do? That caused the arthritis?

Judge B: I think it caused an increase in his need to control.

Judge D: We don't have very good data on this actually. Judge G mentioned that before, and Judge E disagreed with him. In this marriage some things are very clear and some things are very unclear, and I myself feel that the whole picture of this separation from the wives is very much in doubt. We don't know anything about the timing really. We are in the dark here and have to do a lot of interpolation and guessing.

Judge B: This brings up an important question. Maybe we should think about a second interview.

Judge D: I think we need more data on this.

Judge E: We have been talking about this man's separation from his wife. Separation is a word we associate with neurodermatitis and asthma. If this is a case of arthritis, instead of thinking of this as a separation, we think of it as a loss of control. And if it is a loss of control, this fits arthritis.

Judge B: A loss of control of the other person.

Judge E: That's right.

Judge B: To implement this point: the loss of control of the other person creates certain affective states that require increased inner control.

Judge D: Mobilize his rage.

Judge B: Which then he has got to control internally.

Judge E: If this were an arthritis case, we would have to assume that what bothered him was his loss of control. Here he is dominating the woman. The woman has been going along with it.

Judge I: I have another question to ask you.

Judge E: Wait till I answer this one. Now if this was a reaction to separation, then it would point probably toward neurodermatitis. Now, let me try to dramatize that psychosomatically. Let's take the dermatitis situation. The way I would conceive of dermatitis—the separation in dermatitis is that the patient is reaching out to get back the contact that he has lost. I'm using somatic language. But he is reaching out to show himself—invite the parents to take him back. He can't allow himself really to reach out, so he reaches out with his skin symptoms. On the other hand I would say (I'm following now on Judge B's formulation), I would say that a need for a close relationship with a woman is back of the need to dominate her. In our arthritis cases this is something we haven't emphasized, but cases we have been working on bring this out very clearly.

Judge I: That the need for a close relationship with a woman is basic because of the need to dominate, you mean?

Judge E: Let me really try to describe this. The arthritic patients as I can see them—this has entirely come from Judge B's and my work together—the arthritic patient has a close relationship with the mother initially, on the basis of being under mother's control. Mother will accept the patient, on her terms. The patient develops a corresponding attitude of keeping a relationship by controlling the object. This becomes a defense against the possibility of losing the mother—birth of another child, or something. You are afraid you are going to lose mother. Instead of developing asthma, let's say, you just hold her. She is not allowed to move. These are mutual relations. The mother has a similar attitude toward the patient. So now, in the arthritic patient, as I see it, the need to hold on to the mother, or even the fear of losing her, is reacted to by simply clamping down and keeping her under control. She is not to be allowed to leave, you see. So now the question comes: when a separation occurs, does the separation occur psychodynamically before or after this clamping relationship has occurred? If it occurs after, then he gets arthritis. If he doesn't have this particular way of holding on to mother, then he is more likely to get asthma or neurodermatitis.

Judge I: This is all very pretty. Supposing we question very carefully, and we find out that the patient developed symptoms two years ago, not after a separation following the remarriage, but the illness began with the remarriage. This would be very disturbing, wouldn't it?

Judge E: Then we would have to find another explanation.

Judge I: I want to remind you that he makes a very interesting remark in response to one of the questions that Judge H asked. He says no, he doesn't think that she brought the psychosomatic illness with her. In other words, he breaks up with his girl friend and he has an emotional reaction. Then he takes back his wife that he got a divorce from, and remarries her. Then he gets his illness. The questions are vague as to whether he gets his illness at the time of the remarriage, or whether he gets his illness at the time of the re-break-up after the marriage. He says, "No, I don't think she brought the psychosomatic illness with her." In other words, it is as though he didn't think it was contagious.

Judge E: You mean he didn't develop it during the marriage, but afterward.

Judge I: No. It suggests that he developed it during. He says he doesn't think that she brought it with her.

Judge E: I think what all this emphasizes is—and this is the thing that I was dissatisfied with—we don't know the facts here as to the timing of this. I wonder if this isn't reason for a second interview—a second interview in which we try to elicit these facts. He may not be able to give them to us. His memory may not be clear. Then there are some other things we can ask. When his wife left him—we could ask was he lonely. We could ask questions that would determine whether he is reaching out toward her.

Judge B: I think there is some information in the record that answers that. For instance, in these two separations there are questions that are asked. He talks about the separation from her in 1950, and the way he controlled her. It is a year afterward that the prodromal symptoms started—while they were separated.

Judge E: He isn't reaching out longingly.

Judge B: He isn't reaching out longingly. He denies any anger or bitterness—which consciously he says. The business of "destroy" is a word that he introduces. Now if we go to page 166, where there is a discussion of the exacerbation in 1956 [*reads material about separation*].

Judge E: This is the second separation—second wife.

Judge B: That's right.

Judge E: "Unhappy"—this could be loneliness.

Judge B: Now what I want to draw attention to is that in both these instances, which involve different women, he denies anger toward the woman, and yet, at least in terms of the first one, the hostility is there. But I did not find any indication that there was an attempt on his part to effect reconciliation. We know that this man has always wanted to take the initiative but rarely does.

Judge I: Kind of a lonely longing.

Judge D: On page 167 we get a lot more data on these marriages than we have been using. The idea that the women wanted to fight and he wouldn't, is described. I think that is extremely important.

Judge E: "You should fuss at me more."

Judge B: That's right.

Judge D: I think that this—to talk diagnosis for a minute—either an asthmatic or a neurodermatitis patient would have no compunctions about fighting.

Judge B: But to not talk diagnosis—what would this mean dynamically?

Judge I: Let's get away for a moment from this. What does it mean dynamically? Let's stick to the facts and see if we can clarify some of these things. Let's go back to page 165.

Judge E: Let Judge D finish.

Judge D: "Would you tell me step by step, in your second marriage, how the relationship began to deteriorate? What would happen? What kind of quarrels would you have?"

"Frankly, we didn't have quarrels. That might have been one of the difficulties. If we had quarrels we would have been able to straighten out things that build up. I am not given to outbreaks unless I am triggered. If you say the wrong thing then I will go out and express myself in no uncertain terms."

"You don't fuss?"

"I don't fuss. But . . . ah . . . if something comes up where you trigger me then I express myself in no uncertain terms and I think I'm through with you."

Later he makes it clear that he is through with the argument.

Judge E: He repudiates that.

Judge D: This irritated the women.

Judge I: Now that's not fact any more.

Judge E: That is fact only it is not in this place.

Judge I: Not in this place.

Judge B: But it is a fact if it is in another place. He says that his first wife used to reproach him—"You don't fuss enough." So that she was definitely disturbed because he didn't express any anger.

Judge I: Well, shall we come back now and see if we can get the actual data about the onset? On page 165, Judge H is trying to clarify the onset for us. He is asking questions about it.

Judge E: I got puzzled by this date of 1956, because somewhere else it seemed to indicate that they broke up back in 1950. Oh, yes, they got remarried then. So they were broken up for a period of six years.

Judge I: That's right.

Judge B: But the implication here is that they got married and the disease started after. That was the remarriage: "not too long before the symptoms started."

Judge I: Your inference is that the remark here implies that they got remarried not too long before the symptoms began. Now we have to make up our minds: did the symptoms begin after the marriage or after the reseparation? Right?

Judge B: He answers that.

Judge I: He goes on and says, "Yes, it would be."

Judge E: Where is this?

Judge I: On page 165. "But she didn't bring the condition with her."

Judge B: *Omission.* We don't know what is omitted here.

Judge I: Let's finish the sentence. But she didn't bring something with her—what does that mean?

Judge B: We don't know what is omitted.

Judge E: But I want to go back before you go to that. "That would not have been too long before [*omission*]."

Judge I: What would not have been too long?

Judge B: Remarriage. The remarriage would not have been too long before [*omission*] and then he explains what the omission was: "[what has not thus far been established as date of disease discovery, or date of exacerbation.]"

Judge I: In other words, the remarriage, then, wasn't too long before the illness.

Judge E: The onset was after the marriage, but we don't know if it was after the separation.

Judge I: Exactly. So then the next sentence is this: "But she didn't bring it with her."

Judge E: But we don't know what the omission is, Judge I. But she didn't bring a change in attitude—goodness knows what the omission could stand for.

Judge I: Let's see what Judge H says. "Maybe not, but nevertheless the timing is fairly close."

Judge B: Then there is the omission, so we don't know what happened.

Judge I: "So that would have meant [disease discovery] took place within a year after you remarried. You said you got remarried and unmarried all in the same year." So it's all within the same year.

Judge B: Remarried, unmarried, and disease.

Judge I: Exactly, that's the point. "In 1956, [*omission*]. Right."
"So that really the disease was not too long after you separated then?"

Judge B: Correct. That's the point. You see in here we can see the dynamics of the interview. He may have said it started in 1956. He may have said he got married in 1956. He may have said he got separated in 1956. And whatever the interviewer did here—and I assume the omission deals with this—he tried to get the patient to delineate when the symptoms started, and what happened. The picture that emerged for me was that there was hope. There is remarriage. He is going to control her again. He is going to have a reestablished relationship. Then comes the separation—then come the symptoms.

Judge E: It seems to be definite that the symptoms occurred after the separation.

Judge I: In my formulation I am not certain about it, that is why I'm arguing.

Judge B: Devil's advocate?

Judge I: Another question I want to raise: Aren't you people who are for arthritis disturbed by the verbal freedom this man has?

Judge B: I have interviewed several cases of arthritis, and I find that there is a great contrast. They are usually very voluble or very tight. Apparently you can have both extremes. I remember one woman—I think most of you got it right too—a lawyer's wife. She talked a blue streak.

Judge I: Well, I'm certain of two things about this case. He is a 43-year-old colored man. In reading over the record I was struck with the emphasis on control, and I was struck with his emphasis on anger, and in my thinking about it I considered the asthma/neurodermatitis diatheses, also hypertension and arthritis. A great deal of emphasis about closeness and loneliness. In fact, he uses somatic language. *[Reads his formulation for neurodermatitis.]* One place he speaks about separation from his wife leaving a scar, and the other place about the fear that a broken marriage would injure his daughter.

Judge E: I know he mentions a scar. The only question is, have you got it right?

Judge B: *[Reads from record, page 166.]*

Judge E: He has been talking about separation, but the scars are not definitely related to separation here. There is quite a little in between.

Judge I: *[Reads formulation.]*

I say that he needs to get the anger out of the way in order to establish a clear atmosphere again. So I say here that he does this because of a strong desire for reconciliation. That's my interpretation. *[Continues to read formulation.]*

Judge E: You use the word "reconciliation" there.

Judge I: That's my word. He does say, in response to a question, that he got married to his divorced wife because of how he felt about the break-up with his sweetheart.

Judge E: Let's get this, because the exact way these things are phrased may be important. Do you know what page that is on?

Judge I: Page 203.

Judge E: Now this phrase "yielding to the second marriage" corresponds with the feeling that I had, that he is yielding to the importunities of his second wife. He is letting her take the initiative again.

Judge I: *[Continues reading page 203.]*

Judge B: What is the point?

Judge I: The point is that he remarried his troublesome wife, whom he divorced, a second time, because of his reaction to the break-up of this marriage. The point I'm making is that he needed closeness—even if it had to do with marrying a person who was going to grate on him.

Judge B: If we look at the timing of what actually happened we see that he was going with this girl, and in typical fashion this girl was another woman who decided to break things up. He didn't break up with this girl friend—the girl friend broke up with him. At the same time the second wife is writing him and saying: "I'll be good, I'll do what you want me to" and so when the girl cuts him off, what he does is to yield to this woman who once more makes overtures to him. This is really part of this man's characteristic way of relating to women.

Judge I: Do we have evidence that she had been writing to him?

Judge E: She had been writing to him.

Judge I: The point I'm making is that it's after this woman breaks up with him that he accepts the offer of the second wife. [*Reads his formulation.*]

Judge B: Do we want to take another week and discuss this case very thoroughly, or do we decide now? If we want another interview, I think Judge H ought to try to get it as soon as possible so we can finish up by the end of June. We have to do a lot of statistical work over the summer.

Judge D: I'm satisfied with this interview.

Judge E: I think most of the questions that I wanted answered we have discussed. Whether another interview could bring out—this would be the only reason—bring out any evidence of loneliness, longing for the second wife, and so on, during the separation. I think that would be the only reason, and I'm not sure we need it.

Judge B: If we decide we don't want another interview I think we should take off time today and go on with the discussion next week. We can give Judge I all the time he needs, and we can check each item as we are going through it.

Judge D: I think we could take fifteen minutes to do that now and finish the case today.

Judge B: And not have a meeting next week? I personally feel that if we want to finish the case without another interview we ought to spend next week on it too. I have a hunch that all of us would benefit from re-reading the material that we already have, in the light of our discussion today.

Judge I: I would like to finish my formulation. On page 185 he (interviewer) is asking him about relationship to his father [*reads his material*]. The point I am making here is that he tells how his daughter was proud of him, and always wanted to show off her daddy. He volunteers that his second wife is "not too warm or affectionate." These are his own words.

Judge E: His own words in answer to the interviewer's question. This isn't a spontaneous response.

Judge I: If this man had an erotization of the skin, and the unconscious fantasy was to be loved and fondled and taken care of, he had a conflict over it because of homosexuality. Here is one area in which it could be very comfortably expressed. Namely, with his daughter, or with his son, whom he wanted to sit on his lap and put his arms around him, and so on.

Judge E: I wish we could find that reference.

Judge I: *[*Continues reading his formulations.*]*

Judge E: On page 202, in answer to the standard question about failure, he said his two marriages were failures. Now I don't know what is the significance of that statement.

Judge I: I think the significance is that it was a reflection on his own narcissistic concept of himself. *[*Reads his formulation.*]* The "Ten Commandments" would fit in with this man's idea of being God-like himself, and would speak of his trying to polish up the soil for exhibitionistic purposes. I didn't say anything about interest in clothes. I think this was already mentioned by Judge G. This about sums it up.

Judge B: There are a couple of other points which you could mention for neurodermatitis.

Judge I: I have a few more points I didn't include in the write-up.

Judge B: For instance, this man likes water, although he doesn't like swimming. Now this may be a point against skin disease.

Judge I: That reminds me of something else—his insomnia. I would like to call your attention to an experience of mine. Very frequently with skin cases—not the skin cases that you are familiar with in terms of guilt about exhibitionistic success, but skin cases in terms of conflict over needs to have the tactile wishes gratified—there may be conflict over the need for love and affection, which is somehow conflictful either because it is painful, because of the hostility toward the object, or because it threatens one's own pride. I have found that these skin cases frequently have insomnia—have difficulty in relaxing and letting themselves go, and falling asleep.

Judge B: But actually we don't know about that. For instance, he mentions "King's Row" and the brutal way of punishing sin, which was by castration. Then he talks about nightmares where they are running after him with knives. Sometimes people are insomniacs because they don't want to face these anxieties in their dreams.

Judge E: Castration fear you get in both skin and arthritis cases.

Judge B: In terms of the skin diagnosis, there are other items. For instance, the buying of an $800 fur coat.

Judge I: And the buying of all the household furnishings. You might say this is an expression of his feminine orientation, but I think it may also be an expression of interest in decorations, and clothing and things.

Judge D: If this is skin it would have to be one of those unambivalent cases.

Judge B: Then there is also the question of his singing as a hobby. This man is a singer, and all of the argument with the minister was because the minister wouldn't let him sing—in the church of his mother.

Judge I: He loves to talk. At the slightest excuse he would get on top of a soap box and give a lecture.

Judge B: The argument with the minister, though, was that the minister excluded these two fellows after he had already given permission. He insisted on having his will be done that they join the church.

Judge E: You mean this was an argument of control.

Judge D: It was an argument of control.

Judge I: I want to point out the conflict over his homosexuality, or his conflict over his love and tenderness.

Judge E: Homosexuality belongs to both arthritis and skin cases.

Judge B: Belongs to everyone.

Judge I: The conflict over it is in connection with the father.

Judge B: But I think fundamentally we still have to keep in mind that dominant in this man's material is the direction, at least manifestly, of wanting very much to control others. In reality he was controlled, and he permits himself to still be controlled as far as women go.

Judge I: You say in reality he was controlled. The question I would raise here—I don't think there has been a very good case made for a genesis for arthritis. The soil has not been really established here.

Judge B: It is clear for me.

Judge E: The father is very insistent.

Judge B: And the mother whips.

Judge G: I am wondering why no question about blushing.

Judge I: He says he blushes to make the other person feel comfortable.

Judge G: Oh, yes.

Judge D: To put the other person at ease.

Judge I: That's quite remarkable.

Judge B: I think we still come back to the question that I raised earlier. Do we want another interview? Do we want another week on this case? Do we want to hear the diagnosis now and talk about the case next week?

Judge D: Let's settle it today, and if it is not arthritis we will have a post mortem next week.

Judge G: Yes, I agree.

Judge B: Well, Judge I, do you want another interview?

Judge I: Yes, I do. I want a more specific expression of the way this man was reared by his father and mother. I want more clarification about the exact onset.

Judge B: You would want more of the genetic background. Second, if we do not get another interview, would you like to take another week discussing it? Or would you rather settle it today?

Judge I: Settle it today.

Judge B: And what is your diagnostic commitment now?

Judge I: Neurodermatitis.

Judge B: OK. Judge D, do you want another interview?

Judge D: No. There are things I would like to get, but I think the way the interviewer asked the questions, he would just ask the same questions again and we would get them the same way. I think that we can stop now.

Judge B: You wouldn't want another week? And what would your diagnosis be?

Judge D: Arthritis.

Judge B: Judge G?

Judge G: Arthritis.

Judge B: And no more interviews?

Judge G: No.

Judge B: Judge E?

Judge E: I am not sure another interview would tell us more, but if Judge I has the feeling that it might be useful, I would be inclined to follow him. If you decide on that, then we should indicate just what questions we want answered.

Judge I: I must point out once more that the argument for arthritis, the element for control and so on, is a very good one. On the other hand, though, I have seen the presence of an arthritic coloration with a skin coloration side by side. Now, what bothers me is the very careful questioning of the interviewer in connection with the onset, about the man's physical activity. The man was very active as a boy, physically. He was very active in sports. He didn't quit sports after high school, but did some more of it in the army; but after that he was no longer physically active in sports. He was only a spectator. It is true that he had physical activity, but there was not . . . . Then the interviewer sums up very clearly, after questioning which would lead you otherwise to the opinion that there was not a significant change in the type of physical activity.

Judge E: That's an argument for interviewer bias.

Judge I: That's right. I don't like that type of argument either.

Judge E: My feeling is—at least this is what I always try to practice—if I suspect interviewer bias I try to disregard it. It seems to me if we go only on the basis of what the patient has said—that he had a decrease in physical activity. Probably not an abrupt one, but a gradual one.

Judge I: The question is: why does this man need physical reasons to get sick? You gave one reason already—that he got frustrated because the wife left him.

Judge B: The need to sublimate. In other words, there are two components to it. One is the control and the other is the increased anger.

Judge E: I don't know whether another interview would help me.

Judge I: I withdraw my request for another interview.

Judge B: Judge E, what would your diagnostic commitment be now?

Judge E: At the present time, arthritis.

Judge B: Well, actually, I think in view of the fact that you feel it wouldn't be necessary for you, and Judge I would be willing to withdraw, I think I would go along with the idea of not having another interview. I think we have not really explored this interview fully. I know that in listening to it—parts of it being read this afternoon—I realized that even though I read the case twice, I didn't completely gain the significance of some of these things. However, based upon our discussion here, in my mind there is little doubt, on the bases of the data we have, that the exacerbation or actual onset occurred after the separation, and not at the time of the remarriage. So that in terms of the timing, I think the information is here as far as the onset. I think once more it is true in terms of the technique that we are using, we have to use inference where facts are not clear. But if one were to come to some kind of feeling about this case, I would be more inclined from my own personal point of view to favor arthritis, and my diagnosis now is only arthritis. So we have four for arthritis and one for neurodermatitis. We have the formulations and diagnoses of those who could not attend today. So now can we hear from Judge H *[interviewer]*.

Judge E: Now we are going to get a shock.

*[*Interviewer joins group.*]*

Judge H: It is arthritis. The thing that you argued so much about, perhaps should have been edited out. "So you did not have any decrease in your physical activity." What I was trying to convey there was that he was insisting that he did not have any, and that all I had been able to bring out was that he had reduced his work compulsivity. I didn't realize that that would be so misleading. I thought it would clarify what he was differentiating between—his major physical activity, about which he made many complaints, lugging garbage cans and all that—and these little things on which he had cut down. I'm not sure that this qualification of a decrease in physical activity is in and of itself utterly necessary for arthritis.

Judge E: When you get a sharp decrease, that is a strong positive evidence of arthritis.

Judge H: I think what this brings out is that the decrease in the compulsive work pattern probably may be an equivalent. To my enormous surprise when I got the medical record for the first time, this man has an ejaculatio praecox, and I think these women left him on account of this—or at least the second woman did. I asked him point blank, "Did they make any complaints to you; were you too passive; did you come too soon?" "No."

Judge D: He couldn't talk about this.

Judge B: This is a very interesting thing because the parallel between this case and a case that I am analyzing, and Judge E and I are working on, is great. One of the complaints of my patient has been ejaculatio praecox, and we have worked out the dynamics of that in terms of the control component, of being able to control the bodily function, and it is actually a very important thing. There is a great deal of narcissistic shame about this symptom.

Judge D: You know my fantasy when I first read the record about his break-up with his first girl that got pregnant, was that she showed him how to do it. Then he came right away and she got pregnant, and then he would have married her but she said I don't want you, you're not a man.

Judge H: I thought his statement about his remarriage to his second wife "I yielded to her" was also very significant. It was difficult to keep this man talking. I don't think he ever would have told me about the ejaculatio praecox. I was quite surprised to find it in the medical record.

Judge E: It seems to me that is not medical information.

Judge H: It is in the medical record. It is medical information.

Judge E: It is in the medical record, but it is psychological information.

Judge H: If I had communicated it to you, it would have been inappropriate.

Judge B: In other words, it may be that, statistically, rheumatoid arthritic males have a higher incidence of ejaculatio praecox than do other diseases. You are saying, why didn't we have it in the record. I would say, if it did not come up spontaneously, I don't think it should be put in.

Judge H: I would assume that they do have a higher incidence. Otherwise what are they doing on their backs? It was interesting that when I was going through this interview, I kept wondering whether this was really an arthritis or just arthritic diathesis. The arthritic character was there, but I simply couldn't get anything very clear as to onset. Apparently the medical editor thought the same. At one time there was a question—the medical editor asked whether it was really an arthritis case. He thought it might be a Strumpell's disease or something like that. Finally, whoever edited it checked the medical record carefully and OK'd it.

Judge E: I'd like to ask a question here. This reminded me of one arthritis case that I interviewed. Was there any evidence of a physical cause for this arthritis? Infection or anything of that sort?

Judge H: No. He kept laying his arthritis at the doorstep of the very hard work.

Judge E: I had a case that bothered me very much, way, way back. I interviewed a man and there was some information suggesting an arthritic personality. I combed the whole situation just as completely as I could. He was one of those inarticulate fellows. I couldn't get the slightest indication of anything I could recognize. This man had had influenza, or some kind of an infection that might have precipitated the arthritis, and it just occurred to me that perhaps not all of the arthritics have a strictly psychological onset.

Judge H: We have his medical history, which I think may have some bearing on this. He came to the hospital first in 1954. Pain in the back. It is recorded that he noticed "gradual change in posture" over the last 12–13 years. However, he also reported that he had gonorrhea in 1937, and he had a urethral stricture for which he was treated in 1954. Complains of various pains, and coming in to have his stricture treated. Chronic prostatitis was noted one time, and so on, and so on.

Judge E: He didn't come in in 1954 for his arthritic symptoms at all?

Judge H: "In February 1954 he came to the outpatient clinic complaining of poor posture for 12 or 13 years and pain in his left hip for one year." Now that poor posture business is carried back to shortly after the first marriage. In other words, every time he mentions it, I edited out "poor posture," because I thought that would be a dead giveaway.

Judge B: Did he mention that hard work was the cause of this?

Judge H: He thought that hard work was the cause.

Judge B: You see this is an important point because in terms of the ulcers —they frequently say it was hard work, or imply it. And here is arthritis where hard work . . . . But here it has a different meaning. In other words, merely to say "hard work"—I think this is insufficient. One has to break down what does hard work mean?

Judge H: The most interesting thing was that this "postural change," which was already present when he was in the service, led him to walk with a peculiar sway which led the men in the service to razz him about being a "homosexual," and I'm sure that what was going on in his back was less important than what was going on in his head in regard to the peculiar sway.

Judge B: If we paid attention to the body language—and I was very much struck by his emphasis on closeness—neurodermatitis would be suggested. I wasn't as impressed by the "scar" idea and the like, although this would also very much be in the context of neurodermatitis. I don't think one can take body language alone. We have got to understand what is the meaning of the particular body language in the total context.

Judge H: This brings up an important point. In this case I had to edit out his most significant body language, namely his repeated references to postural change.

Judge B: This, I think, would be an important point if it could have been in the record without serving as an illegitimate communication.

Judge H: It would have been a medical clue; actually, as he used it, it was body language.

Medical Control Group Reports

Date Protocol Sent to Group: May 22, 1959

The following are the reports submitted by members of the medical control group:

JUDGE	INITIAL DIAGNOSIS		FINAL DIAGNOSIS	
L	Hypertension	7	Hypertension	
M	(did not participate)			
N	Hypertension	7	(did not participate)	
O	Colitis	5	Ulcer	
	Ulcer	2		
P	Ulcer	5	Ulcer	4
	Neurodermatitis	2	Hypertension	3
Q	Arthritis	6	Arthritis	6
	Ulcer	1	Ulcer	1
R	(did not participate)			
S	Ulcer	5	Hypertension	7
	Hypertension	2		
T	Hypertension	5	Hypertension	5
	Ulcer	2	Ulcer	2
U	Hypertension	5	Hypertension	6
	Neurodermatitis	1	Neurodermatitis	1

Judge L's Report

1. Forty-three-year-old Negro male.
2. Onset at about age 43, but possibly earlier, milder symptoms five or six years before interview.

Diagnosis: pure guess, Hypertension 7

Judge N's Report

Small, neat 43-year-old male Negro.
Ill for two years—possibly more.
Married twice.
Very questionable prodromata—not asthma, neurodermatitis.
Page 181, no particular change in physical activity—not arthritis.

Diagnosis: Hypertension 7

Judge O's Report

Reference to vague symptoms a few years before and two years of definite symptoms makes hypertension, neurodermatitis, asthma, and hyperthyroidism unlikely. Arthritis would probably have interfered with work as janitor. Of ulcerative colitis and peptic ulcer, I believe ulcerative colitis is more likely.

Diagnoses: Ulcerative Colitis 5
Peptic Ulcer 2

Judge P's Report

A 43-year-old married colored male who possibly had prodromes of disease five or six years before but was diagnosed only one or two years before. He had been athletic, done heavy labor in the CC Camps and, although slowed down slightly, was continuing his janitor's job as before. He had been in service before the discovery of his disease.

Consideration: Peptic Ulcer 5
Neurodermatitis 2

Judge Q's Report

I have used the following clues:
Page 166, he is a 43-year-old colored janitor whose disease had its onset two years previously. Page 165, onset may have been eight years ago. Page 164, prodromata are mentioned.

The long course and prodromata are against hypertension, hyperthyroidism, neurodermatitis and asthma. Long prodromata suggests ulcer, colitis, and arthritis.

My diagnoses are: Arthritis 6
Ulcer 1

Judge S's Report

Mild onset five or six years prior to interview. No immediate medical care.

Diagnoses: Peptic Ulcer 5
Hypertension 2

Judge T's Report

Had possible earlier attack six years before, but current episode two years ago. Original prodromata not diagnosed. Patient has led a quiet life but has continued working. I think hyperthyroidism is most unlikely although others are possible but because of age and race I'll pick:

Diagnoses: Hypertension 5
Ulcer 2

Judge U's Report

The patient is a 43-year-old Negro janitor and one-time football player. That he was paid to come to the interview for "reasons unknown to the interviewer" could suggest that he suffered from something less typical of his age, race, and build than hypertension.

There is no hint of disability or pattern of the illness. A possible cue is the fuss made by the (medical) editor over whether or not the vague prodromata were genuine. If the illness were asthma, arthritis, neurodermatitis, or colitis, this should not have been so difficult to settle. He does not seem like a man with thyrotoxicosis, and there is no hint to suggest ulcer. From his constitution and possible prodromata:

Diagnoses: Hypertension 6
Neurodermatitis 1

Interviewer Cue Detection Judges' Reports

JUDGE I

Interviewer Cuing Report — *Present Date*: August 4, 1960
Case: Mr. A. O. — *Interview Date*: February 20, 1959

Cue No.	*Page No.*	*Description*	*Categorization by type*	*For Diagnosis of*	*Against Diagnosis of*
1	166–68	Emphasis on anger	#2	Hypertension ++	
2	181	"so no change in physical activity"	#3 #2		Arthritis ++

General Impressions

A good interview, covered all areas and asked all the questions. No distortion in weighting by the doctor, but the material seemed to be heavy in the direction of anger.

Summary Rating

Arthritis		*Asthma*		*Colitis*		*Hypertension*	
For	Against	For	Against	For	Against	For	Against
	++					++	

Neurodermatitis		*Thyrotoxicosis*		*Ulcer*	
For	Against	For	Against	For	Against

JUDGE II

Interviewer Cuing Report — *Present Date*: May 2, 1961
Case: Mr. A. O. — *Interview Date*: February 20, 1959

Cue No.	*Page No.*	*Description*	*Categorization by type*	*For Diagnosis of*	*Against Diagnosis of*
1	166	Disease discovered about age 40–41 (No interviewer cues found)	(medical)	Hypertension Thyrotoxicosis Arthritis	Asthma Neurodermatitis

General Impressions

No general cues noted.

No interviewer cues, specific or general, noted. One medical clue, a very weak one based on age of onset, is against asthma and neurodermatitis and it favors hypertension, thyrotoxicosis, arthritis.

Summary Rating

None given.

JUDGE IV

Interviewer Cuing Report *Present Date*: November 18, 1961
Case: Mr. A. O. *Interview Date*: February 20, 1959

Cue No.	*Page No.*	*Description*	*Categorization by type*	*For Diagnosis of*	*Against Diagnosis of*
1	161	"Ground down on her" . . . "She got too rebellious"	Weighted words	Rheumatoid Arthritis	
2	166	Leading question about anger	Unwarranted assumption	Hypertension	
3	167	"explosive attack of anger"	Unwarranted assumption	Hypertension	

General Impressions

No general cues.

The specific cues listed are only mildly suggestive.

Summary Rating

None given.

Cue Utilization Discussion

Cue Review by Analytic Judges

March 27, 1962

Mr. A. O. (1959) Rheumatoid Arthritis

Judge G: Mr. A. O.—interviewed by Judge H. A Negro man with arthritis. The interview was a very good interview, and brought up all the important features of the disease. It was very, very clear how this patient was controlled very strictly by his father and mother, but mostly by his father. And he then developed a controlling attitude, and I think that there are very few clues in this interview. But I want to mention only two in connection with this controlling attitude. On page 171 he tells the interviewer how he wanted to control his second wife by buying her a fur coat, and the reason why he bought it was quite clear—to control her.

Judge E: He said so?

Judge G: No, he doesn't use this word, but it was quite evident, because also a sister of his wife—sister-in-law—said "you want to have some power over her," or something. So then the interviewer said on page 172, "You know, as you quote your sister-in-law, it sounds as though your sister-in-law thought you were too dominating." And the word "dominating" was used by the interviewer. I think this is perhaps emphasis of the character that this patient is very domineering, but also without this word, without this remark, most of us would have diagnosed rheumatoid arthritis. Then on page 173 he wanted to compensate his controlling attitude toward other people, his wife, by forcing them to be very considerate. And the interviewer said "This desire of yours to be considerate . . . ." "I am as considerate as I know how to be." "This is a desire of yours to be considerate."

Judge E: He repeated his own words?

Judge G: No. He said it is a *desire* of yours. He said, "I am as considerate as I know how to be." And the analyst says, "This is a desire of yours—to be considerate?"

Judge D: As if he really weren't but would like to be?

Judge G: The interviewer mentions a desire to be. This is what you want to be.

Judge E: Do you think that is a cue?

Judge G: I didn't find any cues, and the interviewer asked him all the standard questions and so on, and followed up everything which the patient said—investigated his sexual life very thoroughly.

And it is also interesting from the picture of this case that the patient was very passive with women. He was seduced by women—but he never could take the initiative. When he was 19 he was seduced by a woman who became pregnant, and did not marry her. He married three times, and all three times he divorced—separated, and from the interview it was quite clear that he could not stand his wives whom he could not control, and he desired to control very, very much.

[Judge G reviews all the diagnoses made and then continues his discussion.]

Judge G: Hypertension was considered but without reference to certain of the psychological features. We didn't consider loyalty at the time, but he used to blow his top. The diagnosis of neurodermatitis was based upon his attitude about being alone. We considered that he must have suffered from loneliness. He said it is better to live alone than be unhappy. He preferred being alone —not with his wife—but for the most part he was lonesome. But he didn't have the desire to relate to somebody like the neurodermatitis patients have.

Judge E: Our experience was that neurodermatitis cases were at times diagnosed arthritis—rarely were arthritis cases diagnosed neurodermatitis.

Judge B: If I could just interject one thing: In terms of the valuation, I think it is important that Judge F was arthritis 7A for hunch, and final arthritis 7A. Judge E was arthritis hunch, final arthritis. Judge D was arthritis hunch, final arthritis. Judge C was arthritis 5, hypertension 2, and then went to arthritis 6, hypertension 1. Judge B—hunch arthritis 6, neurodermatitis 1; final—arthritis. Judge A was arthritis 7A—final arthritis 7A. Judge G was arthritis—final arthritis. Judge I was neurodermatitis hunch, and neurodermatitis final. So I think Judge I was really the only one who very seriously considered neurodermatitis. I would say in terms of the group performance there was much consensus on diagnoses and formulations.

Judge G: I don't know whether I have to read all the formulations, but there was very much emphasis on his dependent attitude. It was a very good interview, and everything that the patient brought up, and the sexuality and so forth, was followed up. The dynamic picture of arthritis was very, very clear.

Judge B: In summary: The analytic group, with the exception of Judge I, were all uniform in the preponderant diagnosis of arthritis at the beginning, and even more so at the end.

Now in terms of the cue judges: Judge I finds one mild cue against arthritis, none for arthritis, one (mild) cue for hypertension. "A good interview, covered all areas, asked all the questions, no distortion in weighting by the doctor. But the material seems to be heavy in the direction of anger."

Judge II said that there were no interviewer cues found. "No interviewer cues specific or general noted. One medical clue—a very weak one, based on the age of onset—is against asthma and dermatitis, and favors hypertension, thyroid and arthritis." But essentially no cues.

Judge IV found "No general cues. The specific cues listed are only mildly suggestive." He found one cue for arthritis—words of the interviewer—"ground her down." (Wife got too rebellious.) He felt that this "grinding down" might be a very slight cue for rheumatoid arthritis (weighted word).

Judge E: Where is that?

Judge B: "Ground down on her."

Judge E: The patient ground down on his daughter or somebody?

Judge H: Probably ground down on his wife.

Judge B: He felt that this was a cue—I assume he felt the interviewer introduced it. But he says it is very mild.

So essentially we would say there were no real cues here. Of the medical people only one person made the diagnosis of arthritis—Judge Q—and his evidence is flimsy. I will read his write-up.

"Forty-three-year-old colored janitor whose disease has its onset two years previously. Onset may have been eight years ago, prodromata are mentioned. The long course and prodromata are against hypertension, hyperthyroid, neurodermatitis, and asthma. Long prodromata suggest ulcer, colitis, and arthritis. My hunch is arthritis 6, ulcer 1."

He is the only one who made the correct diagnosis.

Judge E: He didn't have much.

Judge B: He didn't have much. The other people—and I won't read their write-ups—Judge N called it hypertension. Judge U, hypertension 6, neurodermatitis 1. Judge L, hypertension 7. Judge T, hypertension 5, ulcer 2. Judge S, ulcer 5, hypertension 2. Judge P, ulcer 5, neurodermatitis 2. Judge O, ulcerative colitis 5, ulcer 2. None of the write-ups were at all revealing.

Judge E: What led them all to hypertension?

Judge B: I could read Judge U's. It is the longest.

Judge D: Forty-three-year-old colored man.

Judge B: "Forty-three-year-old Negro janitor and one-time football player. That he was paid to come to the interview for 'reasons unknown to the interviewer' could suggest that he suffered from something less typical of his age, race and build than hypertension. There is no hint of disability or pattern of the illness. A possible cue is the fuss made by the (medical) editor over whether or not the vague 'prodromata' were genuine. If the illness were asthma, arthritis, neurodermatitis or colitis this should not have been so difficult to settle. He does not seem like a man with thyrotoxicosis, and there is no hint to suggest ulcer. From his constitution, and the possible vague prodromata, I would consider hypertension."

Judge E: Constitution?

Judge B: Muscular kind of chunky football player type. But essentially I don't think we have to spend much time. I would say that this is a very, very good interview. Judge G found no cues which were unequivocal. Judge I found a cue against arthritis. The analytic group did very well at the beginning and at the end. And I would say this is fine. If all the cases were like this there would be no question.

Bibliography

Chapter One

Abraham, K. 1927. A short study of the development of the libido, viewed in the light of mental disorders. In *Selected Papers*, pp. 418–501. London: Hogarth Press.

Alexander, F. 1935. The logic of emotions and its dynamic background. *Intern. J. Psychoanal.* 16:399–413.

Binger, C. A. L., Ackerman, N. W., Cohn, A. E., Schroeder, H. A., and Steele, J. M. 1945. *Personality in arterial hypertension.* New York: Am. Soc. for Res. in Psychosomat. Probl.

Breuer, J., and Freud, S. 1955. Studies on hysteria. *Standard Edition* 2:335.

Cannon, W. B. 1929. *Bodily changes in pain, hunger, fear and rage.* New York: D. Appleton.

———. 1932. *The wisdom of the body.* New York: Norton.

Deutsch, F. 1939. The production of somatic disease by emotional disturbance. *Res. Publ., Assoc. for Res. in Nervous and Mental Disease* 19:271–92.

Dunbar, F. 1943. *Psychosomatic diagnosis.* New York: Hoeber.

Ferenczi, S. 1916. Transitory symptom-constructions during the analysis. In *Sex in psycho-analysis*, pp. 193–212. Boston: Badger.

———. 1950. *Further contributions to the theory and technique of psychoanalysis.* London: Hogarth Press.

Freud, S. 1957. The psychoanalytic view of psychogenic visual disturbance. *Standard Edition* 11:209–18.

Grinker, R. R., Sr. 1953. *Psychosomatic research.* New York: Norton.

Miller, M. 1942. A psychological study of a case of eczema and a case of neurodermatitis. *Psychosomat. Med.* 4:82–93.

———. 1948. Psychodynamic mechanism in a case of neurodermatitis. *Psychosomat. Med.* 10:309–16.

Mirsky, I. A. 1953. Psychoanalysis and the biological sciences. In *Twenty years of psychoanalysis: A symposium*, ed. F. Alexander and H. Ross, pp. 155–76. New York: Norton.

Weiner, H., Thaler, M., Reiser, M. F., and Mirsky, I. A. 1957. Etiology of duodenal ulcer. I. Relation of specific psychological characteristics to rate of gastric secretion (serum pepsinogen). *Psychosomat. Med.* 19: 1–10.

Weiss, E. 1922. Psychoanalyse eines Falles von nervösem Asthma. *Intern. Zeit. Psychoanal.* 8: 440–55.

Publications of the Chicago Institute for Psychoanalysis Related to the Psychosomatic Specificity Project

Alexander, F. 1932. Psychoanalysis and medicine. *Ment. Hyg.* 16: 63–84.

———. 1933. Functional disturbances of psychogenic nature. *J.A.M.A.* 100: 469–73.

———. 1934. The influence of psychologic factors upon gastro-intestinal disturbances: A symposium. I. General principles, objectives, and preliminary results. *Psychoanal. Quart.* 3: 501–39. (Also in Alexander, F., and French, T. M. 1948. *Studies in psychosomatic medicine*, pp. 103–33.)

———. 1935. The logic of emotions and its dynamic background. *Intern. J. Psycho-anal.* 16: 339–413.

———. 1936. *The medical value of psychoanalysis*, 2d ed. New York: Norton.

———. 1936. Psychological aspects of medicine. *Psychosomat. Med.* 1: 7–18.

———. 1939. Psychoanalytic study of a case of essential hypertension. *Psychosomat. Med.* 1: 139–52. (Also in Alexander and French 1948.)

———. 1941. Clinical versus experimental approach in psychosomatics. *Psychosomatic. Med.* 3: 330–39.

———. 1941. Gastrointestinal neuroses. In *Diseases of the digestive system*, ed. S. A. Portis, pp. 206–26. Philadelphia: Lea & Febiger.

———. 1943. Fundamental concepts of psychosomatic research: Psychogenesis, conversion, specificity. *Psychosomat. Med.* 5: 205–10. (Also in Alexander and French 1948 and in *The Yearbook of Psychoanalysis* [New York: Intern. Universities Press] 1 [1945]: 257–66.)

———. 1944. Proceedings of the meeting on gastro-intestinal disorders of the American Society for Research in Psychosomatic Problems. *Psychosomat. Med.* 6: 74–76.

———. 1944. A psychosomatic study of hypoglycemic fatigue. In *Psychosomatic medicine: The proceedings of the second brief psychotherapy council*, pp. 41–60. Chicago: Inst. Psychoanal.

Alexander, F. 1944. Psychosomatic disturbances of the gastro-intestinal tract. In *Diseases of the digestive system*, ed. S. A. Portis, 2d ed., pp. 826–44. Philadelphia: Lea & Febiger. (Also in Alexander 1950.)

———. 1946. A case of peptic ulcer and personality disorder. In *Proceedings of the Third Psychotherapy Council*, pp. 18–40. Chicago: Inst. Psychoanal.

———. 1946. Training principles in psychosomatic medicine. *Am. J. Orthopsychiat.* 16:410–12.

———. 1948. Emotional factors in essential hypertension. *Psychosomat. Med.* 1:173–79. (Also in Alexander and French 1948.)

———. 1950. *Psychosomatic medicine.* New York: Norton.

———. 1961. Experimental studies of emotional stress. I. Hyperthyroidism. *Psychosomat. Med.* 23:104–14.

———. 1962. The development of psychosomatic medicine. *Psychosomat. Med.* 24:13–24.

Alexander, F., and French, T. M. 1948. *Studies in psychosomatic medicine: An approach to the cause and treatment of vegetative disturbances.* New York: Ronald.

Alexander, F., Ham, G. C., and Carmichael, H. T. 1950. Dynamic aspects of the personality features and reactions characteristic of patients with Graves' disease. *Res. Publ., Assoc. for Res. in Nervous and Mental Disease* 29:451–57.

———. 1951. A psychosomatic theory of thyrotoxicosis. *Psychosomat. Med.* 13:18–35.

Alexander, F., Johnson, A. M., and Shapiro, L. B. 1947. Preliminary report on a psychosomatic study of rheumatoid arthritis. *Psychosomat. Med.* 9:295–300. (Also in Alexander and French 1948.)

Alexander, F., and Menninger, W. C. 1936. The relation of persecutory delusions to the functioning of the gastro-intestinal tract. *J. Nervous Mental Disease* 84:541–54.

Alexander, F., and Pollock, G. H. 1959. Experimental study of psychophysiological correlations. Reports presented at the Annual Meeting of the Amer. Psychosomat. Soc. Atlantic City, N.J.

Alexander, F., and Saul, L. J. 1937. The human spirogram. *Am. J. Physiol.* 119:396–97.

———. 1940. Respiration and personality—A preliminary report. Part I. Description of the curves. *Psychosomat. Med.* 2:110–18.

Alexander, F., and Szasz, T. S. 1952. The psychosomatic approach in medicine. In *Dynamic psychiatry*, ed. F. Alexander and H. Ross, pp. 369–400. Chicago: Univ. of Chicago Press.

Alexander, F., and Visotsky, H. 1955. Psychosomatic study of a case of asthma. *Psychosomat Med.* 17:470–72.

Bacon, C. L. 1934. The influence of psychologic factors upon gastrointestinal disturbances: A symposium. II. Typical personality trends and conflicts in cases of gastric disturbance. *Psychoanal. Quart.* 3:540–57.

French, T. M. 1939. Psychogenic factors in asthma. *Am. J. Psychiat.* 96:87–89.

———. 1949. Emotional conflicts and allergy. *Intern. Arch. Allergy Appl. Immunol.* 1:28–40.

French, T. M., and Alexander, F. 1941. *Psychogenic factors in bronchial asthma.* 2 vols. Washington, D.C.: Natl. Res. Concl.

French, T. M., and Johnson, A. M. 1944. Brief psychotherapy in bronchial asthma. In *Psychosomatic medicine: The proceedings of the second brief psychotherapy council,* pp. 14–21. Chicago: Inst. Psychoanal. (Also in Alexander and French 1948.)

French, T. M., and Shapiro, L. B. 1949. The use of dream analysis in psychosomatic research. *Psychosomat. Med.* 11:110–12. (Also in *The Yearbook of Psychoanalysis* [New York: Intern. Universities Press] 6 [1950]:123–28.)

Gerard, M. W. 1946. Bronchial asthma in children. *Nervous Child* 5:327–31.

Ham, G. C. 1952. Psychosomatic investigation and management of gastrointestinal disorders. *J. Med. Soc.* 52:22–50.

Josselyn, I. M., Mohr, G. J., Spurlock, J., and Baron, S. H. 1958. Studies in ulcerative colitis [in children]. *Am. J. Psychiat.* 114:1067–76.

Lee, H. B. 1934. The influence of psychologic factors upon gastrointestinal disturbances: A symposium. IV. Oral trends and oral conflicts in a case of duodenal ulcer. *Psychoanal. Quart.* 3:574–82.

Miller, M. L. 1939. Blood pressure findings in relation to inhibited aggressions in psychotics. *Psychosomat. Med.* 1:162–72. (Also in Alexander and French 1948.)

———. 1942. A psychological study of a case of eczema and a case of neurodermatitis. *Psychosomat. Med.* 4:82–93.

Mohr, G. J. 1943. Studies of eczema and asthma in the preschool child. *J. Am. Acad. Child Psychiat.* 2:271–91.

———. 1948. Psychosomatic problems in childhood. *Child Development* 19:137–42.

———. 1963. Family dynamics in early childhood asthma: Some mental health considerations. In *The asthmatic child,* ed. H. I. Schneer, pp. 103–17. New York: Hoeber.

Saul, L. J. 1935. A note on the psychogenesis of organic symptoms. *Psychoanal. Quart.* 4:476–83.

Saul, L. J. 1939. The physiological effects of psychoanalytic therapy. *Res. Publ., Assoc. Res. Nervous Mental Disease* 19:305–17. (Also in Alexander and French 1948.)

———. 1939. Hostility in cases of essential hypertension. *Psychosomat. Med.* 1:153–61.

———. 1941. Psychosomatic knowledge in case work. *The Family* 22:219–27.

———. 1941. Some observations on the relations of emotions and allergy. *Psychosomat. Med.* 3:66–71. (Also in Alexander and French 1948.)

———. 1944. Physiological effects of emotional tension. In *Personality and the behavior disorders*, ed. J. McV. Hunt, 1:269–305. New York: Ronald.

———. 1953. Psychosomatic aspects of peptic ulcer. *Samiksa* 7:225–35.

Saul, L. J., and Bernstein, C., Jr. 1941. The emotional settings of some attacks of urticaria. *Psychosomat. Med.* 3:349–69. (Also in Alexander and French 1948.)

Shapiro, L. B., Gottschalk, L. A., and Serota, H. M. 1950. Psychologic conflict and neuromuscular tension. I. Preliminary report on a method as applied to rheumatoid arthritis. *Psychosomat. Med.* 12:315–19.

Szasz, T. S. 1948. Psychiatric aspects of vagotomy: A preliminary report. *Ann. Internal. Med.* 28:279–88.

———. 1949. Psychiatric aspects of vagotomy. II. A psychiatric study of vagotomized ulcer patients with comments on prognosis. *Psychosomat. Med.* 11:187–99.

———. 1949. Factors in the pathogenesis of peptic ulcer. Some critical comments on a recent article by George F. Mahl. *Psychosomat. Med.* 11:300–304.

———. 1949. Psychiatric aspects of vagotomy. IV. Phantom ulcer pain. *Arch. Neurol. Psychiat.* 62:728–33.

———. 1950. Psychosomatic aspects of salivary activity. I. Hypersalivation in patients with peptic ulcer. *Res. Publ., Assoc. Res. Nervous Mental Disease* 29:647–55.

———. 1951. Oral mechanisms in constipation and diarrhoea. *Intern. J. Psycho-anal.* 32:196–203.

———. 1951. Physiologic and psychodynamic mechanisms in constipation and diarrhoea. *Psychosomat. Med.* 13:112–16.

———. 1952. Psychiatric aspects of vagotomy. III. The problem of diarrhoea after vagotomy. *J. Nervous Mental Disease* 115:394–405.

———. 1952. Psychoanalysis and the autonomic nervous system. A bioanalytic approach to the problem of the psychogenesis of somatic change. *Psychoanalyt. Rev.* 39:115–51.

Szasz, T. S., Levin, E., Kirsner, J. B., and Palmer, W. L. 1947. The role of hostility in the pathogenesis of peptic ulcer. Theoretical considerations with the report of a case. *Psychosomat. Med.* 9:331–36.

Van Der Heide, C. 1940. A study of mechanisms in two cases of peptic ulcer. *Psychosomat. Med.* 2:398–410.

———. 1943. Psychosomatic medicine. *News-letter of the Amer. Assoc. Psychiat. Soc. Wrkrs.* 13:13–20.

Wilson, G. W. 1934. The influence of psychologic factors upon gastrointestinal disturbances: A symposium. III. Typical personality trends and conflicts in cases of spastic colitis. *Psychoanal. Quart.* 3:558–73.

———. 1938. The transition from organ neurosis to conversion hysteria. *Intern. J. Psycho-anal.* 19:23–40.

Reports and Brochures of the Chicago Institute for Psychoanalysis

Cohn, A. E. 1941. *Psychoanalysis in Medicine.*

Review for the Year 1932–1933, p. 47.

Review for the Year 1933–1934, p. 52.

Review for the Year 1934–1935, p. 46.

Five-Year Report 1932–1937, p. 70.

Supplement to the Five-Year Report 1932–1937, p. 15.

Ten-Year Report 1932–1942, p. 80.

Report of the Five-Year Period 1942–1947, p. 68.

Index